teach
yourself

the first world war

the first world war
david evans

For over 60 years, more than
40 million people have learnt over
750 subjects the **teach yourself**
way, with impressive results.

be where you want to be
with **teach yourself**

For UK order enquiries: please contact Bookpoint Ltd, 130 Milton Park, Abingdon, Oxon OX14 4SB. Telephone: +44 (0) 1235 827720. Fax: +44 (0) 1235 400454. Lines are open 09.00–18.00, Monday to Saturday, with a 24-hour message answering service. Details about our titles and how to order are available at www.teachyourself.co.uk

For USA order enquiries: please contact McGraw-Hill Customer Services, PO Box 545, Blacklick, OH 43004-0545, USA. Telephone: 1-800-722-4726. Fax: 1-614-755-5645.

For Canada order enquiries: please contact McGraw-Hill Ryerson Ltd, 300 Water St, Whitby, Ontario L1N 9B6, Canada. Telephone: 905 430 5000. Fax: 905 430 5020.

Long renowned as the authoritative source for self-guided learning – with more than 40 million copies sold worldwide – the **teach yourself** series includes over 300 titles in the fields of languages, crafts, hobbies, business, computing and education.

British Library Cataloguing in Publication Data: a catalogue record for this title is available from the British Library.

Library of Congress Catalog Card Number: on file.

First published in UK 2004 by Hodder Arnold, 338 Euston Road, London, NW1 3BH.

First published in US 2004 by Contemporary Books, a Division of the McGraw-Hill Companies, 1 Prudential Plaza, 130 East Randolph Street, Chicago, IL 60601 USA.

This edition published 2004.

The **teach yourself** name is a registered trade mark of Hodder Headline Ltd.

Typeset by Transet Limited, Coventry, England.
Printed in Great Britain for Hodder Arnold, a division of Hodder Headline, 338 Euston Road, London NW1 3BH, by Cox & Wyman Ltd, Reading, Berkshire.

Hodder Headline's policy is to use papers that are natural, renewable and recyclable products and made from wood grown in sustainable forests. The logging and manufacturing processes are expected to conform to the environmental regulations of the country of origin.

Impression number 10 9 8 7 6 5 4 3 2 1
Year   2010 2009 2008 2007 2006 2005 2004

contents

01

Europe in 1914 and the coming of war

This chapter will cover:
- the situation in Europe before the outbreak of war in 1914
- the nature of the relations between Europe's royal dynasties
- the reasons for the rivalry between the major powers and the stages by which Europe became divided into two armed camps
- crises and confrontations
- assassination at Sarajevo and the outbreak of war.

'Wherever I look ... everything is restless and unsettled and everyone except ourselves is getting ready for war. This frightens me.'

(General Sir Henry Wilson in 1913)

Europe in 1914

A map of Europe in 1914 is very different from that of today. In the west, the frontiers of Portugal, Spain and France have remained much the same but in central and eastern Europe there have been significant changes. Germany was much larger then than it is today and Austria-Hungary, sometimes called the Habsburg Empire, dominated central Europe. Today, Austria and Hungary are two separate countries and the rest of that Empire is now a cluster of small independent states – the Czech Republic, Slovakia, Croatia and Bosnia. Present day countries such as Finland, Poland, Estonia, Latvia, Lithuania, Belarus and the Ukraine were then part of the vast Russian Empire but now

figure 1 Europe in 1914

they are all independent nations. At this time, although the struggle for home rule had begun, the whole of Ireland was part of Great Britain. The changes that have occurred since 1914 are the result of wars, revolutions and other political and social upheavals. No event contributed more to these changes than the First World War – the Great War of 1914–18.

The great European powers

Before 1914, Europe was dominated by five great powers – Britain, France, Germany, Austria-Hungary and Russia. Britain, major industrial nation and so-called 'workshop of the world' was also a great imperial power with an Empire that stretched across the world and over which, so it was claimed, 'the sun never set'. Her Empire provided her with raw materials for her industries and markets for her manufactured goods. The world's greatest fleet, the Royal Navy, guarded her important trade routes and it was a time when Britannia really did rule the waves! With such advantages Britain could stand aside from world events and concentrate on her own affairs and those of her Empire. During this time, often referred to as her period of 'splendid isolation', Britain faced numerous problems. In 1899, Britain became involved in a war in South Africa against the descendants of the early Dutch settlers, the Boers. To outsiders, the Boer War seemed a 'David and Goliath' affair and many regarded Britain as a colonial tyrant. Some European countries, particularly Germany, were sympathetic to the Boers and the German Kaiser went as far as to hint that he might help the Boers in their conflict with Britain. During the same period, Britain very nearly went to war with France over quite a trivial issue – the ownership of a small town in the Sudan called Fashoda.

France, another great imperial power, also faced major difficulties. In 1870, she was tricked into a war with her neighbour, Prussia, and the Franco-Prussian War ended in her humiliating defeat. Afterwards, she had to pay the costs of the war and surrender the provinces of Alsace and Lorraine to Prussia. Even worse, the Prussian chancellor, Otto von Bismarck, used the occasion to declare the birth of a German Empire and Wilhelm I was proclaimed first Kaiser of the new Empire that embraced nearly all the German-speaking states in central Europe. In France, these events nearly led to a revolution and the French people voted to become a republic, the Third Republic. Their disgraced emperor, Napoleon III, and his family were forced to spend their last years living in exile in England. Humbled and embittered, the French looked for a chance to avenge their humiliation and regain their lost provinces.

It is often not appreciated that Germany did not exist as a nation until 1871. The creation of a united Germany was virtually the work of one man, Bismarck, nicknamed the 'Iron Chancellor'. In 1888, Frederick III who was married to Victoria, daughter of Queen Victoria, the Queen of Britain, succeeded his father but he reigned for less then four months before he died of throat cancer. The German throne next passed to Kaiser Wilhelm II, soon to be infamously known as 'Kaiser Bill' who quickly rid himself of the restraining influence of Bismarck, and began to follow reckless policies that were to endanger the peace of Europe.

The Emperor Franz Ferdinand, already in his mid-sixties, ruled over the ramshackle multi-racial empire of Austria-Hungary. Famed for his austere living – it is said that his spartan bedroom only contained a bed and washstand – his life was dogged by a series of unusual personal tragedies. His brother, the self-appointed Emperor of Mexico, was executed by rebels whilst his son, Rudolf, shot himself as part of a suicide pact with his mistress at Mayerling. In addition, his wife, the Empress Elizabeth, was stabbed to death by an anarchist whilst another son, Karl Ludwig, died from typhoid after drinking the waters of the River Jordan whilst on a pilgrimage. By this time, the heir to the throne of Austria-Hungary was his remaining closest relative, his nephew, Franz Ferdinand and it was the assassination of this nephew that was to lead directly to the outbreak of war in 1914.

Tsar Nicholas II who ruled the massive Russian Empire that stretched from Europe across Asia to the Pacific Ocean in the east also faced difficulties. Dominated by his German-born wife and influenced by a self-styled holy man, the evil Rasputin, a tragedy of his life was that his only son, Alexei, was a haemophiliac. Nicholas's autocratic rule was under threat from revolutionary groups who sought to overthrow the monarchy and introduce a democratic style of government and bring about other much needed reforms. In 1904, Nicholas foolishly tried to gain popularity by becoming involved in a war against small and presumably weak Japan, as he thought he could gain an easy victory. However, it was a folly and the Russians were defeated and humiliated on land and sea. This led to even greater unrest amongst the Russian people and an attempted revolution. Faced by strikes and demonstrations, order was restored when Nicholas offered a range of concessions to the Russian people including an elected assembly. Even so, the situation in Russia remained fraught with danger.

The feuding royal dynasties

Apart from republican France, royal families ruled the major powers of Europe. The leading royal dynasties were the British House of Hanover, the German House of Hohenzollern, the Russian House of Romanov, the long established House of Habsburg in Austria-Hungary and in Italy, the House of Savoy. Although intermarriage had created close ties of kinship, it in no way prevented the royal families from feuding.

QUEEN VICTORIA
married Albert of Saxe-Coburg-Gotha

| Victoria married FREDERICK III Kaiser of Germany (Mar–Jun 1888) | EDWARD VII King of Great Britain (1901–1910) | Alice married Ludwig of Hesse |

| WILHELM II Kaiser of Germany (1888–1918) | GEORGE V (1910–1936) | Alexandra married NICHOLAS II Tsar of Russia (1894–1917) |

figure 2 the feuding royal houses

Of the nine children of Queen Victoria, the Queen of Britain, the eldest, Princess Victoria, married the German Kaiser, Frederick III, popularly known as Fritz. In 1859, she gave birth to a son, Wilhelm who, as Wilhelm II, became Kaiser in 1888 and was to rule Germany during the First World War. Victoria's second child, Edward, a portly high-living prince, succeeded his mother to the throne in 1901 and reigned until his death in 1910 when he was succeeded by his son, George V. Alice, Victoria's third child, married the German prince Louis of Hesse. Their daughter, Alexandra, married Nicholas II, Tsar of Russia. This meant that the British King, George V, was a cousin of both the German Kaiser, Wilhelm II, and Alexandra, the Tsarina of Russia. Since their mothers were Danish princesses and sisters, George V was also a cousin of Nicholas II and although they got on well, neither liked nor trusted their German cousin, Wilhelm II. It is interesting to note that in 1901, her son, King Edward VII, her grandson, Kaiser Wilhelm, and Tsar Nicholas II of Russia all attended Queen Victoria's funeral. Yet within 20 years, two would themselves be dead and the third facing self-imposed exile.

Great power rivalry

Each of the great powers was ambitious, mindful of its own needs and jealous of the others. As the years passed this jealousy turned first to bitter rivalry. Frenchmen looked forward to what they considered would be an inevitable war with Germany during which they would gain revenge for their defeat in 1870 and which would give them the chance to regain Alsace and Lorraine. For his part, the German Kaiser was jealous of Britain's colonial expansion and commercial prosperity and wanted to extend his own country's influence in the world. He was convinced that the future greatness of Germany was dependent on her becoming a naval power. As he put it, 'We have fought for a place in the sun and won it. Our future is on the water.' Naturally the British became alarmed when Germany seemed intent on challenging her long-standing supremacy on the seas.

The scene changed dramatically in 1906 when the British launched the first of a new class of powerful, ironclad warships. Called HMS *Dreadnought*, its range, speed and firepower outclassed German battleships and made them obsolete. The Germans referred to their own battleships as being *fünf-minuten* ships, 'five-minute ships', the time they would last when confronted by a *Dreadnought*. During the years that followed, Britain and Germany became involved in a naval race to build the greatest number of *Dreadnought*-class battleships. As

figure 3 the Balkans in 1914

Admiral von Tirpitz masterminded the building of a powerful German fleet, so the British government dithered as to the number they should build. The British public had no such doubts. A popular British music-hall song of the day was 'We want eight and we won't wait'. The effects of this rivalry were serious; the building of such ships proved a great financial burden for both countries.

Austria-Hungary and Russia had long been rivals in an area of south-east Europe known as the Balkans. The whole region had once been part of the Ottoman Empire and had been ruled by the Turks. As the Turkish Empire fell apart, so both powers tried to take advantage of the situation and extend their influence in the area. Both had common frontiers with the former Turkish provinces whilst Russia claimed the additional advantage of sharing the same Slav heritage as many of the Balkan peoples.

In the squabble between the two countries, Kaiser Wilhelm firmly backed Austria-Hungary. Germany had also tried to get on good terms with the Sultan of Turkey by building a railway that linked Berlin with Baghdad and promising financial and military aid. Neither Austria-Hungary nor Russia seemed to appreciate that the peoples of the Balkans hoped to set up their own independent Slav state free from their influence. One Balkan country more than any other stood firmly against Austrian domination – little Serbia.

From rivalries to alliances and ententes

Alliances are formed when nations bind themselves together by treaties and this often happens when countries share a common fear and look for security on the basis of safety in numbers. During the years when Bismarck was the Chancellor of Germany, he planned a series of alliances with other countries that were intended to safeguard Germany from any possible threat from Russia or the chance that France might wage a war of revenge. In 1879, he formed a Dual Alliance with neighbouring Austria-Hungary by which the countries agreed to help each other if attacked by another. The Dual Alliance became a Triple Alliance when they were joined by Italy who was, at best, a half-hearted member. Although the Kaiser claimed that the Triple Alliance was defensive in nature, the existence of such a powerful bloc of nations in central Europe spread alarm amongst their neighbours. Since both France and Russia thought the Triple Alliance was aimed at them, it was inevitable that they would come together to gain greater security and this they did in 1894. The threat posed by Kaiser Wilhelm's Germany also made it necessary for Britain and France to settle their differences. Many hatchets had to be buried before the two countries could reach a closer understanding and in 1904, an Anglo-French Entente was agreed. It became popularly known as the Entente Cordiale. An entente is not a formal alliance but more an agreement to settle differences and work more closely together. Eventually a Triple Entente was formed that embraced France, Britain and Russia. It was now the Kaiser's turn to be alarmed since it appeared that the Entente powers encircled Germany. More significantly, the creation of a system of alliances and ententes meant that the European great powers were now divided into two hostile armed camps, clearly posing a threat to the future peace in Europe.

figure 4 Europe divided – the Triple Alliance and the Triple Entente

In such a situation all that was needed was a provocative act, a spark, to plunge Europe into war. The German Kaiser, described as having 'the touchiness of a prima donna and the conceit of a small child', was not best suited to dealing with such a situation.

'Now tell us all about the war,
And what we fought each other for.'

(Robert Southey, 1774–1843)

The coming of war

A crisis is a decisive moment, a turning point when at a time of danger, things can go either one way or the other. There were two areas in Europe where provocative acts led to crises which might have led to war – Morocco in North Africa and the Balkans.

In 1905, Kaiser Wilhelm II challenged French rights to be involved in the affairs of Morocco when he travelled to Tangier to pay a courtesy call on the Sultan. During his visit he made a provocative speech openly supporting Moroccan independence and challenging the right of France to exercise authority over the country. The French were outraged by the Kaiser's audacity and the following year the major European powers attended a conference at the Spanish port of Algeciras to discuss the issue. If Wilhelm's aim was to test the solidarity of the Triple Entente, he would have been disappointed since Britain and Russia stood firmly behind France. The outcome was an unwelcome rebuff for the German Kaiser but the issue of Morocco was far from settled. In 1911, tribesmen attacked the Moroccan town of Fez and the French sent troops to restore order and garrison the town. The German response was to dispatch the gunboat *Panther* to the nearby port of Agadir on the pretext of safeguarding their country's interests in the area. This was a rash act of brinkmanship. Once again Britain stood by France and even went as far as to begin the partial mobilization of the Royal Navy! Not wishing to risk war, the Kaiser was forced to

THE BOILING POINT.

A *Punch* cartoon of 1912 which shows the leaders of the great European powers sitting on a pot marked 'Balkan troubles', indicates their concern as the situation in the region reaches boiling point.

back down. Wilhelm had once again lost face and the affront angered the German people who put the blame squarely on Britain. Britain was now seen as the main enemy and a wave of anti-British feeling swept Germany. The years that followed were the most frantic in the naval race between the two countries and with the Kaiser angry and frustrated, he was likely to act even more irresponsibly than before.

In 1898, Bismarck commented, 'If there is ever another war in Europe, it will come out of some dammed silly thing in the Balkans'. How true his prophecy turned out to be. In 1908, Austria-Hungary annexed Bosnia. It was an act that infuriated Bosnia's neighbours and unsettled the whole Balkan region.

During the year 1912, the Balkans was torn by unrest that ended in war. The First Balkan War of 1912 lasted barely 50 days and the following year this was followed by the Second Balkan War. The outcome of the wars led to much bitterness and was to decide which side the various Balkan states would join in the event of any future war.

Assassination at Sarajevo

At around 11 a.m. on the morning of Sunday 28 June 1914, the heir to the throne of Austria-Hungary and his wife were assassinated by a teenage student in Sarajevo, the capital of Bosnia. Bosnia, forcibly annexed by the Austrians in 1908, was a dangerous country for any member of the Austrian royal house to visit. The state visit by the heir to the Austrian throne was a provocative act and always likely to attract a response from one of the secret societies that were part of the Pan Slav movement. The victims were Archduke Franz Ferdinand and his wife Sophie. As we have seen, the Archduke became heir to the throne as the result of the number of bizarre tragedies that befell the Emperor's family. He was said to have been 'a humourless, hectoring man, who killed animals in large numbers, but was conscientious and not unintelligent'. He was certainly a devoted family man. He married Sophie, who came from an aristocratic but poor Czech family, against the wishes of the Emperor. The marriage was declared morganatic which meant that any children would be debarred from succeeding to the throne. The assassin, Gavrilo Princip, had three accomplices. They were Serbians who belonged to Union or Death, a secret society better known as the Black Hand.

The Archduke arrived in the Bosnian capital fully aware of the risks he was taking. It was also his wedding anniversary. Together with his wife, he proceeded from the railway station to the town hall in a procession of open cars. On the way, a bomb was thrown at their car but it fell on the folded roof and bounced under the car following behind. Even though 20 people were wounded, the Archduke did not lose his composure. Sadly, his good fortune did not survive their return journey. His driver lost his way and as he stopped to reverse the car, Princip ran from the crowd of onlookers and fired at his victims from point-blank range. The stricken Archduke cried out to his wife, 'Sophie, Sophie don't die. Live for our children.' The Duchess died first followed by the Archduke, his jugular vein severed by a bullet. No murder in history has had such calamitous consequences.

'War by timetable'

The sequence of events that followed the assassination of Archduke Franz Ferdinand seemed to follow a prescribed order and has been described by the historian A. J. P. Taylor as 'War by timetable'. He wrote, 'Sarajevo had set in motion machinery which could not be stopped' (*War By Timetable*, 1969).

Even though an investigation by Austrian officials failed to find any link to connect the Serbian government with the murders, the matter was not allowed to rest. In the Austrian capital, Vienna, there were politicians and military leaders who urged war and saw the assassination as a heaven-sent opportunity to eliminate Serbia, who was regarded as the champion of Pan Slavism in the Balkans.

Crucial to the outcome was the attitude of Germany, Austria-Hungary's powerful ally. In the event, the Kaiser let it be known that Germany would 'stand faithfully by Austria-Hungary, as required by the obligations of their treaty'. In effect, the guaranteed backing of Germany gave the Austrians carte-blanche, complete freedom of action, to do as they wished. They sent an ultimatum to Serbia listing ten demands. The Serbs reply was conciliatory and they rejected only one demand that appeared to infringe their country's sovereignty. As Austria-Hungary began to mobilize her forces for war so Britain and France called for a conference to discuss the crisis. On 28 July 1914, Austria invaded Serbia. Although the Tsar's confidante,

Rasputin, warned, 'Let papa not plan war, for with the war will come an end of Russia and yourselves', Nicholas's reaction was to put his own forces on a war footing. When a German demand for an end to these preparations was ignored, Germany declared war on Russia. Next the Germans sought an undertaking of neutrality from France. The French government replied that it would be 'guided by her own interests' and began to mobilize for war. On 3 August 1914, the Germans falsely claimed that French aircraft had dropped bombs on a German city and declared war on France.

The British involvement

Although Britain was a member of the Triple Entente, she was not committed to joining the war. At home, public opinion was divided. One view was expressed by a newspaper that commented 'We care as little for Belgrade (the capital of Serbia) as Belgrade cares for Manchester' but others thought that, as a matter of honour, Britain should immediately side with her Entente partners. But in the end the matter was settled for them. Years before the war, the Germans had devised a plan, the Schlieffen Plan, that was intended to bring about the speedy defeat of France and avoid the possibility of having to fight on two fronts. In order to be able to outflank the French armies, the plan required the Belgian government to agree to the passage of German troops across their country. When the request was turned down, German troops invaded Belgium. Years before in 1839, Britain and other European powers including Germany had agreed to a treaty by which they collectively guaranteed the neutrality of Belgium. The British government sent an ultimatum to Germany demanding the withdrawal of their troops and that the neutrality of Belgium be respected. The Kaiser ignored the demands after being advised that Britain would be unlikely to go to war 'just for a scrap of paper'. When, on 4 August 1914, the time set for a response to the ultimatum expired, Britain declared war on Germany. As the last minutes of peace ticked away, the British foreign secretary, Sir Edward Grey, standing in the window of his office in Whitehall likened what was happening in Europe to the actions of a man in the street below who was dimming the gaslights. He famously remarked, 'The lamps are going out all over Europe; we shall not see them lit again in our lifetime.'

BRAVO, BELGIUM!

A *Punch* cartoon of August 1914 shows plucky Belgium standing firm against German threats.

What became of the assassins?

Immediately after he had fired the shots that killed Franz Ferdinand, Gavrilo Princip attempted to commit suicide. He failed and was dragged to the local police station. Under torture, he betrayed the names of his accomplices and they were arrested. Their trial lasted a month and at the end all but Princip were sentenced to death. The actual assassin was under age and escaped the hangman's noose by just a fortnight. Instead he was sentenced to spend 20 years in an Austrian prison. The Austrian authorities did not intend him to live and he died in April 1918 with one arm amputated and suffering from tubercular ulcers.

Prior to his execution, one of Princip's accomplices, Nedeljiko Cabrinivic, wrote a letter to his three-year-old daughter:

'My child, the only thing that your father can leave you is his honest and untarnished name ... When you grow up and you will hear about those tumultuous times in which your father lived. If you understand them, you will forgive him ... Be honest and love the people whose roots are your own.'

To the Slav people, the assassins were heroes. Later, a museum was built in Sarajevo to commemorate Princip's bravery and was named in his honour.

02

the opening moves on the Western Front

This chapter will cover:
- the initial reaction to the outbreak of war
- the Schlieffen Plan
- the importance of the retreat from Mons and the Battle of the Marne
- the Christmas truce of 1914.

'Tramp, tramp, the grim road from Mons to Wipers
I've 'ammered out this ditty with me bruised and bleedin' feet.
Tramp, tramp, the dim road – we didn't 'ave no pipers,
And bellies that was 'oller was the drums we 'ad to beat.'

(*The Red Retreat, Rhymes of a Red Cross Man*,
Robert Service, 1916)

Reactions to the outbreak of war

Press reports and rumour meant that the last weeks of peace had
something of an unreal quality. There was no mood of
impending crisis and people continued with their everyday lives
and enjoyed their summer pleasures. In Germany, the Kaiser left
for a yachting holiday in the Norwegian fjords; in France, the
President made plans to visit Russia; in Britain, the King opened
a conference on the issue of home rule for Ireland. However,
once war was declared, governments found it easy to stir up
patriotic fervour. Jubilant crowds in jingoistic mood took to the
streets in Berlin, Paris, Vienna, St. Petersburg and London to
cheer and sing. In Britain, military leaders spoke of a war that
would be 'over by Christmas'. In Berlin, the German Chancellor
remarked solemnly, 'Just for a scrap of paper, Great Britain is
going to make war with a kindred nation that desires nothing
better than to be friends with her.' Whilst the Kaiser reflected,
'To think that George and Nicky have played me false! If my
grandmother [Queen Victoria] had been alive, she would never
have allowed it', his son, the Crown Prince took a different line
and claimed to be delighted at the prospect of 'a gay and jolly
little war'. He further jested that it would be a case of 'lunch in
Paris, dinner in St. Petersburg'. In towns and cities across
Europe, men queued to 'join up' for what they regarded as the
start of a great adventure. They might have better considered
the words of a wise American president, 'Older men declare
war. But it is the young that must fight and die.'

Opening moves and the Schlieffen Plan

As nations continued to mobilize their armies and fleets,
Germany had already worked out a master plan for the quick
and decisive defeat of her enemies. The German military leaders
had long feared the prospect of engaging two enemies
simultaneously – Russia in the east and France in the west.

Count Alfred von Schlieffen, the former German Chief of Staff, calculated that it would take Russia longer to mobilize her forces than France and therefore decided to use the bulk of the German army to win a speedy and decisive victory over the French. France defeated, he would then turn to the east and deal with the Tsar's armies. His plan, the 'revolving door technique', required the German armies to sweep through neutral Belgium into northern France and advance to the west of Paris. The Germans would then swing south in a wide arc to outflank the French armies defending their common border with Germany and force them to surrender. If the Belgians resisted, the main obstacles to the German advance would be Liege and Namur since these fortress towns would be stoutly defended. The plan also involved risks – the Russians might mobilize more quickly than expected and the invasion of Belgium might draw Britain into the war. Schlieffen, who died in 1912, did not live long enough to see his plan put into effect. On 4 August 1914, German troops invaded Belgium and within a fortnight Brussels had fallen and Antwerp was under siege. Meanwhile a British Expeditionary Force (BEF), under the command of Field Marshal Sir John French, had sailed for France. Once landed, it took up position next to the French in the path of the advancing Germans.

Mons and the Marne

The BEF was made up of some 70,000 regular soldiers and reservists. Referred to scathingly by the German Kaiser as 'a contemptible little army', they were highly trained infantrymen and what they lacked in numbers they more than made up for in their professionalism and skilled use of their main weapon, the Lee-Enfield rifle.

The first British encounter with the enemy occurred close to the Belgian coal-mining town of Mons when Irish Dragoons came face to face with a force of Uhlans, German cavalry. At Mons, the BEF fought the Germans to a standstill among the slag heaps close to the Mons-Conde Canal and the battle gave birth to the legend of the 'Angels of Mons' when some British soldiers claimed to have been helped by angel-like English archers from a bygone age. The rumour was repeated by returning wounded soldiers who were probably delirious but it was nevertheless believed by some. The early British success at Mons was short lived. To the south the French were in retreat and this meant that the BEF risked being outflanked. They had no choice other than to retreat. The historian John Terraine has written, 'Mons scarcely rates as a battle at all, there was certainly no evidence that it slowed the Germans to any noticeable extent' (*Mons*, 1960).

The retreat from Mons was a slow rearguard action doggedly fought by exhausted and footsore British infantrymen described by Terraine as 'men stumbling more like ghosts than living soldiers, unconscious of everything about them, but still moving under the magic impulse of discipline and regimental pride'. At Le Cateau, British units under Major General Smith Dorrien stood to fight the Germans who were in hot pursuit and there they briefly held overwhelming forces. Fighting from shallow, hastily prepared trenches, both the Germans and the British inflicted and suffered heavy losses before continuing their retreat. Afterwards, the British commander-in-chief, Field Marshal Sir John French, showed his resentment at Smith Dorrien's decision to stand and fight by removing him from command on the pretext of bad health. Heavily outnumbered, the BEF aimed to delay the German advance long enough for the French to regroup and rush forward fresh reserves. After only ten days of fighting, the Germans were still surging forward and closing in on Paris. Only one obstacle lay in the way – the River Marne.

Although the speed of the German advance had been impressive, it had created problems. As they advanced, so their lines of communication became stretched and with the Russians mobilizing more speedily than expected, troops had to be withdrawn and sent to the east. At this point, the German High Command decided to tinker with Schlieffen's original plan. Instead of sweeping to the west of Paris and encircling the French capital, they decided to pursue the retreating French to the east of the city. This proved to be a major blunder. The move weakened the left flank of the German army and gave the Allies, the name now given to those fighting on the side of France and Britain, the chance to counterattack. In Paris, the governor of the city assembled reserves and sent them forward to the front line in taxis, the famous 'taxis of the Marne'. For two weeks, the Battle of the Marne raged along a 250-kilometre (155-mile) front. As the German position became increasingly precarious, so they were forced to retreat from the River Marne to a new defensive line to the north-east along the River Aisne. The outcome of the battle has been referred to as 'the miracle of the Marne' and because of its significance, some have gone as far as to regard it as 'the most important of the twentieth century'. It halted the German advance, ensured the failure of the Schlieffen Plan and brought about the dismissal of senior German generals. It is only possible to speculate on what the effect a German victory might have had on the outcome of war and even the future history of Europe. What was certain was that any chance of a quick end to the war had finally gone and the war would definitely not be over by Christmas!

The 'race to the sea' and the Ypres salient

The Germans next turned their attention to the flat coastal region of Flanders – the northern border area between Belgium and France – and here each side struggled to outflank the other as they tried to reach the coast in what became known as the 'race to the sea'. The German aim was to extend their front line to the Channel coast and gain control of the strategically important ports of Dunkirk, Calais and Boulogne. All now depended on the ability of the British and Belgians to hold on to the coastal strip around the River Yser and, inland, the city of Ypres.

The battle that followed, the First Battle of Ypres, was the last major battle fought on the Western Front in 1914. It lasted a month and, helped by the arrival of French reinforcements and flooding of a stretch of the coastal region, the Germans failed to break through. During the battle, British casualties totalled nearly 60,000, the majority being original members of the BEF It was but a taste of things to come since Ypres, or 'Wipers' as British soldiers called it, was to witness further bloody encounters and even greater loss of life.

The German failures on the Marne and at Ypres led to a position of stalemate as each side tried, but failed, to dislodge the other. The nature of the warfare was such that soldiers could only find safety by 'digging in' and it was at this stage of the war that the construction of trenches began in earnest. Soon a continuous network of trenches stretched the 800 kilometres (497 miles) from the English Channel to the Swiss border.

figure 5 the Western Front – the front line at the end of 1914

The Christmas truce of 1914 – did it really happen?

Christmas Day 1914 witnessed one of the most notable and unusual events of the First World War. An unofficial truce occurred along sections of the Ypres battlefield during which British and German troops openly fraternized in the land between the opposed trenches, no man's land. It began during a lull in the fighting on Christmas Eve when, after dark, the Germans lit up a Christmas tree and began to sing carols before men on both sides climbed over the top of their trenches, shook hands and wished each other 'a merry Christmas'. They exchanged gifts of cigarettes and cigars as well as souvenirs such as cap badges and family photographs and some even exchanged addresses so that they could make contact after the war. On Boxing Day, a football match was arranged and photographs taken. The truce, which was not general and only took place in sections of the lines, involved hundreds of soldiers and gave both sides the opportunity to bury their dead. The event, described as 'an oasis of sanity in a deadlocked war', gave rise to concern in both the British and German High Commands since they saw it as a threat to the fighting spirit of their troops. They took steps to ensure that the episode would never be repeated.

One explanation of this unusual event is that earlier in the year the Pope had proposed a Christmas Day truce and many of the German soldiers involved came from Bavaria, a largely Roman Catholic area of Germany. It is possible that the unofficial truce came about as an attempt to implement the Pope's wishes.

03 stalemate and a widening war

This chapter will cover:
- the situation on the Western Front during 1915
- the involvement of Turkey and Italy in the war
- the war on other fronts
- the fate of Germany's colonies.

'When all is said and done, the war was mainly a matter of holes and ditches.'

(*Memoirs of an Infantry Officer*,
Siegfried Sassoon, 1930)

The situation at the start of 1915

Although the First World War (1914–18) never became truly a world war to the extent of the Second World War (1939–45), its military operations did extend widely across several fronts in Europe and beyond into the Middle East, Africa and even the Pacific. This was brought about because other powers such as Turkey, Italy and Japan became involved in the conflict and also because Britain, France and Germany had overseas possessions that bordered on each other.

It should also be remembered that imperial powers such as Britain, France and Germany soon involved their colonies in the conflict. In the case of Britain, this meant that Australia, New Zealand, Canada, India and South Africa came to the assistance of their 'Mother Country'. In order to exploit Britain's dependency on imported foods and raw materials and hinder the passage of imperial forces to Europe, German surface raiders ranged across the Atlantic, Indian and Pacific Oceans tracking down and sinking British merchant ships and troopships. Meanwhile on the Western Front the stalemate continued.

The Western Front during 1915

During 1915, Allied and German generals set out to break the deadlock on the Western Front no matter what the cost. The first major offensive came when British troops tried to recapture the village of Neuve Chapelle that the Germans had occupied at the end of the previous year. Although the British were successful in their objective, the battle highlighted two important issues – it revealed the first signs of a shortage of shells and it also provided the first evidence of the human cost of launching frontal attacks against an enemy holding well-prepared defensive positions. The Germans were surprised by the tactic used by the British, which presented them with a target of a solid wall of khaki men, side-by-side and even more so by the fact that once one line had been mowed down by machine-gun fire, another appeared. The lesson was not learned by the British and a same familiar pattern was to be followed time and time again with dire consequences. In the spring came the Second Battle of Ypres, chiefly remembered for the first use of chemical warfare in the form of chlorine gas. The first victims were French colonial troops who panicked, threw away their weapons and fled, then two days later gas was used against the Canadians at St. Julian. Since it was known that ammonia present in urine had the effect of minimizing the effects of chlorine gas, and with no respirators available at this stage of the war, the best the Canadians could do was tie pieces of cloth soaked in urine over their mouths and nostrils. Imagine how awful this was – although there was much worse to come!

During the battle little ground was yielded to the Germans but at a cost – 60,000 casualties. In the autumn, British and French forces combined to launch another offensive along the River Aisne and although the Germans were driven back, they regained the lost ground in a series of counterattacks. During the offensive, French casualties totalled 120,000, British, 50,000 and German, 165,000. In spite of the carnage, once again nothing was achieved but it did lead to the dismissal of the British commander-in-chief, Field Marshal Sir John French.

New nations involved

The outcome of the Second Balkan War decided the nature of the expansion of the war in the Balkans. With Serbia supported by the Allies, because of the earlier Balkan wars, it was inevitable that Bulgaria would join the Central Powers, the name applied to Germany and her allies. In 1916 Romania joined Britain and France, to be followed by Greece in 1917, but even more significant was the entry of Turkey into the war.

Although generally regarded as a nation in decline, Turkey was in a position to blockade the Dardanelles and control entry into the Black Sea and she was also strategically placed to threaten Egypt and the Suez Canal. Before the war, both Britain and Germany had gone to great lengths to win the friendship of Turkey. Sixty years earlier, at the time of the Crimean War, Britain and France had fought to defend Turkish interests against her traditional enemy, Russia, but now Britain and France were allies of Russia, and Turkey faced a conflict of loyalties. Within the Turkish government, factions supported both sides but most influential was the pro-German nationalist,

Enver Pasha, who had once been employed in the Turkish embassy in Berlin. Whilst the Germans had built the Berlin to Baghdad railway and sent their officers to help train and modernize the Turkish army, the British had agreed to build two *Dreadnought*-type battleships for the Turkish government and these were nearing completion in British shipyards. At the start of the war, Winston Churchill, the First Lord of the Admiralty, ordered the seizure of the two ships and this outraged the Turks who accused the British of bad faith and treachery. The matter was finally decided when two German battleships, the *Goeben* and the *Breslau*, outran British warships in the Mediterranean Sea to reach Constantinople and once there, the Germans generously offered them to Turkey to compensate for 'England's theft'. The Turks next closed the Dardanelles to Allied shipping, an act that effectively blockaded Russia since it prevented shipments of armaments reaching her Black Sea ports. Within a week Britain, France and Russia declared war on Turkey. The first Turkish move was to invade the neighbouring Russian province, the Caucasus, with the intention of threatening the Baku oilfields but their troops, unprepared for the harsh winter conditions, were routed. However, as we shall discover, Turkey still had an important part to play in the war.

Since Italy still distrusted France and had no quarrel with Germany, Italian opinion was divided about the war and it was only after much diplomatic manoeuvring that Italy abandoned her membership of the Triple Alliance and joined the Allies. Italy had long coveted regions along her borders with Austria-Hungary and Italian nationalists saw involvement in the war as a means of acquiring those territories. In 1915, Italy agreed the Treaty of London with the Allies. At the time, the terms of the treaty were kept secret but they included a promise that, after the war, Italy would gain the south Tyrol, Trieste, Istria and a part of the Dalmatian coast. It was also agreed that Albania, just across the Adriatic Sea, would become an independent Muslim state with Italy responsible for her foreign policy. In May of that year Italy finally declared war on Austria-Hungary but it would be another year before she finally entered the war against Germany. From an Allied point of view, Italian entry into the war would provide them with important bases for their Mediterranean operations and at the same time, open up a new front that would divert Austro-Hungarian resources from the Eastern Front where Austria-Hungary was fighting Russia. Clearly Italy was tempted into the war on the side of the Allies by promises of a share of the spoils once victory was won but to Britain and France her involvement in the war soon proved to be more a liability than an asset. With her soldiers inadequately trained, lacking in fighting qualities, inadequately supplied with munitions and other war materials and, General Cardona apart, led by officers of poor quality, Italy was far from prepared for war.

The war on other fronts

The involvement of Turkey and Italy added a new dimension to the war. In addition to the Western and Eastern Fronts, the armies of the Allies and the Central Powers now faced each other in Serbia and Salonika, on the Italian Front and along Turkey's common border with Russia. To these would soon be added a campaign on the Turkish mainland, in Palestine, Mesopotamia and against German colonies in east and south-west Africa.

figure 6 military operations in Europe during 1915

figure 7 Serbia finally overrun

Although isolated from her Allies, Serbia caused problems for
Austria-Hungary and at the start, the Austrian offensive against
Serbia turned into a humiliating failure and was easily repulsed.
Although poorly equipped, the Serbs fought well and by the end
of 1914 were able to launch their own offensive and expelled
the invaders from their country. Enough was enough and the
Germans sent Field Marshal August von Mackensen to sort
things out and organize a combined Austrian, German,
Bulgarian offensive against troublesome Serbia. With Austro-
Hungarian forces crossing the River Danube and advancing
from the north and west and the Bulgarians moving from the
east in an outflanking movement, the Serbs had no choice but to
retreat westward. Led by a hero of earlier years, the wily,
67-year-old Radomir Putnik, the Serbs avoided encirclement by
making their way across the mountains of Albania in most
appalling weather conditions to reach the Adriatic Coast and
there some 150,000 were taken on board Allied ships and
transferred to the island of Corfu. Meanwhile, to the south a
British and French force had landed in Salonika to help 'plucky
little Serbia' but with their attempt to advance northwards
blocked by the Bulgarians, they had no choice other than to dig
in. Isolated and involved in little action, they became nicknamed
the 'Gardeners of Salonika'.

After declaring war, the Italians attempted a series of offensives
against the Austrians in the Alps and along the River Isonzo in
the general direction of Trieste. Warfare in the Alps was always

destined to be hard going and require special skills and powers of endurance and the severe weather and hazardous conditions soon blighted the initial enthusiasm of the Italians. The struggle to win control of the high ground and mountain ridges ended in stalemate and both sides were forced to dig in along the Isonzo.

The fate of Germany's colonies

In accordance with her alliance with Britain and with the hope of expanding her territories in the Pacific, Japan declared war on Germany in 1914. The Japanese were quick to occupy Germany's island possessions – the Palau, Caroline, Marianas and Marshall Islands and also besieged and captured Tsingtao, a port on the Chinese mainland that had been leased by Germany. Also during 1914, New Zealand took possession of Samoa whilst Australian troops occupied Papua and New Guinea.

figure 8 Germany's colonies in the Pacific and Africa

During the nineteenth century, Germany had taken part in the stampede to colonize Africa, the so-called 'scramble for Africa'. By 1914, German colonies in Africa included Togo, the Cameroons, German South-West Africa (present day Namibia) and German East Africa (present day Tanzania) and all were adjacent to British and French colonies. At the start of the war, Togo was overrun by British and French forces during a three-week campaign and by the end of the year, the Cameroons had also been taken following a jungle campaign involving British, French and Belgian troops. German South-West Africa, which lay next to British South Africa, presented more of a problem. In South Africa, memories of the Boer War were still fresh and the cause of much animosity and many former Boers, now known as Afrikaners, remembered with great bitterness that the British had burned down their homesteads, rounded up their women and children and interned them in concentration camps where thousands had died of disease and malnutrition. Now they looked for the opportunity to avenge these atrocities by supporting Germany. In 1914, a rebellion broke out led by the former Boer leader, Solomon Maritz. The rebels attracted the support of over 10,000 men but after some initial success, their efforts came to nothing. Fortunately, for the Allies, the majority of the Boers, including their former generals Louis Botha and Jan Smuts, were prepared to join their former enemy in the war against Germany. Led by Botha, South African forces invaded the German colony and in spite of the fact that thousands of South African soldiers deserted to the Germans, loyal South Africans forced the colony to surrender.

The Allies experienced the greatest resistance in German East Africa where a force largely made up of Askaris, native soldiers, and commanded by the formidable soldier of genius, Colonel Paul von Lettow-Vorbeck, successfully resisted Allied attempts to invade the colony. However, faced by overwhelming numbers, Lettow-Vorbeck divided his army into small units of irregulars and during a brilliantly fought guerrilla campaign continued to harass the Allies. He managed to evade capture and his irregulars managed to hold down over 130,000 British and Empire troops until he finally surrendered in 1918 – a fortnight after an armistice had been signed in Europe.

04

the Eastern Front

This chapter will cover:
- Russia's entry into the war
- the nature of the war on the Eastern Front
- the successes of Hindenburg and Ludendorff
- the reasons for the Russian failures on the Eastern Front.

'… very shaken, part of it altogether smashed and the rest falling back.'

(A Russian officer's view of his army in 1915)

Russia's involvement in the war

Russia entered the war with the same enthusiasm shown by the other major powers, and as part of an effort to rally popular support for the Tsar, a large crowd outside the Winter Palace cheered Nicholas. Amongst his first actions was to change the name of his capital city from the German-sounding St. Petersburg to the more acceptable Russian version, Petrograd and in an effort to prove her loyalty, Alexandra, the Tsarina who was German by birth, became involved in hospital work. At the start of the war, the Tsar wanted to assume command of the Russian armies himself but he was prevailed upon to appoint his uncle, the Grand Duke Nicholas Nicholaievich. The Grand Duke, the nephew of a former tsar Alexander II, was unusually tall and full of energy, he was also a good administrator but a man of only limited experience as a military commander. Even so, as a soldier and strategist he was far superior to the generals who served him. The Russian Minister for War was Vladimir Sukhomlinov, a devious man who was flattered to win favours and was both corrupt and inefficient. Jealous of Grand Duke Nicholas who despised him, Sukhomlinov was to be more responsible than any other for the disasters that lay ahead.

The Eastern Front

The Eastern or Russian Front stretched from the Baltic Sea southward across East Prussia and the Russian province of Poland to Galicia in Austria-Hungary and along this front, the armies of Tsar Nicholas II confronted those of Austria-Hungary and Germany. The Germans, who had placed great emphasis on winning a speedy victory against France in the west, hoped that the Austro-Hungarians would be able to hold a defensive line and counter any Russian moves in the east with minimum German involvement. Unfortunately these hopes were dashed by the failure of the Schlieffen Plan and the unexpected speed with which the Russians mobilized their armies. On the face of it the Russians had one major advantage – they possessed near limitless manpower resources. The Russian regular army's pre-war strength was 1.4 million to which mobilization added a further 3.1 million and behind these lay umpteen millions of peasants willing to join the ranks and die for 'Mother Russia'. With the capacity to overrun their enemy by sheer weight of numbers, it was not surprising that it was known as the 'steamroller army'. Against this, the Russian armies were badly equipped and lacked modern weapons and whilst they did reasonably well against the Austro-Hungarians, they fared badly against the Germans who showed the value of their superior military training and modern weaponry. Unlike the Russians, the Germans were also able to benefit from a modern railway network that allowed them to move their troops speedily from one battlefront to another. In addition, they also had the advantage of being forewarned of their enemy's movements since they were able to intercept uncoded messages sent by the Russians on their radio transmitters. During the winter months, the harsh conditions on the Eastern Front would prove to be exceptionally demanding for the men of both sides.

The opening campaigns

It was in response to an urgent appeal from France to relieve pressure brought by the German onslaught in 1914 that the Russians launched their first offensive into East Prussia. There, Generals Paul von Rennenkampf, a Russian in spite of his German-sounding name, and Alexander Samsonov won an unexpected victory that caused the Germans some immediate concern. The German response was to transfer units from the Western Front and send Generals Paul von Hindenburg and Erich Ludendorff to take charge of their armies and sort things out. Hindenburg came from a Prussian landowning family that could trace its aristocratic and military traditions back to the thirteenth century, he was a veteran of many campaigns and during the Franco-Prussian War had been awarded the Iron Cross. It was said that he won promotion 'by ordinary process, not brilliance', and unlike most officers of his rank lacked both influence and money. He retired from the army in 1911 but was recalled in 1914 at the age of 67. Erich Ludendorff was a man of far more modest origins. Son of an impoverished landowner, he was commissioned into one of the less fashionable regiments. Nearly 20 years Hindenburg's junior, he was ambitious, a man of great mental and physical energy and of the two, he was the

figure 9 campaigns on the Eastern Front during 1914 and 1915

true military genius. As the war progressed, the aged Hindenburg and dynamic Ludendorff, 'twinned by their triumphs in East Prussia', gradually emerged as the real power in Germany in both military and political affairs.

With the two Russian armies separated by the Masurian Lakes, Ludendorff decided to concentrate on the one advancing from the south and at the Battle of Tannenburg, the Germans won a resounding victory and took 90,000 prisoners. Afterwards, the disgraced Samsonov took his own life. During the following month, the Germans turned their attention to the second Russian army and at the Battle of the Masurian Lakes they were again victorious. This time, the Russians lost some 120,000 casualties and were forced to retreat in disorder and so the legend of the invincibility of Hindenburg and Ludendorff was born.

1915 – A year of mixed fortunes for Russia

Although the Russians had suffered at the hands of the Germans, they continued to make progress against the Austrians and in the spring of 1915 were able to fight their way across the Carpathian Mountains and advance towards the River Danube before shortages of supplies and ammunition brought their advance to an abrupt halt. Within the German High Command there was some disagreement as to whether greater emphasis should be given to the Eastern or Western Front. Some, such as General Erich von Falkenhayn, favoured an offensive in the west but Hindenburg wanted to press home their advantage in the east and force Russia out of the war. In the end the views of the more influential Hindenburg prevailed. Strengthened by the arrival of reinforcements from the west, the Germans launched an offensive that took the Russians by surprise. First, their defences were shattered by a massive bombardment during which 700,000 shells were fired in four hours and then with the Germans advancing along the whole front, the Russians found themselves facing the risk of being caught in a pincer movement between the Austrian armies now advancing from Galicia in the south and German armies advancing from East Prussia in the north. The Russians had no other choice than to retreat and this allowed the Germans to advance rapidly and capture Warsaw first and then Brest-Litovsk. A Russian general reported to the Tsar '...a third of the men have no rifles. These poor devils have to wait patiently until their comrades fall so they can pick up their weapons. The army is drowning in it's own blood'. Driven from Poland, the Russians retreated further eastward so that they were now fighting on their own soil. Although the Russians fought bravely enough and resisted strongly, the Germans were able to advance nearly 500 kilometres (311 miles) before the Grand Duke's armies were able to establish a new defensive line that extended from Riga on the Baltic Sea to Romania in the Balkans. It was soon to become 'six hundred miles of mud and horror' along which Russian casualties stood at 2 million with a further million lost as prisoners. The suffering of the soldiers was horrendous, yet disastrous as the whole episode may have been, the Russians had made it impossible for the Germans to concentrate all their efforts on the Western Front. In addition, they had provided the French and British with sufficient breathing space to call up reservists, begin to train new recruits and bring to Europe the armies being raised in the British Empire – Australians, New Zealanders, Canadians, Indians and South Africans. Now Russia herself was in desperate need of help from her allies.

What went wrong on the Eastern Front?

In spite of their superiority in numbers, during the early stages of the war the Russian army gained only limited success against the Austro-Hungarians in Galicia before being badly mauled by the Germans in East Prussia and forced to retreat. Its disasters were accompanied by calamitous losses. What went wrong?

In the first place, the soldiers of the so-called Russian 'steamroller' army lacked adequate training and were poorly led and whilst Grand Duke Nicholas was considered to have done as well as circumstances allowed, his subordinates were ineffective to the point of being pathetic. Recruits drafted in as replacements for the losses were often sent to the front line without weapons and had to use agricultural implements such as scythes and pitchforks or wait to take weapons from the dead and wounded. In addition, they were inadequately equipped, clothed and fed and their armies possessed inadequate artillery and very few aircraft. During their offensives they still depended heavily on the success of the old-fashioned cavalry charges but even such skilled horsemen as the Cossacks were no match for German machine gunners. Of the slaughter, Hindenburg wrote, 'Sometimes we had to remove the mounds of enemy corpses from before our trenches in order to get a clear field of fire against fresh assaulting waves.' The historian John Erickson summed it up adequately when he wrote, 'The Russian infantryman, ill-equipped and under-fed, performed great feats of endurance and showed raw, unflinching courage, but manpower could not continually match the murderous enemy firepower.'

Vladimir Sukhomilov, the Russian Minister of War and a man said to 'have grown fat on inefficiency', must carry the blame for the appalling state of affairs. A friend of Tsar Nicholas and one of the favourites at court, he was described as being 'short and soft with a cat-like face, neat whiskers and beard and with an ingratiating almost feline manner that captivated those he set out to please'. He retained favour by being servile, flattering and entertaining and instead of discussing important military matters he preferred to tell jokes and be a figure of fun. He was partly responsible for his country's ill-advised entry into the war in 1914 and assured the Russian government, the Duma, that their army was ready for war and would be able to deal with any demands placed on it. From the start, Sukhomilov was at loggerheads with Grand Duke Nicholas and as the war progressed the two men came to hate each other. The Grand Duke blamed the disasters of 1914 and 1915 on Sukhomilov's apathy and incompetence and some Russians went as far as to suggest that Sukhomilov was secretly in the employment of the Germans. This was certainly not the case but unknowingly he did have two German spies on his staff and had borrowed sums of money from them. In the summer of 1915, a commission of inquiry found him guilty of incompetence and he was dismissed. Shortly afterwards he was tried, convicted for corruption and treason and sent to prison. On his release, he moved abroad and died in Berlin in 1926.

05 the Dardanelles fiasco

This chapter will cover:
- the differing views on the need for a campaign in the eastern Mediterranean
- the failure of the naval attack on the Dardanelles
- the preparations for the Gallipoli campaign and the involvement of the ANZACs
- the nature of the Gallipoli campaign
- some unusual episodes during the campaign
- the reasons for the failure of the Gallipoli campaign.

'Fair broke the day this morning,
Against the Dardanelles;
The breeze blew soft, the morn's cheeks
Were cold as cold as shells
But other shells were waiting
Across the Aegean Sea,
Shrapnel and high explosive,
Shells and hells for me.'

(From an untitled poem by Patrick Shaw-Stewart,
1888–1917)

Easterners versus Westerners

The entry of Turkey into the war meant that Britain had to take steps to protect her interests in the Persian Gulf and Egypt where the Suez Canal, her all important lifeline to India and the Far East, had to be safeguarded at all costs. The involvement of

figure 10 the strategic importance of the Dardanelles and the Gallipoli peninsula

Turkey was also significant to developments on other fronts. During the early months of 1915, two major problems confronted the Allies – what steps should be taken to break the deadlock on the Western Front and how could Britain and France best help to sustain Russia's flagging war effort and ensure that she remained in the war? A diversionary attack might provide a solution, but then there would be the question of where. Allied generals and politicians were divided on the whole issue.

In Britain, the War Council discussed different strategies. A plan to land along the Belgian coast behind the German lines was considered but quickly discounted before David Lloyd George, the Chancellor of the Exchequer and soon to be Minister of Munitions, and Winston Churchill, the First Lord of the Admiralty, argued that it was time for Britain to use her naval might to turn the tide without the further loss of millions of lives. An urgent appeal for help from Grand Duke Nicholas in Russia made an expedition against the Turks the most obvious choice and so Lloyd George and Churchill backed by Maurice Hankey, the Secretary of the War Council, and Admiral Sir John Fisher, made plans for 'a great amphibious operation' in the eastern Mediterranean. Collectively referred to as Easterners, they argued for a campaign aimed at securing the Dardanelles, the narrow straits that separated that part of Turkey in Europe from the Turkish mainland. The Dardanelles was also the seaway that by way of the Sea of Marmara connected the Aegean Sea, at the eastern end of the Mediterranean, with the Black Sea. Such a plan would fulfil two important aims – it would make it necessary for the Germans to send troops to reinforce the Turks and so possibly weaken their position on the Western Front and it would also bring into play the Royal Navy. Britain's greatest asset could be used to force a sea route to beleaguered Russia and make it possible to supply her with war materials and also give the chance of capturing Constantinople, which Churchill boldly, if unrealistically, forecast would take three weeks, and might even force Turkey out of the war altogether.

The scheme was controversial and had its opponents. These, known as Westerners, were mainly British and French generals in the High Command who were firmly of the opinion that in the long run, the war would be won or lost on the Western Front. They thought that there should be no slackening in the Allied efforts against Germany and claimed that the Dardanelles venture would at best, be a sideshow. Lord Kitchener, the British Minister for War, went further and insisted that no men be taken from the Western Front since this might weaken the Allied position there. Eventually a compromise was agreed by which an attempt would be made to force the Dardanelles by using naval power only. The British War Council resolved that the Royal Navy should 'prepare an expedition to bombard the Gallipoli peninsula with Constantinople as its objective'. Agreed without adequate consultation with military leaders or a realistic consideration of the difficulties posed by studying maps of the region, it was an ill-advised scheme. Furthermore no investigation had been held to discover if sufficient ships were available for the operation. The historian A. J. P. Taylor summed up the situation when he wrote, 'The War Council assumed that great armadas could waft non-existent armies to the ends of the earth in the twinkling of an eye' (*Struggle for the Mastery of Europe*, 1954).

The naval attack on the Dardanelles

figure 11 March 1915 – the naval attack on the Dardanelles

The first attack came when naval units under Admiral Sackville Carden attacked and largely destroyed the Turkish forts guarding the entrance to the Dardanelles but bad weather prevented their work being completed. Next mine sweeping trawlers manned by civilian crews and commanded by naval officers were sent to clear Turkish mines laid at the approach to the stretch of waterway known as the Narrows. Here, at a point where the channel was barely two kilometres (1.2 miles) wide, the Turkish guns situated on both sides of the water opened fire on the trawlers and forced them to retreat before the mines had all been cleared. A further problem arose when the sickly Admiral Carden fell ill and had to be replaced by his second-in-command, Admiral John de Robeck. A month later, an Allied fleet made up of 18 ships, many of them obsolete and considered expendable, sailed towards the Narrows with the intention of bombarding the Turkish gun positions and disrupting their communications. At first things seemed to go well until one French and two British battleships struck mines. Altogether the Allies lost six battleships and the disheartened de Robeck refused to continue the attack without adequate military support.

The Gallipoli campaign – the onset of a disaster

The failure of the naval attack finally persuaded Kitchener that the use of ground troops was essential. To avoid withdrawing men from the Western Front, a force of some 70,000 men was assembled consisting of the Australian and New Zealand Army Corps – the ANZACs – as well as British and French units. The force, under the command of a British general, Sir Ian Hamilton, was assembled on the Greek island of Lemnos. Although a man of charm and with a wealth of military experience, Hamilton was to prove an unimaginative and indecisive military leader and it is said that his knowledge of the Dardanelles was limited to maps in a tourist guidebook. He was to prove a far from ideal choice. From the start there were problems caused by the lack of adequate artillery and medical supplies and the fact that to make good the shortfall in landing craft, vessels had to be bought from the Greeks. Furthermore, with so much activity going on, the Turks were well aware that something was being planned.

figure 12 the Gallipoli campaign – April 1915–January 1916

The intention was to invade and occupy the Gallipoli peninsula and to achieve this, British and French forces would land on the tip of the peninsula at Cape Helles and the ANZACs further to the north near Gaba Tepe. In an attempt to mislead the Turks, a series of diversionary operations were planned but as the Allied intention became patently clear, the Turkish army, commanded by the German general, Liman von Sanders, dug in, improved their defences and transferred additional forces to the peninsula. The omens for the Allies were not good.

At dawn on 25 April 1915, the first troops ashore were the Australians. Either human error or the strength of the tide led them to land two kilometres (1.2 miles) north of the intended beach and they found themselves in a cove, later known as Anzac Cove, surrounded by high cliffs. Their landing was only lightly opposed and they were able to press ahead inland until strong Turkish resistance forced them back. At the time, the Turkish commander was Mustapha Kemal, a skilled military tactician and a born leader of men, and his inspired leadership was to play an important part in sustaining Turkish morale and the events that were to lead to their eventual victory. Later, as Kemal Ataturk, he became the leader of his country and was responsible for reforms that turned Turkey into a modern secular state.

The Australians now found themselves fighting desperately to hold on to the cliffs that overlooked their original landing site and the following day, the beach became a shambles as men wandered aimlessly about and stores piled up on the sand. It was, said one journalist, 'like a shipwreck'. During the months ahead, this area was to witness some of the most ferocious fighting of the Gallipoli campaign. On most other beaches, the landings were more successful but at Cape Helles, the Allies suffered another disaster. Here, the plan was for an old collier, a coal-carrying ship the *River Clyde*, to be run aground close to an old fort so that the soldiers could easily wade ashore and storm the beaches. The Allied military commanders didn't realize that the area was strongly defended by the Turks and that the water was too deep for the men to wade ashore. As a result, hundreds were either drowned or mown down by machine-gun fire as they tried to scramble from their grounded ship. On a neighbouring beach, men came under such murderous fire that later reinforcements 'waded ashore through a sea that was literally crimson with blood'. From a ship offshore, General Hunter-Weston, known to his men as 'Hunter-Bunter', seemed unaware of the catastrophe and continued to order his troops to land on an already hopelessly overcrowded beach whilst Hamilton, at his headquarters on board the battleship HMS *Queen Elizabeth* described the scene as 'too monstrous, too cold blooded; like watching gladiators from the dress circle'. Even so and in spite of many disturbing reports, he decided not to interfere with the decisions being made by 'the men on the spot'.

The remainder of the campaign

During the months that followed, the British and French on Cape Helles launched a series of offensives in an attempt to advance further inland but they suffered considerable losses and made only limited gains. At Anzac Cove, the front line changed little as the Australians and New Zealanders struggled to hang on to their narrow bridgehead. Unable to break out and with the Turks unable to drive them back into the sea, a stalemate was reached. With the opposed trenches often less than 100 metres (328 feet) apart, the fighting was usually hand-to-hand, grim and bloody and one Turkish attack against the ANZAC positions was so murderous that a truce had to be called to allow both sides to bring in their wounded and bury their dead. Trenches were sometimes blocked with the bodies of the dead and dying whilst the smell of decaying corpses was ever present and overpowering. The soldiers in the trenches were infested with lice and fleas and pestered by hordes of rats and when eating had to blow away swarms of flies before they could put food in their mouths. It was claimed that flies caused more casualties than bullets as men suffered from malaria, dysentery, a form of chronic diarrhoea, and other stomach disorders. Open wounds were soon covered with maggots and those transferred to the hospital ships sometimes found themselves being treated by veterinary surgeons and unqualified orderlies. A shortage of fit men meant that the wounded were often returned to the front line before they were fully recovered. During the summer months, the blazing sun made the heat overbearing and water was always in short supply. In one instance, a New Zealander sentenced to death for desertion was sent back to the front line where he fought bravely yet the following morning he was still executed as planned. With 'Johnny Turk' proving himself a far better soldier than expected, the Allied front line positions were constantly being shelled and any reckless movement was likely to attract the attention of a Turkish sniper. A final attempt was made to end the deadlock when Allied soldiers landed to the north at Suvla Bay, a move that was intended to coincide with an attempted breakout by those at Anzac Cove. For once the Turks were taken by surprise and the men on the two Allied beaches were able to link up.

Some unusual episodes

Born in 1892 at Durham in the north of England, John Simpson Kirkpatrick was 17 when he left home to work as a stoker on-board ship. He eventually settled in Queensland, Australia where he gained a reputation for brawling and a love of animals. At the start of the war, he enlisted in the Australian army under the name John Simpson and served in the 3rd Field Ambulance. Sent to Gallipoli, he landed at Anzac Cove and soon found himself a donkey. He used the animal to carry wounded men down from the front line to the beach and on his return journeys he took much-needed water supplies to the forward positions. Acting on his own initiative, he and his donkey became a familiar sight at Anzac Cove and, known for his whistling and wisecracking, he was ever cheerful and seemed oblivious to the dangers of snipers and shellfire. Simpson's bravery and good humour made him a legend until he was killed by machine-gun fire as he helped two wounded men down to the beach. Buried at Anzac Cove, he was later recommended for a Victoria Cross but the award was never made. He is still remembered with great affection by Australians and recently he featured on one of their postage stamps.

It was King George V's idea that some of the men serving on his Sandringham estate should form a company to serve in the war. The Sandringham Company, as it was known, was largely made up of servants, grooms and gardeners and became part of the 1/5th Battalion of the Norfolk Regiment and was commanded by Captain Frank Beck, the King's land agent on the estate. In August 1915 the Company landed at Suvla Bay. On 12 August 1915, Beck led his men forward across a section of the Suvla Plain towards the Turkish lines and they were never seen again. Afterwards rumours abounded about the 'vanished battalion', and some eyewitnesses went as far as to claim that they saw a yellow mist descend that formed a cloud and carried the men heavenward to safety. As was later discovered, the truth was far more ugly. The fact was that the men ran into a hail of machine-gun fire and the survivors, when surrounded, surrendered. As prisoners of war they were taken to a nearby barn and there in turn shot in the head. In 1999, the BBC made a film *All the King's Men* which told of this event with David Jason playing the part of Captain Frank Beck.

The end of the campaign and the evacuation

In London and Paris there was increasing concern about the conduct of the Gallipoli campaign since it had failed to achieve its aims and the Allies were suffering heavy losses. Winston Churchill was blamed for conceiving the idea in the first place and was forced to resign. In Britain, people began to question the ability of Hamilton and he was recalled and replaced by General Sir Charles Monro. The new commander immediately came to the conclusion that the campaign had to end, and the Gallipoli peninsula evacuated. A bitter Churchill commented, 'He came, he saw, he capitulated'. Although the forced withdrawal from the Dardanelles was a blow to Allied prestige, the final stage of the campaign proved a complete success. Ingenious plans were made to confuse the Turks so that they thought the Allied front line was still being strongly defended and then during the course of just two nights, the troops slipped quietly away from their positions at Anzac and Sulva. For a few weeks the British and French troops remained at Cape Helles until they too were finally evacuated and the disastrous episode came to an end.

The Dardanelles campaign – some considerations

General Hamilton once said 'The most fatal heresy of war is to believe that battles can be won without heavy losses'. The Dardanelles campaign was a dismal failure – it achieved nothing but still incurred heavy losses – and there is no doubt that the leadership of the Allied forces was inferior to that of the Turks. The intellectual Hamilton turned out to be more a frustrated poet than a military commander and he, together with other Allied commanders, completely underestimated the fighting qualities of Turkish soldiers. Many of them may have been illiterate peasants but they fought with great bravery to rid their country of the unwelcome invaders.

As the campaign progressed, the Australians and New Zealanders came to regard it as a 'British bungle'. The ANZACs disliked Hamilton intensely and thought he represented the worst of the British class system; they also considered General Hunter-Weston, alias Hunter-Bunter, 'a worthless buffoon'. His case was not helped by such worthless comments as 'Casualties? What do I care about casualties?' The ANZACs own commanding officer, Major-General William Birdwood, was certainly a far more gifted officer who showed a greater concern for the welfare of his men. The Australians and New Zealanders did not like the 'spit and polish' mentality of the British army and were slow to salute officers, particularly British officers. Only four men were shot at dawn by firing squads during the campaign largely because the Australians refused to allow their soldiers to be subject to the death penalty.

The Dardanelles campaign ruined political and military reputations and wasted thousands of lives. The total number of Allied casualties came to just over 250,000 and of these, 21,555 were British, 10,000 French, 8,702 Australians and 2,701 New Zealanders. No one knows for certain how many Turks lost their lives but the number is thought to be similar to that of the Allies. For Australia and New Zealand, the Dardanelles campaign was the most significant event in their history. Today, those 'pages of history written in the blood of their soldiers' are regarded as the birth of their national awareness and even their nationhood.

06

the Western Front: the men and their weapons

This chapter will cover:
- the recruitment of men for the British army
- army life
- British, French and German soldiers
- the weapons used in the trenches
- other weapons introduced during the war.

'This bloody steel
Has killed a man.
I heard him squeal
As on I ran.'

(From *The Bayonet*
by Wilfred Gibson, 1887–1930)

The general situation in 1914

There can be no doubt that at the start of the war Germany possessed the best trained and equipped army on mainland Europe. The French army, still suffering from an inferiority complex after its humiliation by the Prussians in 1870, though adequate in numbers, could not match the efficiency of the Germans. Russia could call on massive manpower reserves but did not have generals of any quality to lead them nor the necessary means to equip and support them in the field. During the nineteenth century, the British army had not enjoyed the best of fortunes. Between 1854 and 1856, it had fought a largely inconclusive war against Russia, the Crimean War, and a year later struggled to put down a rebellion against British rule in India, the Indian mutiny. In 1879, at the Battle of Isandlwana in South Africa, the British army suffered its greatest ever defeat at the hands of native warriors, the Zulu, but later on the same day, this was in part redeemed by the heroic defence of Rorke's Drift. General Gordon's expedition to the Sudan in 1885 ended in disaster until Kitchener reconquered the country 13 years later. The British army also failed to cover itself in glory during the Boer Wars and it was only after Boer women and children had been rounded up and placed in concentration camps that the last Boer resistance ended and they were forced to seek peace.

Against the expressed wishes of the military establishment, significant changes took place in the British army when Edward Cardwell, the Secretary for War during the 1870s, abolished the 'purchase system', a long-established system by which officers bought their rank. Infantry regiments, long known by numbers, changed to county titles so that, for example, 14th Foot became the West Yorkshire Regiment, and 28th Foot became the Gloucestershire Regiment. Cardwell also abolished flogging as a punishment in the army and reduced the number of years that a soldier could be expected to serve abroad. Between 1905 and 1912, the Secretary for War, R. B. Haldane, introduced a further series of organizational reforms that placed the command of the army under a General Staff and created a Territorial Army. He also provided for the rapid mobilization of an expeditionary force that could be sent abroad with little notice and it was this, the British Expeditionary Force (BEF), that first crossed to France in 1914. Unfortunately many of Haldane's reforms were largely copied from the German system and, accused of having German sympathies, he was forced to resign.

The British situation in 1914

In common with all the other belligerent European powers, at the outbreak of war Britain experienced a surge of patriotic fervour accompanied by a rush of volunteers keen to serve their 'King and Country'. The government's first action was to send a well-trained army of regular soldiers to France, the BEF, and these were soon to be joined by Reservists, those who had once been in the army and were liable to recall, and Territorials. The 64-year-old Field Marshal, Lord Kitchener, was made Secretary for War but in the long run it would prove an unhappy appointment.

Kitchener realized that the conflict would not 'be over by Christmas' and launched a recruiting campaign aimed at raising a new army of 500,000 volunteers capable of fighting a lengthy war. Great pressure was put on men to get them into khaki. Kitchener's famous poster, 'Your Country Needs You' immediately appealed to one's sense of patriotism and was used to great effect. Others used subtle emotional blackmail – a girl asking her father, 'Daddy, what did you do in the war?' was typical. Girls handed white feathers, a sign of cowardice, to men of military age who were still out of uniform and the opening line of a popular music-hall song of the day ran, 'We don't want to lose you but we think you ought to go'. In churches and chapels, clergy used their sermons to urge men to volunteer for military service. Across the country men wishing to join the Colours besieged recruiting offices with under-age youths and over-age men using all sorts of ploys to deceive the recruiting officers. It was quite usual for men to join with their friends, work mates and others from the same trade and they formed the so-called 'Pals Battalions' such as the 'Accrington Pals', the 'Cardiff Pals', and the 'Grimsby Chums'. Clerks and office workers came together to form units such as the 'Newcastle Commercials' whilst the 'Glasgow Tramways' was made up of transport workers from the city. One battalion consisted of members of the Boys' Brigade whilst another was made up entirely of public schoolboys. Kitchener was not entirely happy with the idea of 'Pals Battalions' since he feared that men's loyalties might be more to their locality than their regiment and country. By the end of 1914, some 1.19 million men had come forward and so great was the number of volunteers that it was not necessary to introduce conscription until January 1916. Unfortunately, the rush to join up caused problems with recruits having to be accommodated in makeshift camps, and with insufficient uniforms to go around, men had to drill in their civilian clothes with imitation rifles. There was also an acute shortage of officers and this meant that officers serving in the Indian Army and young men fresh from Officer Training Corps at public schools and universities had to be drafted in to make up for the shortfall.

'Joining up' – army life and organization

When a volunteer first joined up, he was allocated an army number, 'kitted out', provided with his uniform, clothing and equipment and given his 'dog-tags' – identity discs bearing his name, army number and religion that were worn around the neck. He would then complete his basic training at an army camp where he would be taught how to drill, sent on route marches and instructed in the use of weapons. At the start of the war, he could join a regiment of his choice, usually his own county regiment, but as the war progressed and casualties mounted he would be more likely to be drafted to a unit in need of replacements. Apart from the county regiments, there were also regiments of guards, such as the Coldstream and Grenadier Guards, and cavalry regiments with distinctive names such as the Dragoons, Hussars and Lancers. The infantry was supported by a wide range of specialist units and corps such as the 'gunners' of the Royal Artillery, the 'sappers' of The Royal Engineers and the Royal Army Medical Corps. Later in the war, the Tank Regiment and the Royal Flying Corps were to appear.

The organization and chain of command in the army were complicated. On joining, a new recruit would be allocated to one of the battalions of his regiment. A battalion consisted of something approaching 1,000 men and was commanded by a lieutenant-colonel or colonel. During the First World War so many men rushed to join the army that it became necessary to create many extra battalions. Hence a soldier might say that he was serving in the 7th Royal West Kents or the 16th Lancashire Fusiliers. Within his battalion, a soldier would be allocated to a company, within his company to a platoon and within his platoon to a section.

A new recruit would have to get used to the daily routine of the army – parades, cleaning his boots and polishing his buttons, kit inspections and the round of unpleasant duties given as punishment for minor offences. He had to learn to recognize and salute officers and be aware of the various bugle-calls – reveille at daybreak, the call to the cookhouse at mealtimes and the 'Last Post' for lights out. Many young soldiers became homesick and found army discipline excessively demanding. A colonel is said to have commented, 'They're a rough crowd and a tough crowd: but they're a stout crowd. By gad! We'll make them a credit to the old regiment yet.'

Within the army, a battalion would represent a relatively small unit. Battalions were drawn together from different regiments with artillery and other support units to form a brigade. Brigades were combined to form a division and divisions were organized into corps. Finally corps were brought together to form an army. Armies operating together in the same battle area would be placed under the command of a field marshal and during the course of the war, the British armies in France were first commanded by Field Marshal Sir John French and later by Field Marshal Sir Douglas Haig. The commander-in-chief and his staff would be based at general headquarters (GHQ) that would be situated well behind the front line and from here, they would dictate the course of the war and the fate of thousands of soldiers. Generally speaking, the most senior officers found in the front line would be the battalion commanders, the lieutenant-colonels and colonels but staff officers or 'top brass' as they were called, seldom visited the front line.

The British soldier

The vast majority of the men who joined the army served as private soldiers or privates. Immediately above them were non-commissioned officers or NCOs of which the most junior was a lance corporal and then came corporals and sergeants. Their rank was indicated by chevrons (V-shaped stripes) on the arm. Immediately above the NCOs were the warrant officers, the company and regimental sergeant majors who were usually noted for their dedication to discipline, their insistence on 'spit and polish' and their ability to shout on the parade ground! Officers, as the term is usually understood, were commissioned officers and such men were said to hold the king's commission that had to be acknowledged by other soldiers with a salute. The most junior officers were subalterns, that is second lieutenants and lieutenants. If promotion came, they might eventually be promoted to captain, major, colonel and, at the very top, to that of general and field marshal. During the First World War, stars (pips) and crowns on the cuff of his uniform indicated a commissioned officer's rank. Almost all officers were drawn from the upper-classes and were public-school educated and promotion from the ranks was unusual. However, as the war progressed and the number of casualties increased, it became more common. Many young subalterns serving in the trenches were aged 18 and only just out of school.

Non-commissioned officers and warrant officers wore their badges of rank on their sleeves. Officers carried their badges of rank on their tunic cuffs.

A lance-corporal
B corporal
C sergeant
D colour sergeant
E company sergeant major
F regimental sergeant major
G second lieutenant
H lieutenant
I captain
J major
K lieutenant-colonel
L colonel
M brigadier-general
N major-general
O lieutenant-general
P general
Q field marshal

Apart from their badges of rank, soldiers wore regimental badges in their caps and regimental shoulder titles. They also carried patches and signs to indicate their brigade and division.

Badges of rank in the British army

Ordinary British soldiers wore khaki-coloured battledress made out of rough, serge material and the tunic was single breasted and fastened at the neck. The trousers extended down to puttees, strips of cloth wound spirally around the leg from the ankle to just below the knee, and for headgear, they had cloth peaked caps. Stoutly made army boots caused men to suffer agonizing blisters particularly after marching for miles along the *pavé*, French cobbled roads. Each soldier was also provided with webbing equipment, a belt, braces and buckles to which he could attach a haversack, pack, ammunition pouches, a waterbottle carrier, a 'frog' to hold his bayonet and a carrier for his entrenching tool. Steel helmets were first issued in February 1916 but were not in general use until a year later. Officers' uniforms were made of superior, worsted-type material, barathea, and included a jacket with patch pockets that opened at the neck to show a shirt and tie, above breeches and riding boots or leggings. The most distinctive item of clothing of an officer's uniform was his 'Sam Browne' – a leather shoulder strap, belt and revolver holster named after General Sir Samuel Browne who first designed it. Both officers and men carried canes known as 'swagger sticks'.

In order to be accepted as a volunteer, a man had to be physically fit, over 1.6 metres (5.2 feet) tall and aged 18 to 38 or up to 45 if he had previous military service. Later, men below the minimum height requirement were recruited and nicknamed 'Bantams', and they formed special units for undersized men and were often subject to ridicule. Eventually the name was discontinued and the units disbanded. A volunteer, who was expected to enlist for the duration of the war, received 35 pence a week with food and clothing provided free. To support his wife and children, he had to contribute an allotment to a Separation Allowance so that his wife received 62 pence weekly – 45 pence allowance plus her husband's own 17 pence allotment. The total payable to a wife with two children was 87 pence weekly. Once enrolled, a soldier became subject to military law, King's Regulations. It should be remembered that a man's reasons for joining the army were not always motivated by patriotism or the desire to serve one's 'King and Country'. There were also other considerations such as the need to escape the drudgery of their everyday work, slum living conditions and to escape the threat of unemployment. In 1914, the average wage of a manual worker was about one pound a week and half of that would be spent on rent! The average weekly expenditure of a working man's family was about 50 pence so that there was seldom anything left over for any extras or even the smallest extravagance. Unemployment brought with it dire poverty and even those in work all too often lived in poverty in overcrowded, insanitary slums where a high death rate was an accepted fact of life. For such men, the demands and risks of army life were not such a bad deal. There were also those who were taken in by the belief that it would be a short war – 'over by Christmas' – and had volunteered in order not to miss out on what they judged to be an adventure with the promise of foreign travel and the chance to meet French *mesdemoiselles*.

British, French and German soldiers – a comparison

A British soldier fully dressed in Field Marching Order would be heavily burdened with packs and equipment that would vary according to season and whether or not he was on the march. Normally he would be expected to carry a third of his own weight, about 35 kilos (77 pounds). As the war progressed his burden was increased by the addition of a steel helmet and gas mask.

At the start of the war, a French soldier was dressed in a dark blue *capote*, a long cloak-like tunic, with red trousers and a red and blue forage cap or *kepi*. Such colourful clothing clearly had disadvantages and before the end of 1914 a far more modest blue-grey uniform had replaced it.

The most famous item of clothing of a German soldier would have been his *pickelhaube* or spiked helmet. His uniform, field grey tunic and trousers, was worn with calf-length jackboots. During 1916, his style of helmet changed to a *Stahlhelm* that gave added protection to the back of the neck.

Weapons used in the trenches

The main weapon of the British soldier was a .303, bolt action Lee-Enfield rifle with a magazine that held ten rounds of ammunition. An experienced infantryman could fire 25 rounds a minute whilst skilled sharpshooters and snipers had rifles with specially fitted telescopic sights. The most popular German rifle was the *Mauser* whilst the French used the *Lebel*. British officers carried Webley revolvers and the Germans, the famous *Lugars*.

Every soldier also carried a bayonet that was simply a blade attached to the end of the rifle and used against the enemy in close hand-to-hand fighting. The British bayonet was knife shaped, the French, pencil shaped whilst the Germans used a 'saw-back' blade with a row of teeth on the back edge.

Far more devastating than the rifle was the machine gun. The machine guns used by both sides during the war were largely based on the original design of the American inventor Hiram Maxim. At the start of the war the main British machine gun was the Lewis gun, the so-called 'Queen of the battlefield' which was mounted on a bipod and fed by a pan-shaped magazine fitted on the top. More lethal was the Vickers machine gun which was water cooled with a metal jacket around the barrel and could fire 600 rounds a minute. Mounted on a tripod, it could be set to fire along a fixed line between two points and this meant that there was no need to aim and machine gunners just swept the area ahead with a hail of bullets. Little wonder the machine gun was nicknamed the 'Devil's Sprinkler'. The machine gun used by the French was the Hotchkiss and by the Germans, the *Maschinengewehr*.

Another weapon much used in trench warfare was the hand grenade that was thrown at the enemy. The British Mills grenade, which was made of cast iron and segmented so that it broke into pieces of shrapnel more easily when it detonated, was fitted with a timed fuse that was connected to a lever held in place by a pin. The pin had to be removed in order for it to explode. Later the grenade was modified so that it could be fired from a rifle. Germans used the *Stielhandgranate* or 'stick bomb' that had a handle and the *Kugelhandgranate* which was ball shaped and known to the British as the 'pineapple grenade'. There were also trench mortars that were fixed to a base, shaped like a drainpipe and used to throw shells short distances into the enemy positions.

Flame throwers were first used by the Germans. At first their *Flammenwerfers* were primitive, used ordinary petrol and were very unreliable. Canisters were liable to explode and so cause the user to perish in the flames of his own weapon. So hated were flame throwers with their terrifying bursts of liquid fire that prisoners of war thought to have been involved in their use were liable to be shot out of hand.

Finally, when all other forms of weaponry had been used up, men fought hand-to-hand. As they wrestled they used their fists, clubs, entrenching tools and anything else that was available.

Other weapons

Artillery played a major role throughout the war with both sides
using a great variety of field guns and howitzers that fired
shrapnel, high explosive and gas shells. Field guns were intended
to fire shells across open country whilst howitzers, with their
higher trajectory, could drop shells into hollows and trenches.
Some shells disintegrated into small fragments called shrapnel
that caused horrendous injuries whilst high explosive shells
caused enormous material damage and left massive craters.
Guns were classified according to their calibre, that is the
diameter or bore of the barrel, and shells according to their
weight. British artillery included the 18-pounder field gun with
a range of six kilometres (3.7 miles), the 60-pounder field gun
with a range of nearly ten kilometres (six miles) and the massive
30 cm (12-inch) howitzer that had to be moved by rail and had
a range of 13 kilometres (eight miles). None of these could
match the German long-barrelled gun that had a staggering
range of 65 kilometres (40 miles). Nicknamed 'Big Bertha',
supposedly after the manufacturer's wife, this most famous
Krupp-built howitzer could send a shell weighing a tonne over
13 kilometres (eight miles). Exploding shells not only killed and
maimed but also buried men alive and caused a nervous
disorder known as 'shell shock'. Empty shell cases became one
of the most common souvenirs of the war and even today can
still be found in many homes.

Although outlawed by the Geneva Convention of 1899, the
Germans first used gas as a weapon of war on the Ypres salient
in 1915. The first to be used was chlorine gas that came in
clouds visible to the eye and had a distinctive smell described as
a mixture of pineapple and pepper. It produced unpleasant side
effects and caused soldiers to suffer a lingering death by
suffocation. Later in the war phosgene gas was introduced
which was also derived from chlorine but being 18 times
stronger was far worse. It had the smell of rotting fish and since
it was heavier than air, it was liable to linger in shell craters and
trenches for days after first being dispersed. However it was
dicloroethyl sulphide or mustard gas that became the most
feared. Its effects were not immediately apparent but after some
hours blisters appeared that affected the eyes and bronchial
tubes so that affected soldiers were liable to be blinded or drown
in their own blood. In 1915, a reporter for *The New York
Tribune* described the effects of 'violent nausea and faintness
followed by utter collapse. It is believed that the Germans, who
charged in behind the gas, met no resistance at all, the French at

their front being virtually paralysed'. In the trenches, empty shell cases were used as gongs to warn of the approach of gas. To start with, soldiers had no protection other than the ammonia in their own urine and bicarbonate of soda, if it was available, to part neutralize the effects of the gas. Soon many thousands of specially manufactured protective pads of cotton waste wrapped in muslin and held in place by tape were sent to the front as a stop gap before the first gas masks or respirators arrived. The first were grotesque bags with goggle-type eye pieces that covered the whole head and these were followed by more refined respirators which consisted of a mask that fitted tightly around the face connected by a tube to a canister hung in front of the wearer's body. The canister contained charcoal through which the poison gas filtered. The gas masks were cumbersome, difficult to wear and gave only limited protection. None were totally effective against mustard gas.

Tanks and the need for mobility

A few imaginative officers in the British army recognized the need to develop a mechanized armoured vehicle capable of passing through barbed wire to provide cover for troops advancing across no man's land towards the enemy's positions. Lieutenant-Colonel Ernest Swinton suggested using armoured tractors to carry infantry and guns and although the idea was rejected, a Landships Committee was set up to investigate the possibility of designing armoured vehicles. Following lengthy delays, the prototype of the first landship appeared. Nicknamed 'Little Willie', it was no more than a large metal box on tracks but in order to maintain secrecy, the model was officially called Tank Mark I. As a result, the name 'tank' later came to be applied to similar types of vehicle the world over. Although 'Little Willie' had many shortcomings since it could not cross a gap more than two and a half metres (8.2 feet) wide and had a maximum speed of only five kilometres (three miles) an hour, it was to be the basic model on which future tanks would be designed. The first variation was called 'Mother', it weighed 28 tonnes, had a crew of eight but its maximum speed remained the same and the British High Command remained far from impressed. Kitchener dismissed it as a 'pretty mechanical toy' and others expressed the view that the war could not possibly be won by such machines. When the first tanks went into production, Mark I came in two varieties – male tanks armed with two six-pounder guns at each side and female tanks with four Vickers machine guns mounted on the sides. Later a wooden beam was attached to the front to help it cross fields of mud and a wire canopy stretched across the top in order to deflect grenades thrown at it. For the crews of the tanks conditions inside were horrendous with the engine giving off stifling fumes and heat, the deafening noise and the crew being thrown around as the tank lurched from side to side. If the tank commander wanted to communicate with those outside, he had to open the door and shout through a megaphone. The first British tanks arrived in France in August 1916.

During the course of the war, whatever advances were made in the technology of warfare by one side were soon copied by the other. Although the Germans were first to use poison gas and flame throwers, both were in use by the British and French armies by the end of 1915. It is interesting to note that in October 1918, a 29-year-old corporal serving in a Bavarian infantry regiment was temporarily blinded by British gas – his name was Adolf Hitler. Likewise, the Germans worked to design their own tank and this resulted in the development of the A7V *Sturmpanzerwagen* that weighed 33 tonnes, required a crew of 18 and had a top speed of 12 kilometres (7.5 miles) an hour. Only 20 were built and the majority of tanks used by the Germans during the war were those captured from the British.

The role of horses

No account of the First World War would be complete without mention of the important part played by horses on the Western, Eastern and Italian Fronts and in the campaigns against the Turks. Tens of thousands of horses were employed in a range of different roles and thousands were killed or so badly mutilated that they had to be put down. The cavalry was considered by many to be the elite of the army and many senior officers including French, Haig, Allenby, Hamilton and Robertson were drawn from its ranks. At the start of the war, units of cavalry – Dragoons, Hussars and Lancers – crossed to France and those in command were convinced that the cavalry still had a major part to play in offensive warfare. British cavalrymen together with French *Curassiers* were soon involved in skirmishes with their German counterparts, the *Uhlans*. It was hoped that the cavalry units would be the shock-troops of the battlefield and it was intended that they would charge, breach the enemy's positions and then deploy in the countryside beyond. The

Cavalry Training Manual of 1907 still championed the horse as the main offence weapon of war and stated, 'It must be accepted as a principle that the rifle, effective as it is, cannot replace the effect produced by the speed of a horse, the magnetism of the charge and the terror of cold steel.' Although the cavalry played some part in the retreat from Mons and the Battle of the Marne, it was gradually realized that the day of the charge was over and instead their use was limited to that of scouting and reconnaissance. In 1915, an impatient Field Marshal French wrote, 'How I would love to have a real go at them with lots of cavalry ... and run them down to earth'. As the war progressed, the limitations of cavalry against machine-guns and other advances in the technology of warfare became increasingly obvious and although held in reserve on the Somme in 1916, cavalry units never had an opportunity to exploit a breakthrough. Elsewhere in Mesopotamia and Palestine, cavalry was used with some success but on the Western Front it ceased to be an effective fighting force and by the end of the war most cavalrymen had abandoned their horses to become infantrymen.

The most important role played by horses was in providing mobility. Most artillery was horse drawn and horses were used to move wagon of munitions, supplies and provisions from the rear to the forward areas. In performing these duties, they had to survive on insufficient fodder and were often overworked so that once exhausted to the point where they could go no further, they were shot out of hand. Close to the front line, soldiers became distressed at the sight of horses still moving with their entrails exposed and one senior officer witnessing the slaughter of horses and mules commented, 'Human corpses are all very well but it seems wrong for animals to be dragged into the war like this'. The demand for horses became so great that at home they had to be requisitioned in spite of the protestations of their owners.

07

trench warfare

This chapter will cover:
- the need for a system of trenches
- the construction of the trench system
- everyday life in the trenches
- matters relating to morale and discipline
- the care of the wounded
- soldiers at rest away from the front.

'The firing trench is our place of business – our office in the city, so to speak. The supporting trench is our suburban residence where the weary toiler may betake himself periodically (or, more correctly, in relays) for purposes of refreshment and repose.'

(From *The First Hundred Thousand*
by Ian Hay, 1876–1952)

The need for trenches

Trenches and trench warfare were not new. Advances in the technology of warfare meant that as weapons acquired greater range, became automatic and increased their firepower, men had to dig into the ground in order to survive. Trenches had already been used during the Crimean War, the American Civil War, the Franco-Prussian War and the Boer Wars, and during the First World War trench warfare was not confined to the Western Front but occurred in every battle area. On the Western Front, months of stalemate allowed a network of trenches to develop which honeycombed the battle-scarred countryside from the North Sea to the Swiss frontier. The trenches may have provided shelter from bullets and shrapnel but they only allowed the most primitive living conditions and for tens of thousands of men, trench warfare became a way of life, even a subculture. On their arrival in France, men were sent for additional training at a base camp that was intended to prepare them for the realities of life at the front. One such training area was the notorious Bull Ring at Etaples, known to the soldiers as 'Eat Apples' it was later to be the scene of a major army mutiny. Then it was off to the front either by train or by completing a series of gruelling route marches. On the march, men burdened with rifles and full packs were expected to cover 30 kilometres (18.6 miles) a day with ten minutes of each hour allowed for rest and it was during these marches that soldiers sang the songs that were to become so famous – *It's A Long Way To Tipperary, Mademoiselle From Armentières* and *Pack Up Your Troubles In Your Old Kit Bag*. The versions sung by the soldiers were very much cruder than those that became popular at home.

Trenches and the trench system

Basically, a trench is an extended hole dug into the ground that is a little over two metres (6.5 feet) deep and a little less than two metres wide. Some of the earth that was removed when digging the trench was used to create a parapet to the front that increased its height to nearly three metres (9.8 feet) whilst the remainder was piled to form an earthwork at the rear, a parados. The sides of the trench were reinforced with sandbags intended to absorb the impact of bullets and shrapnel. Trenches were not dug in straight lines but in irregular sections known as firebays and traverses that, from the air, resembled the battlements of a castle. The line of trenches closest to the enemy was known as the front line and behind this was a vast warren-like network of support and reserve trenches connected by communication trenches. Running forward from the front line towards the enemy, narrow and much shallower trenches were dug which were known as saps. Soldiers used these to crawl forward and observe the enemy's movements more closely. Within each trench there was a ledge or firestep on which men stood to see and fire over the top. Another feature of the trenches was the dugouts – these were shelters scooped out of the back of the trenches to provide the crudest living accommodation. The front of a dugout might be no more than an overhanging groundsheet that allowed minimum privacy and barely any shelter from the elements. The floor of the trench was lined with planking – duckboards that allowed soldiers to move more easily in the mud. The area separating the two opposed front lines was known as 'no man's land' and whilst the distance between them varied, in places it was 50 metres (164 feet) or less. At one point near La Boiselle on the Somme, it was claimed that the trenches were close enough for the British and Germans to shake hands over the top! Apart from the towns such as Etaples ('Eat Apples') Poperinge ('Pop'), Ypres ('Wipers'), soldiers also gave trenches, local woods and other landmarks nicknames – Blighty Wood, Crucifix Corner, Death Valley, Devil's Wood (Delville Wood), Hawthorn Ridge, Mucky Farm (Mouquet Farm), Owl Trench and Sanctuary Wood.

The cattle ranchers on the Great Plains of North America were the first to use barbed wire. On the Western Front, barbed-wire entanglements were used to guard the approaches to front-line trenches and for obvious reasons the barbed wire had to be pitched at least a grenade's throw away. Erecting and repairing the barbed wire was a dangerous business that was usually done at night using padded mallets or corkscrew-like supports that did not have to be hammered into the ground and so possibly alert the enemy.

figure 13 a cross section of a trench

Life in the trenches

Once at the front, new arrivals would be 'shown the ropes' by 'old sweats', the men already well experienced in the daily routine that was trench life. It would be very wrong to assume that life in the front line was always hectic with constant attacks and counterattacks since the amount of activity varied and there were times when soldiers went for weeks without being involved in any action. Men were divided into watches and allocated duties and most of their day was spent engaged in boring routine that included rifle inspections, repairing trenches, digging latrines and other fatigues. They also enjoyed rest time when they could eat, sleep and write letters home. Even so, there was always a need to be on the alert against enemy-raiding parties and snipers. The critical periods of the day when the enemy was most likely to attack were at dawn and dusk and at these times, men had to 'stand to'. Darkness added to the need for caution and sentries were posted to keep watch across no man's land and report any movement. Men were also liable to be called upon to take part in night patrols to see what the enemy was up to. Of course, there was always the chance of encountering an enemy patrol. Night also provided an opportunity to repair the barbed wire and search for dead and wounded comrades. When star shells or Verey lights were fired high into the sky they illuminated the whole landscape and this was the time when men in no man's land had to stand motionless since the slightest movement was likely to attract a burst of machine-gun fire. 'Going over the top' as part of a raiding party or worse, to take part in a major offensive against the enemy demanded exceptional bravery and often resulted in a heavy loss of life.

In the trenches, maintaining any level of personal cleanliness was fraught with difficulties. Water, both for drinking and washing, was in short supply since it had to be brought forward from the rear and when water was available, men used their steel helmets as wash basins but often even a daily wash and shave was impossible. Baths were luxuries only to be enjoyed once out of the line. Lavatories or latrines were dug at the edge of the trenches and once full, they had to be filled in and new ones prepared. This work was the most disliked punishment imposed on soldiers for minor offences. The trenches were the breeding ground of millions of rats and other vermin that thrived on the scraps of food, litter, excrement and the remains of decomposing bodies. The loathsome creatures grew to an enormous size and became sufficiently bold to attack men whilst they were sleeping. They were also responsible for the contamination of food and the spread of disease. Men found ingenious ways of trapping and killing them although there were instances when they were kept as pets. Lice and fleas were other scourges of the trenches that infested men's hair and clothing and caused great discomfort. Some relief was to be found by cutting one's hair short or shaving it off altogether and men tried to rid their clothing of lice and fleas by running the seams of their underclothing over the flames of candles. Lice also caused a condition known as trench fever and infected soldiers needed up to 12 weeks to recover. In the summer, swarms of flies infested the trenches and dugouts where, like the rats, they fed on the dead and decomposing bodies that were riddled with their eggs and maggots. From the onset of autumn until late spring when the rainfall was at its highest, the trenches were filled with water and the landscape around became a morass of clinging mud. Although the trenches were lined with duckboards and the men had waterproof groundsheets and thigh-length gum boots to protect them against the ooze, many suffered from a form of foot rot known as trench foot. The usual remedy was the regular application of grease made from strong-smelling whale oil. Even more serious was frostbite that was the result of exposure to extreme cold and could lead to gangrene and even the need to amputate the affected limbs. To reduce the chances of soldiers suffering from these ailments, officers carried out regular foot inspections.

Food-wise, a British soldier was supposed to receive 4,193 calories a day. In practice, his daily ration depended on circumstances and therefore varied in quality and quantity with bully beef, akin to present day corned beef, biscuits and jam, almost invariably plum and apple, the common foods most readily available. Hot meals that included meat and vegetables were supplied by field kitchens and then sent forward to the men in the trenches but by the time it reached them it was often cold and unappetizing. Although it was officially forbidden, soldiers devised their own means of heating food by using a 'Tommy Cooker' which was a small, pocket-size stove fuelled by solidified alcohol that gave off some heat. Even so, there were sometimes long periods when men went without food of any sort. Every soldier carried with him iron rations which was dehydrated food that could only be used in a dire emergency and with the permission of an officer. All drinking water was chlorinated which made it safe but foul tasting. Dire and even fatal consequences resulted when men were tempted to drink from the polluted water found in craters.

Morale in the army varied from unit to unit and depended on such factors as the progress of the war, news from home, local conditions, casualty levels, the quality of the officers and the level of *esprit de corps*. Of necessity, discipline had to be strict. Lesser misdeeds were dealt with on the spot and punished by stoppages of pay and the imposition of additional duties and fatigues but for more serious offences, men were court-martialled. During the course of the war some 169,000 men were tried for offences ranging from being drunk and insubordinate to striking an officer, falling asleep on duty, cowardice, desertion and even murder. With soldiers entitled to a quarter of a litre of rum weekly and with liquor freely available behind the lines, drunkenness was a problem and over 35,000 men were charged with this offence. Much hated was Field Punishment Number 1 which was known as 'crucifixion'.

It humiliated the unfortunate offender by tying him to a fixed object for a number of hours each day in full view of his comrades. Although some 3,342 men were tried for crimes that merited the death sentence, only 343 were actually shot at dawn.

During the course of the war, the total number of British casualties reached some 2.69 million of which about a quarter were killed and over half the British soldiers involved in the war suffered a wound of one sort or another. In action, it was forbidden for a soldier to stop to help a fallen comrade and each man carried with him an emergency dressing which he could use to attend to his own wound. Otherwise, he had to wait to be discovered by stretcher-bearers of which every company possessed four. Bullet wounds were usually clean cut and much easier to deal with than wounds by shrapnel that could cause ghastly mutilation. The wounded were first taken to a regimental aid post located in the reserve trenches where they would be seen by a medical officer who would dress their wounds and administer any needed pain killers, usually injections of morphine. Next they would be moved to an Advanced Dressing Station where emergency surgery might be attempted and then on to a Casualty Clearing Station where teams of doctors were able to provide a wide range of more advanced treatment. The most seriously wounded would then be transferred to hospital by mobile ambulances or ambulance trains where they would be able to enjoy the long forgotten luxuries of clean sheets and good food. Doctors and nurses had to deal with the most appalling injuries which might require amputation and lead to disfigurement and cope with those suffering from gas blindness and shell shock. The symptoms of shell shock, a nervous disorder brought about by battle fatigue, were a vacant expression, ready smile and nervous facial twitch. Some medical officers refused to recognize the condition and considered such men to be malingerers. Have no doubt, there were those soldiers who 'tried it on' and would have been delighted to receive a 'blighty one' – a wound that was not life threatening but severe enough for them to be sent home. Injured soldiers were awarded a wound stripe and once they had recovered, sent back to the trenches. The dead were usually buried close to where they fell but in the heat of battle this was sometimes impossible and so bodies were interred in the bottom of the trench. Cemeteries were often established close to Casualty Clearing Stations but the problem was that the land was liable to be fought over time and time again so that exploding shells might disturb the ground and the location of the graves be lost forever. Not surprisingly, some of the dead were too badly decomposed or mutilated to be recognized and 160,000 British soldiers killed in the war have no known graves. To this day, building contractors in France and Belgium often unearth human remains that are still buried with full military honours.

In matters of religion, soldiers received guidance from army chaplains and padres. A chaplain's life was taken up with a range of emotive tasks – comforting the dying, taking down messages intended for next-of-kin, attending burials, consoling those at the end of their tether and being present at executions. Whenever it was possible, chaplains organized church services, known as drumhead services because the makeshift altar was often made of drums. Often Roman Catholic chaplains were called upon to go into the front line to administer last rites to the dying. Geoffrey Studdart-Kennedy, a much beloved Anglican clergyman, went into the trenches even when they were under enemy fire and handed out cigarettes to the troops. Nicknamed 'Woodbine Willy', his bravery earned him the Military Cross and he later became chaplain to King George V. At his funeral in 1929, old soldiers placed packets of Woodbines on his coffin as a mark of their respect and gratitude. At Poperinge in Belgium, 'Pop' to British soldiers, Colonel Reginald Talbot appointed a clergyman, Philips Clayton, to turn a house into a rest and recreation centre. 'Tubby' Clayton, as he became known, called the building Talbot House. In army signal jargon, it became known as Toc H and it was the first branch of an organization that was to spread worldwide. The original Toc H house in Poperinge remains open to visitors to this day.

Away from the front

The length of time a soldier spent in the front line varied according to circumstances. A typical arrangement would be for a man to spend four days in the front line, four in a support trench, eight in reserve and then enjoy a period of rest behind the lines but there were occasions when men spent 30 days and even longer in the front line without relief. Serving men looked forward to their annual leave of ten days, which included the time taken to reach home and return to his unit. Again, it was not uncommon for men to go much longer without seeing their families and there were instances when men on home leave committed suicide rather than return to the trenches. Letters from home were always most welcome as were parcels containing knitted gloves and scarves, chocolate, home-made delicacies and of course cigarettes. The troops loved their 'fags', which were often their only comfort in their otherwise miserable existence in the trenches. Sadly, not all the letters brought welcome news since some included news of a family bereavement or details of a wife's infidelity, a 'Dear John' letter. Such letters added to a soldier's discomfort and misery and might make him apply for compassionate leave.

Once at rest behind the front line, the first thing a soldier wanted was a wash, shave, change of clothes and sleep before they went in search of relaxation. Concert parties, film shows and sports events were organized for soldiers and the Young Men's Christian Association (YMCA) and other voluntary organizations ran canteens that provided tea and refreshments. Unfortunately not all the forms of relaxation they sought were that wholesome. With some soldiers gambling became an obsession and many lost their money playing 'Brag' whilst others preferred dice or Crown and Anchor. Many made their way to the *estaminets* in local towns and villages and there drank themselves senseless on beer and cheap wine. Others went off in search of brothels, *maisons de tolérance* as they were known, which sported the traditional red light and were uniform in their seediness. Even so, men queued at the door for their few minutes of pleasure and it was not surprising that venereal disease became a major problem. During the war there were over 150,000 reported cases of syphilis amongst British soldiers and those with VD were treated at a special hospital set aside for the purpose. The disgrace of 'having caught a dose' and penalties such as stoppages of pay and the cancellation of leave did little to reduce the number of cases. Occasionally units taken out of the line were not sent for rest but to camps where they were subject to drills, excessive 'bull' (spit and polish) and additional military training. As you can imagine, this was most unpopular and contributed to a number of army mutinies including one at Etaples in 1917.

Life in the trenches was harsh and brutal particularly for men who a few months earlier had been in civilian employment and had enjoyed quiet family lives. Even so, they were able to forge a sense of camaraderie that would help them share the dangers and suffering they were forced to endure with fortitude and unbelievable courage.

The language of the trenches – everyday words and phrases used by British soldiers

blighty	home
blighty wound	a wound serious enough for a a soldier to be sent home
bully beef	tinned beef like corned beef
Canary	a drill instructor
chit	a written message
crump	an exploding shell
'Digger'	an Australian soldier
dixie	a food container
'Doughboy'	an American soldier
duckboard	a board used to line the bottom of a trench
egg	a hand grenade
estaminet	a bar, a place where soldiers went to relax
fags	cigarettes, usually Woodbines
fatigues	duties sometimes given as a punishment
fleabag	a sleeping bag
'Fritz'	a German
'Froggies'	Frenchmen
funk hole	a place to shelter
going over the top	moving forward from the trenches
Hun	a German
iron rations	packs of emergency food
Maconochie	tinned food known by the manufacturer's name
maisons de tolérance	brothels
minenwerfter	a large German shell also known as a 'Moaning Minnie'

no man's land	the land between the opposed lines of trenches
pavé	a French cobbled road
phutt	to go phutt – to stop working
Plug Street	Ploegsteert, a Belgian town
Pop	Poperinge, a Belgian town
pork and beans	Portuguese soldiers
Red Cap	a military policeman
san fairy ann	from the French '*Ce ne fait rien*' – it doesn't matter
sapper	an engineer
shell shock	a nervous condition brought about by proximity to exploding shells
stand to	waiting in readiness for an enemy attack
Toc H	Talbot House
Tommy	a British soldier
Top Brass	senior officers
trench fever	a fever that affected men in the trenches carried by lice
trench foot	a condition of the feet arising from exposure to wet and cold
whizzbangs	German shells
Wipers	Ypres, a Belgian town
Yank	an American soldier

08

issues of bravery and cowardice

This chapter will cover:
- the award of medals and how acts of bravery were recognized
- some men who won the highest award for bravery – the Victoria Cross
- courts martial
- some men who were shot at dawn
- mutinies in the British army.

'Courage is willpower, whereof no man has an unlimited stock and, when in war it is used up, he is finished. A man's courage is his capital and he is always spending.'

(Lord Moran of Manton, 1882–1977,
The Anatomy of Courage, 1945)

Reaction to fear

During the First World War there was ample evidence of the courage shown by men of all ranks and social backgrounds. Altogether 633 Victoria Crosses (VCs) and a great many other medals for gallantry were awarded to men serving in the armed forces of Britain and the Dominions. Of the VCs, 187 were awarded posthumously since, as was often the case, men found themselves in extreme situations where acts of bravery were needed to save the day and there were heroic men prepared to sacrifice their lives in order to save their comrades. Many headstones in British military cemeteries in France carry the biblical inscription 'Greater love hath no man than this, that a man lay down his life for a friend'. Of course, there were also those whose bravery was born of boldness and indifference to their own safety. On the other hand, 3,342 men were sentenced to death for a range of crimes that included cowardice and desertion. In a great many cases they had done their best but, as Lord Moran (later to become Winston Churchill's own personal physician) says, simply ran out of their stock of courage. Many of those sent for trial by courts martial fell victims of flawed judgements and miscarriages of justice.

Acknowledging acts of bravery

Servicemen receive medals for long service, good conduct and for being involved in a particular war or campaign. However, the most prestigious medals are those awarded for bravery. The few that are awarded the same medal twice receive a clasp or 'bar' to their original medal. Soldiers who served in the early stages of the First World War became eligible to receive the 1914 Star, sometimes called the Mons Star, as well as the 1914–15 Star. At the end of the war, all servicemen were awarded the British War and Victory Medals. A Star, War and Victory Medals were collectively nicknamed 'Pip, Squeak and Wilfred' whilst the War and Victory Medals alone were referred to as 'Mutt and Jeff' after two popular cartoon characters.

The highest award for gallantry was the Victoria Cross. This decoration which bears the inscription 'For Valour' and is only awarded to those who perform outstanding acts of bravery in battle, was founded by Queen Victoria during the Crimean War and was made from the metal of Russian guns captured during the siege of Sevastopol. During the war, one officer, Captain Noel Chavasse, an officer in the Royal Army Medical Corps (RAMC), twice won the medal in France in 1916 and again in Belgium in 1917. The Distinguished Service Order (DSO) was awarded to officers for meritorious service in time of war. Another medal awarded for bravery made only to officers was the Military Cross (MC) and over 37,000 were awarded during the war and of these 2,992 gained a bar, 116 a second bar and four a third bar. The similar award to other ranks was the Military Medal (MM) of which 121,554 were awarded. The Distinguished Conduct Medal (DCM) was also awarded for bravery in battle as well as a wide range of medals made available to servicemen from the Dominions.

Medals awarded to British and dominion servicemen 1914–18	
Victoria Cross (VC)	633
Distinguished Service Order (DSO)	8,981
Military Cross	40,236
Military Medal	121,554
Distinguished Conduct Medal	24,591
Mons Star	365,622
1914–15 Star	2,078,183
British War Medal	6,610,000
Victory Medal	5,725,000

Battlefield commanders and commanders of ships at sea sent dispatches home for the attention of those in higher authority and in them it became the practice to mention by name those who had made some significant contribution to the success of any action. It was a lower grade of recognition and brought no award and it has been calculated that 2 per cent of all servicemen were 'mentioned in dispatches'. For British consumption, details of all awards appeared in the *London Gazette*, an official newspaper that also listed the names of men who had been commissioned. Amongst French awards for bravery were the *Légion d'honneur*, the *Medaille Militarie* and the *Croix de Guerre* whilst German servicemen received the

Eiserne Kreuz, the Iron Cross. This long-established medal dated back to 1813 and was awarded at two levels – First and Second Class.

Examples of men whose bravery earned them the Victoria Cross

Corporal Cecil Noble and Company Sergeant Major Harry Daniels

From Bournemouth in Dorset, England, Cecil Noble was a corporal serving with the Rifle Brigade. In March 1915 at Neuve Chapelle, France, German machine-gun fire and barbed wire entanglements held up the advance of his battalion and together with Company Sergeant Major Harry Daniels, he went forward and succeeded in cutting the wire. Both men were wounded and Noble later died of his injuries but Daniels survived and was later promoted to the rank of lieutenant-colonel. He died in Leeds in 1953.

Able Seaman William Williams

From Stanton Lacy, Shropshire, England, William Williams was a member of the crew of HMS *River Clyde*. In April 1915 at Cape Helles, Gallipoli, standing chest deep in the sea and under continuous Turkish fire, he held on to a rope that was securing smaller ships alongside. Severely wounded, he was killed by a shell whilst efforts were being made to rescue him. He was, said his commanding officer, 'the bravest sailor I have ever met'.

Private William McFadzean

Twenty-one-year-old Private McFadzean came from Lurgan, County Armagh and served in the Royal Irish Rifles. In July 1916 at Thiepval Wood, he was in a trench crowded with men when the safety pins fell out of two grenades. He immediately threw himself on top of the grenades that exploded and killed him instantly. By showing immense heroism, the young soldier gave his life in order to save his comrades.

Captain Noel Chavasse

Son of the Bishop of Liverpool, Noel Chavasse was a doctor attached to The King's Liverpool Regiment. In August 1916, he ignored heavy enemy fire to tend wounded men in no man's land and his bravery earned him the Victoria Cross. The following year at Wieltje in Belgium, although badly wounded himself, he refused to leave the front line and went in search of wounded men. He later died of his wounds and for his courage was awarded a second Victoria Cross.

Private Thomas Cooke

A New Zealander serving with the Australian Imperial Force, Thomas Cooke was awarded the Victoria Cross for his bravery at Pozières in September 1916. After a Lewis gun had been disabled, he was ordered to take his own gun to a dangerous part of the line where he soon came under heavy enemy fire. The only man left, he stuck to his post, continued firing and was later found dead beside his gun.

Sergeant Robert Bye

A sergeant in the Welsh Guards, Robert Bye came from Abercynon in South Wales. In July 1917, during an attack on German positions near the Yser Canal in Belgium, he noticed the havoc being caused by two German block-houses. He rushed at one and put it out of action before leading his men against the other. In accomplishing this, he killed 70 of the enemy and took many prisoners. Bye lived until 1962 when he died in Nottingham.

'Shot at dawn'

Under British Military Law there were numerous offences for which a serving soldier might be charged and if found guilty, face the death penalty. They included desertion, cowardice, mutiny, murder, quitting post, disobedience, striking a superior officer, sleeping on post and casting away arms. During the course of the war 348 men and three officers suffered this fate and of these some 268 were found guilty of desertion.

Executions of British and Dominion servicemen 1914–18	
Desertion	268
Murder	37
Cowardice	18
Quitting post	7
Disobedience	5
Striking an officer	5
Mutiny	4
Sleeping on post	2
Casting away arms	2

There were four types of courts martial. A Regimental Court Martial dealt with relatively minor offences and the maximum penalty it could impose was 42 days' detention but more serious cases were considered by a District Court Martial that had the power to sentence a man to two years of hard labour, reduce him to the ranks or discharge him with ignominy. A General Court Martial which in wartime, of necessity, became a Field General Court Martial, sat to consider the most serious cases and could impose the death sentence. A man accused of an offence that carried the death penalty would be kept under close arrest until the time of his trial. The soldier involved would be offered the services of an officer to act as his defence council but the officer, known as the 'prisoner's friend', would be unlikely to have had any legal training. Sometimes soldiers chose to defend themselves but this was not a good idea since the man might only be of limited education and unable to express himself adequately. Before his trial one soldier wrote home to his mother, '... I'm in a bit of trouble now and won't get any money for a long time. I will have to go in front of a court. I will try my best to get out of it, so don't worry'. He was shot.

At such a court martial, the soldier or his representative, the 'prisoner's friend', had the right to call witnesses and cross-examine them and if the case could not be proved, the soldier was released immediately. If found guilty, the soldier might be sent to serve a period at an army detention centre with or without hard labour but if guilty of a capital crime, he would be sentenced to death. The sentence would not be carried out until the papers dealing with the case had been sent first to the man's battalion commander and then his brigade, division and corps commanders for them to add a recommendation. The papers would then reach the commander-in-chief for him to make a final decision.

A matter of justice?

The final decision as to whether a man should have his sentence commuted and live or confirmed and face the firing squad depended on a range of considerations – the soldier's previous record, details of his medical condition and any recommendations for mercy. The weight given to a soldier's previous record varied and some men with exemplary records were executed as were a few that had earlier been awarded medals for gallantry. Medical officers had varying views about possible extenuating circumstances such as the state of the man's health. They also disagreed about the impact of psychological factors – the effects of a long period in the front line and whether or not the soldier was suffering from shell shock. A commanding officer's concern at a decline in morale and the fighting spirit of his men might lead him to support the decision to execute a man simply *'pour encourager les autres'* – to encourage the others. Field Marshal Haig, himself, commented 'Moral fibre … men who possess little or none of this would give way at the moment of stress were it not for the makeweight of the daily fear of punishment'. It is claimed that at one stage of the war there was unrest in the ranks because no officer had faced the firing squad and that this caused Haig to ensure that an officer charged would be shot. It should be noted that 40 per cent of the men executed had been volunteers who had enlisted at the outbreak of war and that they had offered to fight for their country but once at the front, had been unable to cope with the rigours of war. There were occasions when court martial procedures were not followed and some where they were totally ignored. It should also be remembered that only a small minority of soldiers found guilty of a capital crime were actually shot – 343 out of 3,080, just 11 per cent. Of those executed, two thirds had previously been convicted of a breach of military law and 37 were murderers when the sentence would have been mandatory. There were instances when men shot their own comrades in drunken brawls; one man shot a fellow soldier after he had discovered that he had not fairly distributed the loot after they had jointly burgled a house; two others conspired to shoot their unpopular sergeant-major and shot the wrong man!

Executions

The first execution took place on 8 September 1914 just four weeks after the war started when Private Thomas Highgate, who was just 19 years old was shot for desertion. During the course of the war 13 gunners of the Royal Artillery were executed, 12 men from the West Yorkshire Regiment and five men from the same battalion of the Worcestershire Regiment were shot on the same day. Executions took place at dawn and were usually carried out by a firing squad drawn from the man's own battalion. It was an unpopular task and selected men were known to plead not to be included and it was said that 'self-respecting soldiers … screamed out begging not to be made into murderers'. After writing his last letter home and spending some time with the chaplain, the unfortunate man, probably bolstered with rum, would be taken to the place of execution where he would be formally identified, blindfolded and his hands fastened behind him. Tied to a post or made to sit in a chair, a square of white material would be placed over his heart to serve as a target for the firing party. No point would be served in aiming off since, if there were still signs of life after the volley had been fired, the officer in charge had to deliver a *coup de grace* with his own revolver. At the start of the war, the soldier's family was informed of the soldier's disgrace and any allowance paid to his wife and children stopped but Haig reversed this so that the family was not informed, the allowance continued to be paid and the soldier buried amongst other fallen comrades. In spite of considerable pressure, the Australian authorities refused to allow the death penalty to be applied to their soldiers. Although estimated at only 48, the Germans have never made known their figures, but they did express surprise at the number executed by the British. Although records indicate that only 133 Frenchmen suffered the death penalty there is reason to believe there may have been many more following army mutinies in 1917.

Some famous cases

Private Albert Ingham

Before the war, Albert Ingham had worked as a clerk for the Lancashire and Yorkshire Railways. In 1914, he was amongst the first to volunteer and joined the Manchester Regiment. After serving in Egypt, he arrived on the Western Front and survived the Battle of the Somme. By October 1916, he had endured enough and together with a friend, Alfred Longshaw, he deserted. The two men reached Dieppe and managed to get on board a Swedish ship before being discovered and handed over to the Military Police. At their court martial, both men were sentenced to death and in spite of efforts to save the doomed men, they were both executed on 1 December 1916. Ingham's father was told that his son had died of wounds and when he discovered the truth, he asked that his son's headstone carry the inscription 'Murdered by the British army'. This was refused but it was agreed that it could read 'Shot at dawn. One of the first to enlist. A worthy son of his father.' The inscription is unique since it is the only headstone to indicate the true cause of death of an executed soldier.

Sub-Lieutenant Edwin Dyett

At the start of the war, Cardiff-born Edwin Dyett, the 19-year-old son of a merchant navy captain and the brother of a serving naval officer, volunteered to join the Royal Navy. Unfortunately, a surplus of sailors meant that many were transferred to serve in the Royal Naval Division which meant that they effectively became soldiers. Dyett, a sub-lieutenant in the Nelson Battalion, was sent to serve in the trenches on the Western Front. A nervous young man and quite unsuited to soldiering, Dyett was recognized as an inferior officer and kept in reserve but unfortunately the high casualty rate made it necessary for him to be sent to the front line. On 13 November 1916, in the confusion of battle, Dyett got lost and instead of following orders, attempted to make his own way back to his lines and ended up sheltering in a shell crater. Most officers found unsuitable for trench warfare were sent home and given a desk job but this was not to happen in the case of Dyett. Charged with desertion, he was found guilty and sentenced to death. There were said to have been irregularities about his trial and much of the evidence against him came from an officer who bore him a grudge. When giving evidence himself, Dyett did not mention his family's naval connections or the fact that he was distantly related to Field Marshal Sir John French. Everyone assumed that his sentence would be commuted but on 5 January 1917, he was shot. It has since been claimed that because soldier–sailor relations were not good, Dyett was a scapegoat and his execution a political gesture. On hearing the news, his father emigrated overseas and swore never again to set foot in Britain.

Private George Everill

Private George Everill of the North Staffordshire Regiment must have had one of the worst military records in the British army. Originally a placid and well-behaved soldier, in March 1916 he faced his first charge of insubordination and was sentenced to one year's imprisonment with hard labour but the sentence was suspended. Five weeks later, he was charged with wilful defiance and was sentenced to ten years' penal servitude but once again his sentence was commuted to only two years. In March 1917, Private Everill was charged with being absent and his one year sentence was commuted to 90 days' Field Punishment Number 1. Shortly after his release he was charged with using threatening language to a superior officer and again his three year sentence was commuted to 90 days. After serving his time, he was charged with showing wilful defiance. At his court martial he declined to question witnesses and, not surprisingly, no evidence was produced of his previous good conduct. This time he had gone too far and was sentenced to death and after Haig had confirmed the sentence, the 30-year-old soldier finally faced the firing squad at Poperinge on 14 September 1917. His wife, who believed that her husband had been killed in action, saw to it that the epitaph on his grave read, 'Thy will be done from his loving wife and children'.

Mutinies

The reaction of some soldiers to the horrors of trench warfare was not limited to trying to get away from it all by deserting and there were incidents of open mutiny by individual soldiers as well as whole units of men. In May 1915, a battalion of the Welsh Regiment undergoing training at home registered their disgust at the bullying of their NCOs, largely drawn from the Guards and the Metropolitan Police, by refusing to obey orders. An attempt at intimidation failed and the military authorities were forced to back down. Later the same year, men from the same regiment again refused to obey orders this time to show their opposition to Field Punishment Number 1, 'crucifixion'. Far more serious was the mutiny that occurred in the military prison at Blargies near Rouen. On this occasion many of the 300 men held in the prison openly protested at the excessive punishments, the poor food and the fact that there were only 14 latrines with each man allocated a daily usage of 45 seconds. When some men resisted being put in leg irons, order had to be restored through the use of armed force. As a result of the courts martial that followed, two men were executed – an Englishman and a New Zealander – but the other ringleaders, being Australians, avoided the death penalty. By far the largest mutiny of the war occurred at Etaples in September 1917.

The Etaples mutiny

Etaples, close to Le Touquet and on the estuary of the River Canche, was a military base at which soldiers received further military training before proceeding to the front line. At the base there were also hospitals and convalescent homes, various facilities for relaxation and a detention camp for offenders. The regime at the base was harsh and the conditions spartan and at the much hated 'Bull Ring', a parade ground on the sand dunes, men were drilled and bullied by instructors known as 'Canaries' because of their yellow arm bands, and the 'Red Caps', the Military Police. To make matters worse, soldiers on leave from the front were sometimes made to drill like new recruits. The situation came to a head in September 1917 when a riot broke out and soldiers ignored sentries and tried to enter the town of Etaples. The base commander's office was broken into and Brigadier-General Thompson himself manhandled. Officers were insulted and one soldier was heard to shout 'Don't listen to the bloody officer. What you want to do is tie a rope round his neck'. With men brandishing red flags and reports of rape and looting in the town, the situation was getting out of hand and troops from the Honourable Artillery Company had to be sent to Etaples to restore order. During the episode, one man was killed and afterwards, another soldier was charged with mutiny and executed.

In 1986, the events of the Etaples mutiny were the subject of a BBC series, *The Monocled Mutineer*, based on a book of the same name by William Allison and John Fairley. The central character of the series was a dashing rogue and anti-hero figure, Percy Toplis, a private in the Royal Army Medical Corps, who, so it was claimed, was one of the ringleaders of the mutiny. Toplis undoubtedly existed and the BBC series claimed that he often masqueraded as an officer and brazenly attended officers' mess functions wearing a monocle. However, subsequent research failed to prove that Toplis was ever at Etaples. After the war Toplis was wanted by the police and finally died in a shoot-out on a country road in the north of England. There were also other riots and mutinies and late in 1917 Chinese and Egyptians employed by the British army in Labour Corps went on strike. Although unarmed, they were fired on and many were killed and wounded. In July 1918, there was further trouble amongst British soldiers at a base near Calais and although the situation turned ugly, it did not develop to match the events at Etaples the previous year.

09

1916 – Verdun and the Somme

This chapter will cover:
- the general situation on the Western Front in 1916
- the significance of the Battle of Verdun
- the reasons for the change at the top when Haig replaced French
- the significance of the Battle of the Somme
- the consequences of both these battles and the situation at the end of the year.

'Where have all the soldiers gone?
    Long time passing.
Where have all the soldiers gone?
    Long time ago.
Where have all the soldiers gone?
    They've gone to graveyards every one,
When will they ever learn?
When will they ever learn?'

(From a song, *Where Have All the Flowers Gone*,
by the American protest singer, Pete Seeger, 1919–)

The situation on the Western Front at the start of 1916

The last months of 1915 had been relatively quiet on the Western Front. It was a period during which both sides considered their options and planned their strategy for 1916. The German High Command was fully aware that it did not

figure 14 Verdun and the Somme – the offensives of 1916

have the manpower or material resources of the Allies and feared the consequences of continuing to fight an indefinite war of attrition. Some thought was given to offensives against Russia and Italy but Erich von Falkenhayn, the German Commander-in-Chief, considered the Russians to already be beaten and was content to leave the Austrians to cope on the Italian Front. The offensive when it came was to be on the Western Front, but where?

By this stage of the war, the Germans had identified Britain as being their major enemy and thought their best ploy was to 'knock her best sword ... out of her hand'. Strangely, the Germans considered the 'best sword' of the British to be the French army and Erich von Falkenhayn sent a memorandum to the Kaiser:

> 'There are objectives within our reach ... for which the French General Staff would be forced to throw in every man they have. If they do so, the forces of France will be bled to death, since there can be no question of voluntary withdrawal ... The objectives of which I speak are Belfort and Verdun ... The preference must be given to Verdun.'

The Battle of Verdun

Verdun – the name is Gallic and means 'powerful fortress' – is a city that lies on the banks of the River Meuse and is strategically based on the road between Rheims and Metz. A fortress city and important military base surrounded by a series of impressive fortresses, it was at the centre of the French defensive system and was the only garrison to effectively resist the invaders during the Franco-Prussian War. Falkenhayn knew that the capture of the city would be a major blow to French morale and that they would defend it irrespective of the cost. He estimated that the fall of the city would lead to a political crisis and the resignation of the French government and his immediate aim was to lay siege to the city for as long as he was able and to slaughter as many French soldiers as possible. Falkenhayn's code name for the offensive was *Gericht*, 'Execution place'. Verdun stood at the point where the front line crossed the River Meuse and the French authorities were of the opinion that a city surrounded by so many fortresses must be impregnable. The truth was that the fortresses were in a state of disrepair, the trench systems between them were inadequate and their heavy guns had been moved elsewhere.

figure 15 the Battle of Verdun

After bad weather had caused the abandonment of the date originally set for the attack, the German offensive finally began on the morning of 21 February 1916. Before Falkenhayn's troops moved forward, the French positions were subjected to a nine-hour bombardment. Even so, their first attempt to break through the line of fortresses failed and they made little progress against strong French resistance. During the following days they had only limited success until 25 February when Fort Douaumont, the most important of the French fortresses, fell to the Germans. The story of its capture is a mixture of disastrous oversight by the French and remarkable good fortune by the Germans. Some 200 metres (656 feet) long and 100 metres (328 feet) wide, the concrete mass of Fort Douaumont was protected by barbed wire, spiked railings and a ditch whilst the surrounding fortifications bristled with machine guns and gun turrets. Yet, in spite of its impressive array of defences, it fell due to the ingenuity of a German sergeant and his party of nine men. Sergeant Kunze and his men took advantage of the fact that the fortress was inadequately defended to reach the wall of the fortress unnoticed and there they formed a human pyramid and climbed into the fortress through a narrow opening. Others followed and by the end of the day, Fort Douaumont was in German hands. That evening, the French appointed a new commander to lead the armies defending Verdun, Marshal Philippe Pétain. From a prosperous peasant family in the Pas-de-Calais, Pétain had only been a colonel in 1914 but promotion came quickly. His immediate task was to restore the morale of his men and famously declaring *'ils ne passeront pas'*, 'they shall not pass', he ordered a series of desperate counterattacks. The ability of the French to defend Verdun depended on reinforcements and supplies that reached the beleaguered city by way of one narrow road, *la Voie Sacrée*, the Sacred Way. Although under constant heavy German shellfire, during one critical week in February, over 25,000 tonnes of supplies and 190,000 men reached Verdun by means of the road. Later it was estimated that a vehicle passed along the road every 14 seconds and that in all, something like 60 per cent of the French army were to pass along it bound for 'the dreadful Calvary of Verdun'. Even though losses on both sides were appalling, the road ensured that the French garrison survived. The Germans next tried to take Fort Vaux but again it was stubbornly defended. During the struggle the French commander lost contact with his headquarters and an urgent request for support had to be sent by carrier pigeon. The brave bird delivered the message but then dropped dead. It was later awarded the *Légion d'honneur*. In spite of these efforts, Fort Vaux finally fell to the Germans. In an attempt to bring his offensive to a successful conclusion, Falkenhayn broadened his attacks but French resistance remained as determined as ever. As G. D. Sheffield has written, 'with all restraints cast to the wind, amid the shattered trenches and shellholes ceaselessly pounded by artillery, two mighty nations were locked in a struggle to the death' (*Leadership in the Trenches*, 2000). A pilot flying over Verdun noted that 'every sign of humanity had been swept away' and 'woods and roads have vanished like chalk wiped from a blackboard'. He concluded that the scene below reminded him of Dante's *Inferno*.

As Falkenhayn slowly came to realize the futility of it all, he tried to end the battle but his superiors insisted that it continue. Yet another German attempt to break through failed and to make things even more difficult, on 1 July the British had launched an offensive to the north close to the River Somme. During the first six months of the Battle of Verdun, Falkenhayn had failed to take the fortress city, lost 280,000 men and worse was to follow. In October, a French counterattack took the Germans completely by surprise and they were able to advance five kilometres (three miles), retake Fort Douaumont and Fort Vaux and capture 9,000 prisoners. Falkenhayn, who had set out to hammer and destroy the French army on 'the anvil of Verdun', had himself witnessed the slaughter of thousands of his men. In the end, the savagery of the ten-month battle resulted in 542,000 French and 434,000 German casualties. In a reshuffle at the top of the German High Command, Falkenhayn was dismissed and replaced by Hindenburg and Ludendorff whilst on the French side, their Commander-in-Chief, Marshal Joffre, gave way to Robert Nivelle.

Changes at the top – French replaced by Haig

At the end of 1915, Field Marshal Sir John Haig replaced Field Marshal Sir John French as commander-in-chief of the British armies on the Western Front. The two men were very different in character and outlook.

John Denton Pinkstone French was born in 1852. He had earlier taken part in the failed mission to rescue General Gordon in Khartoum and gained something of a good reputation during the Boer Wars since he had led the force that relieved Kimberley and for his exploits had been promoted to brigadier-general and received a knighthood. He was next appointed Chief of the Imperial General Staff and in 1913 was promoted to field marshal. In 1914, he took command of the BEF but soon doubts arose about his ability since he appeared to lack an understanding of the overall situation and was thought too indecisive. Some were also of the opinion that he had failed to make the best of the opportunities that arose. Views about him were mixed and he was described as being 'vain, ignorant and vindictive' whilst another general went as far as to consider him 'an ignorant little fool'. On the other hand, Kitchener admired him for 'his soldier-like qualities' and Winston Churchill considered him to be a 'natural soldier'. French was not helped by his womanizing that involved him in several scandals or by the fact that one of his sisters, Charlotte Despard, was a well-known pacifist, socialist, campaigner for women's rights and a supporter of Sinn Fein.

Douglas Haig was born in 1861 into a family of well-known Scotch whisky distillers. Like French, he was a cavalryman who had served in the Sudan and the Boer Wars and of significance was the fact that he was married to Dorothy Vivian, one of the queen's ladies-in-waiting. A deeply religious man, he was considered to be more liberal and forward looking than most other senior officers. In 1914, he went to France as commander of the British First Army and although his early conduct was undistinguished, his determined defence of Ypres enhanced his reputation. From the start, he had doubts concerning the suitability of French to command and made his views known to King George V in a series of secret communications. As we shall see, views about Haig were to become even more controversial than those about French.

Whatever his shortcomings, French had been quick to appreciate the inevitability of trench warfare and in a letter to the King wrote 'the spade will be as great a necessity as the rifle'. A year later he indicated his dislike of what was going on around him, 'War is really a brutal way of settling differences and the more I see of it, the more I hate it'. Haig, on the other hand, was intent on a war of attrition and in 1915, he commented, 'The enemy should never be given a complete rest by day or night, but be relentlessly worn down by exhaustion and loss until his defence collapses.' Finally, dissatisfaction with French's leadership coupled with behind-the-scenes intrigue that undermined his position led to his dismissal.

In June 1916, the Germans approached the French government with peace proposals. From the German viewpoint, the time seemed opportune since they thought the French were in difficulties following their heavy losses at Verdun and imagined they would be in a strong position to gain advantageous peace terms. The Allied leaders saw things very differently since with Verdun still in French hands and a new offensive being planned, they felt far from defeated and were in no mood to consider peace terms. They still wanted nothing other than out and out victory. Significantly, only those at the top knew of the German peace overtures and they saw no need to make them generally known in order to test the reaction of public opinion.

The Battle of the Somme

As early as December 1915, a conference of Allied leaders had met at Chantilly and had agreed to a joint offensive on the Western Front during the coming summer. Haig would have preferred to have waited until his troops had more combat experience and tanks had arrived at the front in sufficient numbers to have an impact. However, by spring the pressure on the French at Verdun had made the offensive an urgent necessity and plans were made for it to take place along a 28-kilometre (17-mile) front that ran from Gommecourt to a point just north of the River Ancre and then southwards below the high ground, Pozières Ridge, and on to the Somme Valley.

figure 16 the Somme battlefield

The major town immediately to the rear of the British lines was Albert. Always full of military, it was heavily bombarded and numerous shells hit the town's basilica surmounted by a statue of a golden Virgin and Child. The statue did not fall but hung precariously over the side at right angles to the ground where British engineers made it secure. There was a legend that the war would not end until the statue fell.

The line of advance was to stretch to the north and south of the main road between Albert and Bapaume with most of this line

covered by the British 4th Army under General Sir Henry
Rawlinson and the French 6th Army responsible for the
remainder. Although Haig was the Commander-in-Chief, he left
the detailed planning of the offensive to the man on the spot,
Rawlinson. Even so, there were sharp differences of opinion
between the two men since Haig wanted an all-out offensive
that would result in a major breakthrough; Rawlinson however
favoured a more gradual approach that would involve 'bite and
hold' operations – a series of offensives each with limited aims.
On paper, the plan produced by Rawlinson was simple enough.
The first stage of the battle would be a week-long bombardment
of the German lines which he supposed would virtually
eliminate any opposition before the infantry moved forward.
Rawlinson was of the opinion that since the majority of his men
were inexperienced civilian volunteers, to avoid any confusion it
would be best if they advanced towards the enemy in an orderly
fashion, line abreast. Their path through their own barbed wire
would be marked with white tape. Once the enemy line had
been broken, the cavalry would charge through into the open
ground beyond and outflank and roll up the enemy. The date for
the opening of the offensive was set for 1 July 1916. Although
Haig had concerns about certain aspects of Rawlinson's plan he
chose not to make them known.

The bombardment of the German trenches began on 24 June and
continued night and day for the next six days. At the same time,
tunnellers made final preparations to explode mines at various
points under the German front line to mark the start of the
assault. As the final hours passed, battalion commanders
emphasized that the attack next morning would be a walkover
and one commander went as far as to tell his men, 'When you go
over the top you can slope arms, light up your pipes and
cigarettes and march all the way to Pozières before seeing any
live Germans'. Another commented, 'Tomorrow, you will be able
to go over the top with a walking stick, you will not need a rifle'
but no one was more optimistic than Captain Nevill of the East
Surreys who provided each of his four platoons with footballs to
kick across no man's land and offered a prize for the first to kick
the ball into the enemy's trenches. Others were less sure. Whilst
on leave, Captain Martin of the Devonshire Regiment made a
model of the area of the front immediately ahead of his battalion
and on his return to France, used it to illustrate that when the
men went forward as suggested, German machine gunners on the
hill opposite would mow them down. His commanding officer
chose to discount his findings. Two days before the battle,

another officer in the same regiment, William Hodgson, wrote a prophetic poem, *Before Action*, that concluded:

> 'I, that on my familiar hill
>   Saw with uncomprehending eyes
> A hundred of Thy sunsets spill
>   Their fresh and sanguine sacrifice,
> 'Ere the sun swings his noonday sword
>   Must say goodbye to all of this:-
> By all delights that I shall miss,
>   Help me to die, O Lord.'

The first day of the Battle of the Somme was to be the blackest day in the history of the British army. In the British trenches, men, with bayonets fixed, and young officers, whistles in their mouths, waited for the last minutes to tick away. Then suddenly at 7.20 a.m. the mines at Hawthorn Ridge and La Boisselle were detonated and explosions sent huge columns of earth into the air. Then ten minutes later the guns fell silent and urged on by whistles and the encouragement of their platoon commanders, the infantrymen rose from their trenches, made their way through the barbed wire, formed lines and advanced forward. The men did not realize that the shelling had failed to destroy the enemy's barbed wire or that many of the shells, one estimate is a third, had not exploded. Even more significant was the fact that because German trenches and dugouts were dug deeper and better constructed than the British, many of their men had survived the bombardment. To the Germans, the end of the bombardment was a signal that the British attack was about to begin and they were quickly out of their dugouts and in position behind their machine guns. Even though a German counterbarrage began to rain shells on them, the British infantrymen came steadily on. Then the Germans began to blaze away at the sitting targets of rows of advancing soldiers. As the lines began to wither away, soon no man's land was piled high with the dead and the dying. John Giles has vividly described the scene as 'a slaughter yard, with wounded men screaming among the mutilated bodies of the dead' (*From Mons to the Marne*, 1977). As planned, Captain Nevill's company set off with their footballs towards the German lines but they didn't get far before the officer and his men were all killed in no man's land. Near Mametz, Captain Martin had also led his men forward and as his model had shown, they came immediately into full view of the enemy and, caught on an exposed slope, they were mown down. His body, together with another 159 men of the

Devonshires, was later buried in the trench from which they had emerged. Another to perish in the same place and at the same time was the poet Lieutenant Hodgson whose poem suggested that he had some premonition of his fate. In spite of the chaos and slaughter elsewhere, at the southern extremity of the line, the British and French gained some success and reached their objectives. This was largely because the men had moved forward into no man's land and then advanced towards the enemy behind a creeping barrage. Such a barrage moves just ahead of the advancing troops and forces the enemy to keep their heads down.

The historian A. J. P. Taylor (1954) wrote, 'Kitchener's army found its graveyard on the Somme'. On the first day alone, the British army suffered 57,470 casualties of which 19,240 were killed, 35,493 wounded and 2,152 missing and in addition the German also took 585 prisoners. In the close-knit communities in which some of the 'Pals Battalions' had been recruited, every street had families that mourned the loss of a husband, father, son or brother. The Accrington Pals suffered 585 casualties, the Leeds Pals 528 and the Bradford Pals 515. Some must have been mystified by the headlines in some British newspapers that were a travesty of the truth!

The first day of the Somme as reported in the British local newspaper, *The Southern Evening Echo*.

The first day of the battle – what went wrong?

At the start, Haig never really challenged Rawlinson over their different views regarding the tactics to be used in the planned offensive. Crucially, the heavy bombardment of the German positions failed in its aim since many shells failed to explode which meant that much of the German barbed wire was left intact. The superior construction of their defensive positions meant that many of the German troops survived and the sudden end to the bombardment provided the signal that the Allied offensive was about to start. The time lapse between the end of the bombardment and the advance of the infantrymen allowed the Germans to get into position to repel the attack. As the infantrymen made their way through the barbed wire along routes indicated by white tape, so they emerged at exit points that attracted the concentrated fire of German machine gunners. The British infantrymen were misled into believing the assault on the German positions would be a walkover and consequently, under instruction, they made their way forward in lines abreast and at a walking pace. They presented an easy target, as did the waves of infantry that followed them. Even worse, they found themselves floundering amongst their own dead and wounded.

The Somme – the slaughter continues

The carnage of 1 July and the failure to achieve a breakthrough did not deter the military command. In a battle that was to continue for the best part of five months, Rawlinson persisted with the same tactics so that each ridge and wood became the scene of a battle with a heavy loss of life. Positions were often taken, lost and then taken again. During the remainder of July, the 28th (Welsh) Division became involved in a costly struggle for Mametz Wood which cost the Welshmen 4,000 casualties whilst the 18th Division lost a further 4,000 men during a six-day battle to take nearby Trones Wood. It was left to the South African Brigade to drive the Germans from Delville Wood and of the 3,153 men that went into action only 773 emerged unscathed. Towards the end of the month, the Australians set out to capture Pozières Ridge and 8,000 lost their lives fighting for the important high ground. In August, it took three weeks of heavy fighting to capture the area around one farm, Mouquet

Farm, 'Mucky Farm' to the British soldiers, which was part of a German defensive line. The following month there was heavy fighting around Flers and it was here that tanks were used in battle for the first time. Of the 13 tanks that set out, 12 reached the German lines and, of these, six advanced as far as the village. Thiepval, one of the original objectives on 1 July, was finally taken on 25 September with both sides suffering terrible losses and it was here that the Ulster Division alone lost 4,000 men. A small wooded mound, the Butte de Warlencourt, beside the road leading to Bapaume was also the scene of bitter fighting. Fortified by the Germans so that it became honeycombed with tunnels, it changed hands time and time again and did not finally fall to the British until February 1917. The battle for the heights above the River Ancre began early in October and it lasted until the capture of Beaumont Hamel and Beaucourt in mid-November. These were the closing events in the Battle of the Somme.

The Somme – was it worth it?

In just over 20 weeks, at the furthest point the Allies had managed to advance 11 kilometres (seven miles). It had been a long and murderous slog that failed to achieve the desired breakthrough and during the course of the battle Allied casualties totalled 614,105 of which 419,654 were British and Dominion soldiers. The cost to the Germans was about 650,000 and a German staff officer later described the Somme as 'the muddy grave of the German field army'. Was the battle an Allied victory? If it was, it was a Pyrrhic victory and Haig must have wondered how many such victories he could afford. In truth, the loss of life affected the morale of the fighting men on both sides and at home, recruiting figures slumped so that the conscription of men had to be considered. No longer was joining the army regarded as the start of 'a great adventure'.

Postscript

Today, the legacy of the battle can still be found on the Somme. Shell cases, ammunition and barbed wire can be found and local farmers turn up what they refer to as their 'Iron Harvest'. They still represent a danger and can still cause fatalities. The battlefield also contains a great many military cemeteries and memorials to those that fell in the battle. The largest is the

Memorial to the Missing at Thiepval which is situated on a ridge and can be seen at a distance from various parts of the battlefield. Designed by Sir Edwin Lutyens, the panels on the central archway and numerous smaller arches list the names of the 73,412 men who died during 1916 and 1917 and have no known graves. At times, much of the Somme and other battlefields became a blaze of red poppies. Their appearance was due to the disturbance of land and the release of seeds caused by the digging of trenches, exploding shells and the burial of the dead. After the war, the former British commander-in-chief set up the Haig Fund to assist ex-servicemen. The Fund, now managed by the British Legion, adopted the poppy as a symbol of remembrance.

10

the war at sea

This chapter will cover:
- the comparative strengths of the British and German navies
- the early encounters in the North Sea
- the threat posed by German surface raiders
- the Battle of Jutland
- blockades and the nature of submarine warfare
- the methods used by the Allies to beat the submarine threat.

'Oh, dear, what comfort can I find?
  None this tide,
  Nor any tide,
Except he did not shame his kind –
Not even with the wind blowing, and that tide.'

(From *My Boy Jack*, a poem written
by Rudyard Kipling in honour of the
teenage hero of Jutland, John Cornwell)

The British and German navies – a comparison

Britain and Germany had begun their struggle to win naval supremacy long before the outbreak of the war. During the period between 1906 and 1915, Admiral Sir John Fisher brought about a revolution in naval construction with the introduction of the ironclad *Dreadnought* and Admiral Alfred von Tirpitz saw to it that Germany did not lag behind in the production of these new ships. Even so, Britain still retained the leadership in all types of vessels.

The British and German navies in 1914		
	Britain	Germany
Dreadnought-type battleships	20	13
Battlecruisers*	8	5
Cruisers	102	41
Destroyers	301	144
Submarines	78	30

*A battlecruiser was a ship with the guns of a battleship and the speed of a cruiser. To make this possible, its armour was lighter than that of a battleship and critics claimed that this made such ships vulnerable.

The greater part of the British Grand Fleet was based at Scapa Flow in the Orkney Islands and there were also other major naval bases at Rosyth, Chatham, Portsmouth and Plymouth. The German High Seas Fleet was located at Bremen, Cuxhaven, Emden, Kiel and Wilhelmshaven. In addition, both Britain and Germany had squadrons of warships scattered across the oceans of the world. The war started with a blow to British naval prestige when the German warships, *Goeben* and *Breslau*, outwitted their pursuers and made their way through the Mediterranean to reach Constantinople. Their success largely contributed to Turkey's decision to enter the war on Germany's side. Elsewhere in Europe, the German navy was content to raid towns along the British East Coast such as Lowestoft, Scarborough and Hartlepool. A major achievement of the Royal Navy during this time was the movement of the BEF across the English Channel to France without loss of life and it also managed to cut the German transatlantic undersea cable and so sever that country's links with North America.

Early North Sea encounters

First blood went to the Royal Navy when in August 1914 four German cruisers were sunk off Heligoland Bight but this was avenged the following month when a German submarine torpedoed three British cruisers with the loss of 1,600 lives. German hit-and-run raids along the British East Coast continued and one such raid caused over 500 civilian casualties but as British radio surveillance improved, so such raids became more hazardous and less frequent. Although the Royal Navy was more powerful than the German *Kriegsmarine*, neither side was keen to risk a major naval engagement that might involve heavy losses. So important was the Royal Navy to British war strategy that Winston Churchill, the First Lord of the Admiralty, said of the British naval Commander-in-Chief, Admiral John Jellicoe that he was 'the only man on either side who could lose the war in an afternoon'. The Royal Navy gained a major advantage when, unknown to the Germans, the Russians managed to obtain a copy of their code books and passed the details to the British. It was because of this that in January 1915, a German cruiser squadron was intercepted in the North Sea and at the Battle of the Dogger Bank, Admiral Beatty's ships drove the Germans off and succeeded in sinking the *Blucher* with the loss of 950 lives.

German surface raiders

Whilst the Royal Navy might have possessed the most powerful fleet in the word, it could not always guarantee the safety of British merchant shipping across the world's oceans. Most troublesome were the activities of German surface raiders that were active along shipping lanes in the Pacific and Indian

Oceans as well as the Caribbean. These German cruisers, the most famous of which were the *Karlsruhe*, *Dresden* and *Emden*, raided shore installations and sank Allied merchant ships.

When Japan entered the war on the side of the Allies in 1914, her forces occupied the German naval base of Tsingtao on the Chinese coast. As a result, Admiral von Spee's squadron, which had been based there, was forced to put to sea and travelled the Pacific Ocean in search of Allied merchant shipping and wrought havoc by attacking British and French shore installations. From time to time, von Spee's ships had to put into harbour to take on coal and food and on one occasion bought supplies from a British trader who was unaware there was a war taking place. In November 1914, von Spee's squadron met up with three British cruisers under Admiral Craddock off the coast of Chile and at the Battle of Coronel, the Germans won an impressive victory and sank all three British cruisers. Out for revenge, a large British force set out and caught up with the Germans in the south Atlantic. The Battle of the Falkland Islands was a major British success and only one German ship escaped and von Spee, together with his two sons and 2,000 sailors, drowned. In the Indian Ocean, the German battleship *Königsberg*, threatened British shipping heading for the Suez Canal. Amongst her victims was the *City of Winchester* that was carrying most of the Ceylon tea crop and she also managed to delay the first Australian and New Zealand troops bound for Europe. Spotted from the air, the *Königsberg* was finally cornered and forced to scuttle in the mouth of the River Rufifi in German East Africa. Yet another German raider, the *Karlsruhe*, attacked Allied shipping until she unaccountably blew up and sank taking with her virtually all her crew. The *Dresden* evaded her pursuers by hiding in the inlets along the Chilean coast until she too was tracked down and forced to scuttle off Juan Fernandez Island in the Pacific.

By far the most famous and successful of all the German surface raiders was the *Emden*. Known as the 'Swan of the East', the *Emden* was an impressive cruiser commanded by a skilful and chivalrous captain, Karl von Muller. He asked permission to act independently and raid shipping in the Indian Ocean and von Spee agreed telling him that 'there are great prizes to be won'. In order to disguise his ship, von Muller added a dummy funnel so that, from a distance, it resembled a British warship and then, sailing southward across the Pacific, the *Emden* reached the Indian Ocean and bombarded Madras where it set fire to

50,000 tonnes of petroleum. The raider next entered Penang harbour in the Malay peninsular and there sank a Russian cruiser and a French destroyer. During the next seven weeks, the *Emden* sank a further 19 British merchantmen representing 70,000 tonnes of shipping. British, French, Japanese and Russian ships jointly organized a search for her and in November 1914, the German warship came face to face with the faster and heavier Australian cruiser, HMAS *Sydney*. Driven aground on a reef in the Cook Islands, von Muller surrendered but some of his crew managed to escape and after an incredible adventure made their way to Arabia before finally reaching Germany.

The Battle of Jutland

The Battle of Jutland, known to the Germans as the Battle of Skagerrak, was the only major sea battle of the First World War. Until this time, the British Grand Fleet and German High Seas Fleet had avoided a direct confrontation but this came to an end during the afternoon of 31 May 1916 when a German fleet under Admiral Reinhard Scheer faced a British fleet under Admiral Jellicoe in the North Sea off Jutland.

The German plan was to bait a trap and tempt Admiral Beatty's battlecruiser squadron out of Rosyth in the belief that it was chasing a relatively small German force. Von Hipper, the commander of the German squadron, would then retire with Beatty in hot pursuit and so draw him unwittingly towards the main German fleet that was some 80 kilometres (50 miles) distant over the horizon. Beatty's ships would then be easily overwhelmed. The Germans were unaware that the British, with access to their secret codes, knew of their plan and were planning a trap of their own by using a near identical plan. Von Hipper did not realize that the bulk of the British Grand Fleet had also put to sea at the same time as Beatty and was out of sight but not far distant from his squadron.

The Battle of Jutland was fought in two phases. In the first, the squadrons of Beatty and Hipper confronted each other until the German admiral ordered his ships to turn about and so draw Beatty towards the German High Seas Fleet. During the long-range duel that followed, the Royal Navy lost two battleships, HMS *Indefatigable* and HMS *Queen Mary*. However, with von Hipper in difficulties, Scheer ordered the German High Seas Fleet to steam forward to support him without realizing that

figure 17 the Battle of Jutland

just beyond Beatty's squadron lay Jellicoe with the British Grand Fleet. The second phase of the battle began when the German fleet came face to face with the main British force. With the British fleet approaching in six lines ahead, Jellicoe immediately ordered his ships to turn to port, to the left, to form an extended line side by side since this would allow them to fire broadside after broadside at the leading ships as they came within range. Outlined against the evening sky, they were easy targets and Sheer, fearing that his fleet might be totally destroyed, ordered his fleet to retire. Battle was later resumed with the ships of both sides milling around firing at each other. Meanwhile, Jellicoe took the opportunity to cut off Scheer's line of retreat by placing some of his ships between the German fleet and their home ports. With dense smoke and the coming of nightfall making visibility increasingly difficult, Jellicoe was forced to alter course to avoid a mass torpedo attack. Once it was dark, Scheer's fleet broke through the British line and disappeared into the night and the next morning Jellicoe's warships searched the sea for remnants of the German fleet but found nothing. Scheer's High Seas Fleet was safely back in port.

Comparative British and German losses at Jutland		
	British losses	German losses
Battleships	0	1
Battlecruisers	3	0
Cruisers	3	5
Destroyers	8	5
Tonnage	115,025	61,180
Lives	6,097	2,545

And so who won? After the battle both sides claimed victory. Without doubt, the Royal Navy's losses were considerably greater than those of the German fleet. From Jellicoe's viewpoint, a major tragedy was the loss of three battlecruisers, *Indefatigable*, *Queen Mary* and *Invincible*, each of which received direct hits that resulted in massive explosions and the ships sank in 30 seconds and with great loss of life. In the case of the *Invincible*, there were only six survivors and when the cruiser *Black Prince* sank, there were none. This provided proof of the inadequacy of the armour on such ships and consequently their inability to withstand direct hits. The German battleships were built with watertight compartments and it was possible to flood the magazines in the event of an imminent threat from exploding shells. The battle also provided evidence of the superiority of German shells and the quality of their gunnery. Later, some blamed Jellicoe for being too cautious in not giving chase to the German fleet when it fled but this is not entirely fair since the British admiral faced the possibility that his ships were being drawn into a trap set by German submarines. In addition, throughout the battle Jellicoe suffered from a lack of up-to-date intelligence so that he had no idea what was going on and with none of his ships reporting directly to him, crucial information that might have helped to locate the enemy failed to reach him. Statistically, the Germans might appear to have a case for claiming the Battle of Jutland as a victory but in reality the real honours went to the Royal Navy. The German fleet had fled and been driven from the high seas. A disgruntled British naval captain lamented, 'We had them stone cold and we let them go.' The neutral press more fairly commented, 'The German fleet has assaulted its jailer, but is still in jail.' Afterwards, British command of the seas was never again seriously challenged since the German fleet never again risked a major confrontation and spent the rest of the war penned up in its ports. However, below the waves it was to be a different matter since the Germans had no alternative but to intensify their submarine campaign against the Allies.

The heroism of 16-year-old John Cornwell

John Travers Cornwell, or Jack as he was usually called, was born at Leyton in Essex in 1900. After briefly working as a delivery boy, at the age of 15 he joined the Royal Navy. As a Boy 2nd Class, he earned two and a half pence a week and all found (food and clothing provided) but after gunnery training he was promoted to Boy 1st Class and his pay doubled. At the time of the Battle of Jutland, he was serving on HMS *Chester* and during the course of the battle, his ship was in the thick of the fighting and received several direct hits. John Cornwell was in the forward gun turret when a shell exploded, killed most of the gun crew and left him badly wounded. In spite of his wounds, surrounded by the dead and dying, he stayed at his post waiting for any commands that might come. Once back in harbour, he was rushed to a Grimsby hospital but died the next day. After an impressive funeral, he was buried in Manor Park Cemetery and later his mother received his posthumous Victoria Cross on his behalf. Afterwards, the Boy Scout movement instituted the Cornwell Badge as the highest award that can be made to a Boy Scout for courage and devotion. Sadly two years later, his brother, Arthur Cornwell, was killed in action in France.

An unhappy postscript to the Battle of Jutland was that on 6 June, barely a week after the battle, Lord Kitchener and his staff were drowned when the cruiser HMS *Hampshire* struck a mine and sank off the Orkney Islands. Some mystery surrounds the sinking of the *Hampshire*, which was taking Kitchener on a secret mission to Russia. Was it a chance occurrence or was it, as some maintain, the result of German espionage?

Naval blockades

The aim of a blockade is to cripple the enemy's economy and starve the people into submission by denying them supplies of raw materials and foodstuffs. For the Allies, it was relatively easy for them to enforce a blockade of Germany and Austria-Hungary. With hostile powers on three sides – Russia to the east, Italy to the south and France to the west – it was left to the Allies to complete the blockade by closing the North Sea and Mediterranean Sea to German shipping. In order to accomplish this, a series of minefields was placed across the entrance to the Straits of Dover, off the coast of German-occupied Belgium and in the North Sea between the Scottish coast and Norway. A decision to intercept and board neutral shipping in search of goods likely to assist the German war effort led to difficulties and in this respect, the British government had to be particularly cautious with complaints from the United States. Nevertheless, the Allied blockade was successful and as the war progressed so the German people began to experience acute shortages which led to widespread food riots. The security of the English Channel was the responsibility of the Dover Patrol, a squadron of destroyers and minesweepers. Being an island people, the Germans were quick to recognize the vulnerability of Britain to a submarine-enforced blockade.

The German U-boat campaign against Britain

Even before the twentieth century there had been numerous attempts to build a craft capable of operating under water, but most ended in disaster and some proved fatal to their crews. Submarines submerge by flooding their ballast tanks and surface by blowing out the water with compressed air. On top is a conning tower with watertight hatches and when submerged, a periscope is used to survey the sea. The most important attributes of a submarine are that it can submerge quickly when spotted by the enemy and that, within limits, it can withstand water pressure and the threat posed by exploding depth charges. The first submarines in operational service were British K-boats but driven by steam engines, the fires of which had to be extinguished before it could dive, they were far from reliable and once the war started, more K-boats were lost due to mechanical failure than enemy action. Driven by diesel engines, German U-boats were far better designed. Although both K-boats and U-boats carried torpedoes, their main armament was a single deck gun. This meant that submarines had to come to the surface in order to engage the enemy. The problem with the torpedo was that is was unreliable and likely to go off course or fail to explode when it hit its intended target. However, when it did explode, it was extremely effective. In the Royal Navy, K-boats soon gave way to E Class submarines and these were to be mainly responsible for the contribution made by British submarines to the war at sea. These had the appearance of a more modern submarine and were powered by turbines when on the surface and an electric motor when submerged. Like all submarines, they travelled more quickly on the surface than when under water. Some submarines were used as minelayers and towards the end of the war experiments were made to discover if they could carry seaplanes.

Although at the start of the war the German navy possessed only 30 U-boats (*Untersee* boats), they had an abundance of targets to attack. The first submarine action occurred in August 1914 when HMS *Birmingham* sank the U15 but this was avenged the following month when the U21 sank the British warship, HMS *Pathfinder*. October saw the start of a new phase in the German submarine campaign when the U17 sank a British merchant ship, the *Glitra*. At this stage of the war, German U-boats surfaced in order to attack merchant ships and the crews were allowed to take to the lifeboats before their ships were sunk but this conduct did not last long. The Germans next began a period of unrestricted submarine action by declaring the seas around Britain to be a 'war zone' and warning that ships entering those waters were liable to be sunk without warning. On 7 May 1915, the Cunard liner, *Lusitania*, was torpedoed off the southern coast of Ireland.

The sinking of the *Lusitania*

On 1 May 1915, the British liner *Lusitania* sailed from New York bound for Liverpool. The Cunard liner, the largest and fastest on the transatlantic service, was carrying 1,906 passengers and crew. In New York, the German embassy had published a warning that the ship was likely to be attacked. Ironically, in some American newspapers the notice appeared next to an advertisement promoting the voyage and giving details of the liner's sailing times. Early on the afternoon of the 7 May, the liner was torpedoed by the German submarine U20 off the coast of southern Ireland. The *Lusitania* sank in 18 minutes taking with her 1,098 passengers and crew of which 128 were Americans. In the United States there was an outcry and a wave of anti-German feeling swept the country but in Germany, the press described the sinking as an 'outstanding success' and a medal was struck to commemorate the U-boat's achievement. Since that time there has been a great deal of controversy surrounding the sinking of the *Lusitania*. Why did the ship sink so quickly? Why was there such great loss of life when the ship was in sight of land? The liner's captain, William Turner, claimed that two torpedoes struck the *Lusitania* but Walter Schweiger, captain of the U20 denied this and said that the second explosion was caused by the detonation of the ship's cargo. Was it possible that the liner was secretly carrying a cargo of armaments and explosives? Whatever the truth, the sinking of the *Lusitania* had the effect of making the American people more supportive of the Allied cause.

The U-boat campaign intensifies

During 1915, German U-boats sank a total of 1,328,985 tonnes of Allied shipping and the monthly total never fell below 300,000 tonnes. Although the Kaiser was uncertain about it and the Chancellor, Bethmann-Hollweg, very much against it, early in 1917, the Germans started a second and far more vigorous period of unrestricted submarine warfare. The German High Command, particularly Ludendorff, was aware that whilst the German armies were engaged in a life and death struggle on the Western Front, large amounts of essential war materials were being carried to Britain on neutral ships. In his view this had to be stopped even if it meant sinking ships bound to British ports from neutral countries and even if it risked bringing the United States into the war, as Americans were still angry at the sinking of the *Lusitania*. Now with 111 U-boats at their disposal, the Germans had even greater success against British shipping. During February 1917, 548,671 tonnes were sunk and in April this rose to a massive 894,147 tonnes with one in every four British merchant ships that left port failing to return. The situation became so serious that it became a real threat to the chances of an Allied victory and with some people doubting Britain's ability to remain in the war, something had to be done.

Allied countermeasures

The entry of the United States into the war changed the situation significantly but even before that, steps had to be taken to deal with the German U-boat menace. David Lloyd George, the British Prime Minister, favoured the introduction of the convoy system. This system would allow merchant ships to group together to sail across the Atlantic protected by a warship escort. Admiral Jellicoe and other high-ranking officers at the Admiralty opposed the idea and argued that a slow-moving convoy would present a bigger target and that German U-boat commanders would have a field day. They also contended that in order to provide escorts, the Grand Fleet would have to give up most of its light cruisers and destroyers and that this would not be in the nation's best interests but in spite of Jellicoe's protests, the convoy system was introduced. Each convoy would consist of some 40 merchant ships surrounded by fast-moving destroyers equipped with depth charges. New tactics and more advanced technology also came into use. Convoys would be protected by both British and American destroyers in home waters with aircraft being used to provide additional cover. Other important developments included the introduction of the hydrophone that made it possible to detect noise under the water and the use of Q-ships. On the face of it, a Q-ship looked like an unarmed merchantman but when it was approached by a U-boat, a range of concealed guns were revealed, capable of blowing its would-be attacker out of the water. The use of Q-ships proved to be a mixed blessing and brought only limited success since U-boat commanders reacted by remaining submerged and invariably used torpedoes to sink their victims without any warning. On the other hand, the introduction of the convoy system was an immediate success. With U-boat commanders no longer able to prey on single defenceless merchant vessels, British losses fell dramatically. By April 1918, the total number of Allied ships launched exceeded the number lost at sea. As Karl Donetz, a U-boat commander said, 'A lone U-boat will sink one or two ships ... but that is a poor percentage of the whole. The convoy would steam on and reach Britain, bringing a rich cargo of foodstuffs and raw materials safely to port.' The German U-boat menace was as good as beaten.

The tragedy of the troopship *Mendi*

During the course of the war, black South Africans were asked to volunteer to serve in the Native Labour Corps on the Western Front. Their function was to dig trenches, build roads and perform other manual tasks but not to engage the enemy in combat. In January 1917, the troopship *Mendi* sailed from Cape Town with 802 members of the South African Labour Corps (SANLC) on board. After calling at Plymouth, the ship set sail for Le Havre and some 18 kilometres (11 miles) off St. Catherine's Point on the Isle of Wight it was in collision in thick fog with the SS *Darro*. As the sea poured into the breach made in the *Mendi*, the ship took only 25 minutes to sink and of the 802 black soldiers on board, 607 were drowned together with

31 of the ship's officers and crew. There is a legend that since there was little chance of many of the men making it to safety, one of their leaders, the Reverend Isaac Wauchope, called them together and said, 'Be quiet and calm, my countrymen, for what is taking place is exactly what you came to do. You are going to die ... Raise your war cries brothers, for though they made us leave our assegais in the kraal, our voices are left in our bodies.' The men then removed their boots and sang and danced their death dance on the slanting deck of the sinking ship.

The Zeebrugge raid

Admiral Sir Roger Keyes, the officer in charge of naval operations in the English Channel, planned another measure likely to reduce the U-boat menace. April 1918 witnessed one of the most daring naval actions of the whole war when Keyes led a naval task force to the Belgian port of Zeebrugge with the intention of blockading the Bruges Canal and so reducing the flow of U-boats into the North Sea. His force included the cruiser, HMS *Vindictive*, two passenger ferries carrying additional marines, and three old warships, the *Thetis*, *Intrepid* and *Iphegenia* which had previously been filled with concrete. At Zeebrugge, the marines first went ashore to take possession of the mole and engage the German defences. Then Keyes manoeuvred the three concrete-filled ships into the entrance to the channel, placed them sideways on and then scuttled them. Whilst this was going on, a British submarine managed to edge its way under a viaduct connecting the mole with the mainland and once the crew had abandoned the submarine, it was exploded and the viaduct destroyed and as soon as the marines were on board, the *Vindictive* withdrew under the cover of a smoke screen. The deed ensured that the German troops defending the mole could not be reinforced. In truth, the raid had little effect on the movement of U-boats in and out of Zeebrugge but in Britain the epic action boosted the morale of the people, particularly since it had taken place on St. George's Day. Winston Churchill later referred to the raid as 'an episode unsurpassed in the history of the Royal Navy'. An interesting postscript to the raid was that Keyes recommended the award of eight Victoria Crosses to some of the heroes involved but his recommendation was turned down on the grounds that 'it was too many and risked lowering the standard of the award'. Even so, in the end Keyes had his way and the eight men received their medals.

11

Spads, Fokkers and Camels – the war in the air

This chapter will cover:
- the early development of airships and aeroplanes
- the role of aircraft in the war
- the struggle to achieve aerial supremacy
- the achievements of the 'aces'.

'Thrice cursed War
Which bids that I
Such death should pour
Down from the sky.'

(*Nox Mortis*, Paul Bewsher 1894–1966 who served in the
Royal Naval Air Service)

Airships and aeroplanes – the beginning

Ever since 1783 when the Montgolfier brothers first
experimented with hot-air balloons, pioneers tried to make
balloon travel a viable proposition. The problem was that
balloons were at the mercy of the wind and weather and before
any real progress could be made, a means had to be discovered
to propel, steer and make balloons capable of carrying
passengers and cargo. In 1900, the German, Count Ferdinand
von Zeppelin, used a petrol engine to propel a navigable or
dirigible balloon. Cigar-shaped, the structure was made of
aluminium covered with cotton cloth whilst inside were a
number of separate balloon units each filled with hydrogen. The
Germans had succeeded in making the first of a fleet of airships
or Zeppelins, as they were known, and these were used to
provide the first passenger air service. In 1903, at Kitty Hawk,
North Carolina, the American aviators Orville and Wilbur
Wright made the first flight in a heavier-than-air machine that
lasted 59 seconds as the aircraft travelled some 260 metres (853
feet). Two years later, the brothers designed *Flier III*, which was
a more practical aircraft capable of banking and turning and
could reach a speed of 56 kilometres (35 miles) an hour. They
brought their famous *Flier III* to Europe and flew it in public. In
Britain, it was an American, the self-styled 'Colonel' S. F. Cody
who first completed a powered flight. More spectacular was the
flight of the Frenchman Louis Blériot across the English
Channel in 1909 that attracted much public attention and first
focused the minds of the military on the potential of aircraft as
a weapon of war. In a remarkably short time, an assortment of
monoplanes, biplanes, triplanes and even seaplanes were
designed and made available. The threat of a European war
accelerated the development of both airships and aircraft for
military purposes.

Early days – the Royal Flying Corps

Before having an identity of its own, the Royal Flying Corps (RFC) was originally an army unit and existed firstly as a Balloon Section and then as the Air Battalion of the Royal Engineers whilst the Royal Navy had its own branch, the Royal Naval Air Service. The pilots and observers needed to serve in the new units were mainly recruited from upper-class families who had access to an aircraft and regarded flying as a hobby; the engineers came from the ranks of skilled tradesmen who would have previously been engaged in vehicle maintenance or such trades as map-making and photography. The majority of British aircraft was made by either the Royal Aircraft Factory at Farnborough or by privately-owned companies such as Sopwith Aviation and De Havilland. In 1914, at the start of the war, four squadrons of aircraft with a total strength of 63 aeroplanes flown and maintained by 860 men, crossed to France to serve with the BEF. Most of their aircraft were two seaters with a maximum speed of just under 100 kilometres (62 miles) an hour that could fly at a height of 1,000 metres (3,281 feet). At that time, the French had 138 operational aircraft and the Germans 230. Aerodromes were no more than fields with maintenance buildings and living accommodation close by.

The role of aircraft

To start with, men were placed in baskets suspended beneath balloons to keep a watch on the enemy's activities. Winched up to a suitable height, the unfortunate men were clearly visible to the enemy and became the targets of both ground troops and aircraft. In the event of their situation becoming too hazardous, they were issued with parachutes to allow them to make a hasty, if perilous, descent. It was originally thought that aircraft should only be used for observation and reconnaissance and no one imagined that they would become involved in aerial combat. During the opening phase of the war, aircraft quickly demonstrated their tactical value when in 1914 they warned the British and French of the German advance on Mons and it was French aircraft that first reported the change in direction taken by the German army and allowed the decisive Allied counterattack on the Marne. In a dispatch, Sir John French noted that aircraft had 'been of incalculable value in the conduct of operations'. Once the situation on the Western Front reached stalemate, aircraft were increasingly used for spotting targets, directing artillery fire and keeping a lookout for troop concentrations or any general movement that might indicate that preparations were being made for an offensive. At first, communications between aircraft and command posts on the ground were maintained either by dropping weighted messages or the use of signalling lamps but once introduced, the use of wireless proved much more effective. The system used for reporting ground positions was known as the 'clock code' by which the area around the target was divided into imaginary circles and each circle allocated a letter to show its distance from the centre. On all operations, pilots and observers were armed with rifles and revolvers.

Since photographs could be closely examined on the ground, aerial photography was essential for gathering accurate military intelligence. Aircraft flew over the enemy lines photographing their trench positions and troop concentrations but it was far from an easy task since the cameras were large, difficult to handle and attached to the outside of the aircraft. In spite of the fact that aircraft flying on such missions came under intense enemy fire from the ground, aerial photography made it possible to produce much-needed detailed trench maps.

From the spring of 1915, aircraft became increasingly involved in strafing enemy positions with machine-gun fire and dropping bombs on supply lines, ammunition dumps and road and railway communications. They were often criticized by the infantry on the ground since their activities were liable to stir up trouble along sections of the line that had previously been quiet. Soldiers also resented the fact that, their missions completed, fliers were able to return to their bases well behind the lines and spend their evenings in the comfort of the officers' mess or a local *estaminet*. The soldiers also disliked the apparent camaraderie shown by fliers on both sides who sometimes seemed more inclined to wave than shoot each other down. There were occasions when pilots that had been shot down were collected and allowed to join in their enemy's celebrations. Infantryman thought that airmen were not involved in the real war and there were times when this bad feeling spilled over into brawls.

Skirmishing and dogfights

To start with there was little fighting between the fliers on both sides but this situation did not last long and soon the skies over the Western Front became the scene of skirmishing between individual aircraft and mass dogfights between whole squadrons. Success in the sky depended on the quality of the aircraft and the individual skill of the pilots. In an aircraft, the crew, usually the pilot and an observer who acted as a gunner, sat in open cockpits and were fully exposed to the elements. Quite incredibly, aircrews were not equipped with parachutes since they were thought to be un-British and liable to undermine the pilot's determination to stay with his aircraft. In most aeroplanes, the fuel tank was situated close to the engine and sometimes directly under the pilot's seat so that with no means of escape from a blazing aircraft, men were liable to become human torches and suffer horrendous burns. Armed only with light weapons – revolvers and rifles – the best fliers could do was take pot shots at other aircraft. Soon British aeroplanes were equipped with Lewis guns fixed to the side of the aircraft or in the case of a biplane, on the upper wing which meant that firing directly ahead involved a risk of shooting off the aircraft's propeller. Some advance was made when propeller blades were fitted with steel blades intended to deflect bullets but the real breakthrough came when a Dutchman, Anthony Fokker, invented an interrupter gear that he supplied to the Germans. This ingenious innovation momentarily prevented the plane's machine gun from firing when the propeller blade passed in front of it.

Solo scouting missions soon gave way to more offensive operations. In order to make the planes less vulnerable to sudden attack, the leader flew at the front of a V-shaped formation and with the remaining aircraft behind in close proximity. When engaging the enemy, the squadron would break up and, left to his own devices, each pilot engaged in individual combat. In dogfights, tactics and manoeuvrability were all important whilst additional height allowed an aircraft to gain extra speed as it swooped on an unsuspecting enemy. The use of cloud cover was also important as was the advantage of having the sun at one's back and Allied pilots were warned, 'Beware of the Hun in the sun'. Aircraft were lightweight and this meant that when in difficulty it was possible for a pilot to land his plane in a field and take off again once it was safe. Since German pilots were equipped with parachutes and they seldom flew beyond the limits of their own front line, their survival rate was considerably higher than that of the British. There were stages in the war when the casualty rates were such that the life expectancy of inexperienced RFC pilots was only a few weeks.

During 1916, the RFC lost an average of two pilots every day and the situation worsened to the extent that during the following year, 50 aircraft were lost weekly. Towards the end of the war German tactics changed when they took to flying in mass formation. Impressive to look at but not over successful, the most famous group was nicknamed 'Richthofen's Flying Circus'.

The struggle for air supremacy

Although pilots became increasingly skilled, their ability in aerial combat counted for little if they did not possess the fastest, most manoeuvrable and best armed aircraft and so as the war progressed, the advantage swung from one side to the other. At the start of the war, both the British DH2 and the French Spad proved adequate but the advantage passed to the Germans when they introduced the Fokker Eindecker equipped with interrupter gear. So superior was the 'Fokker Scourge' in combat that Allied fliers came to regard themselves as nothing more than 'Fokker Fodder' but this changed in 1916 when the French developed the Nieuport XVII and the British the DH4. Before the end of the year the Germans were again able to claim the upper hand with the introduction of the twin-gunned Albatros. During the following months this aircraft wrought havoc and in April 1917, 'Bloody April' as it came to be known, the fortunes of the RFC and French Air Service reached their lowest ebb. Fortunately, the arrival of better designed and armed aircraft including the Sopwith Camel once again turned the tables in favour of the Allies. The Sopwith Camel, so called because of a hump on its fuselage, could out-manoeuvre German fighters in a dogfight and by the end of the war had accounted for 1,294 enemy aircraft. The Germans did produce what might have proved to be an even more superior aircraft, the Fokker CDII, but thankfully, for the Allies, it failed to get it into production in time.

The 'Aces'

Faster and more sophisticated aircraft created a new breed of airmen who developed their own distinctive tactics, the extremely skilled and equally ruthless 'aces'. Irrespective of their skills, the status of an 'ace' depended on the number of enemy aircraft he managed to shoot down and this he indicated with markings on the side of his aircraft's fuselage. Each country had its legendary 'aces' who became contemporary folk heroes. The most famous were the German, Manfred von Richthofen, the Frenchman, Georges Guynemer, and the Briton, Albert Ball.

A regular soldier who had once served in the trenches, Manfred von Richtofen learned his flying skills from another pilot with whom he had earlier flown as an observer. Leader of the famous Richthofen Squadron, he flew in an Albatros and, as if to flaunt his ability, he painted the fuselage bright red. Nicknamed the 'Red Baron' by the British and the 'Red Devil' by the French, during his wartime career, he shot down 80 Allied aircraft. He was finally shot down as he flew over the trenches in pursuit of a British aircraft. A great deal of controversy exists and many books have been written regarding who was responsible for shooting down his aircraft. Credit first went to a Canadian pilot, Captain Arthur Brown, but this was contested by Australians who claim that one of their gunners shot down Richthofen's plane with a single bullet fired from a machine gun in the trenches. A British pilot flew over the German aerodrome and dropped a note informing the Germans of the Red Baron's death. He was first buried in France with full military honours but after the war his body was exhumed and reburied in the family cemetery at Wiesbaden. On Richthofen's death, leadership of his squadron passed to Hermann Goering who later was to become a leading Nazi and commanded the German airforce, the *Luftwaffe*, during the Second World War.

Originally declared physically unfit and rejected for military services, Georges Guynemer eventually succeeded in joining the French Air Service as a mechanic before qualifying as a pilot. Three months later, he destroyed his first German aircraft but then was himself shot down. During the Battle of Verdun, he had a further eight victories and was fortunate to survive a crash landing. By mid-1917, his total score had reached 30 and included four enemy aircraft shot down in one day but by this time his poor health had further deteriorated and his family and superiors urged him to retire. He refused and five days after claiming his fifty-fourth victim, he was shot down and his body never found. The French pilot with the greatest number of victories, his countrymen considered him the 'Ace of Aces'.

The best-known British fighter pilot of the war, Albert Ball, came from Lenton in Nottinghamshire and served with the Sherwood Foresters before transferring to the Royal Flying Corps. Unlike Richthofen and Guynemer, Albert Ball was an individualist who preferred to fly alone. Consequently 60 Squadron allowed him free range and he was known to attack the enemy regardless of their number and the odds stacked against him. On one occasion, he took on six enemy aircraft single-handed and it was said that at times he appeared to be waging a private war against the German air force. His favourite ploy was to dive steeply, position himself behind and just below his enemy and rake the underside of his opponent's aircraft with machine-gun fire. Something of a loner, he was a quiet man whose favourite form of relaxation was playing the violin. During his career, he destroyed 11 enemy aircraft and forced numerous others to land. Ball was awarded the DSO and two bars, the Military Cross and the Victoria Cross. Still aged only 21, he was killed in action in France in May 1917.

Bombers and bombing raids

Neither side felt bound by the Hague Convention of 1899 that prohibited 'the dropping of projectiles and explosives from flying machines'. At the start of the war the Germans had a force of 30 airships or Zeppelins. Between 150 and 250 metres (492 and 820 feet) long and containing up to 56,000 cubic metres (two million cubic feet) of highly-flammable hydrogen, they might appear to have been easy targets but they were reasonably safe from attack from the ground or by aircraft because of the height at which they flew. In September 1914, the British made the first move when their aircraft attacked Zeppelin sheds at Dusseldorf and Cologne and followed this up with more widespread raids in Germany. To begin with, bombs were dropped manually over the side of the aircraft and even when bomb-aiming apparatus was introduced, it was extremely primitive and inaccurate. The Germans reacted to the British raids by using Zeppelins as terror weapons to attack purely civilian targets. The first raid on Britain came in May 1915 when Zeppelins bombed London and succeeded in killing five people and starting some fires. Afterwards there were more substantial raids on the Midlands, East Coast and again on London during which 556 civilians were killed. In spite of the public outcry, there was little that could be done to prevent them since Zeppelins carried out their raids on moonlit nights and at that stage of the war, the British had no night fighters. To those who flew Zeppelins, bad weather was more of a danger than enemy action although the British did have some successes.

Sub-Lieutenant Reginald Warneford was the first to shoot down a Zeppelin when he caught it flying at lower altitude over Belgium and managed to bomb it from above. As the war progressed, a defensive system was gradually put in place around London that included anti-aircraft guns, searchlights and barrage balloons. Then in 1917, 11 Zeppelins were caught in a violent storm and all were lost. Afterwards the Germans began to phase them out and replace them with bomber aircraft, the most famous of which was the Gotha. During the last year of the war these aircraft carried out numerous raids against London and south-east England and were responsible for nearly 3,000 casualties. A new British bomber, the Handley Page, with a range of over 2,000 kilometres (1,243 miles) brought Berlin within striking distance but the war came to an end before it was operational.

During the course of the war, the importance of aircraft became increasingly evident. The tactical use of air power and its ability to influence the outcome of a battle indicated that aeroplanes had come of age. In 1918, the Royal Flying Corps and the Royal Naval Air Service were combined to become a separate branch of the armed services, the Royal Air Force (RAF).

12

'keep the home fires burning' – the home front

This chapter will cover:
- the British reaction to the war
- the problems that faced the British government
- the Easter Rebellion in Ireland
- the issue of conscription
- the extent to which the war affected the everyday lives of the British people.

'Keep the home fires burning
While your hearts are yearning
Though your lads are far away,
They dream of home.'

(A popular song, *Keep the Home Fires Burning*,
written by Ivor Novello, 1893–1951)

Britain at the start of the war

In 1914, at the outbreak of war, Britain had a Liberal
government led by Herbert Asquith. Other leading members of
the government included David Lloyd George, Chancellor of the
Exchequer, Sir Edward Grey, Foreign Secretary, and Winston
Churchill, First Lord of the Admiralty whilst Lord Kitchener
was appointed Secretary for War. The declaration of war led to
a wave of anti-German feeling that sometimes turned to
mindless hysteria. People with German-sounding names had
their windows smashed and their businesses ransacked, lecturers
of German or Austrian origin were abused by their students
even if they had long been naturalized British citizens. Many,
even though they were old and infirm, were interned and some
were even driven to suicide. The writer D. H. Lawrence was
insulted because his wife was a member of the Richthofen
family; Prince Louis of Battenberg, forced to resign from the
Royal Navy because of his German connections, changed his
family name to Mountbatten. The Royal Automobile Club
(RAC) banned members of German or Austrian origin and it
was even considered unpatriotic to own a dachshund dog. In his
magazine *John Bull*, Horatio Bottomley advised his readers, 'if
one day in a restaurant you are being served by a German
waiter, you will throw your soup in his foul face; if you find
yourself sitting next to a German clerk, you will spill the inkpot
over his foul head'. At the same time the country was affected
by spy mania and much of this was caused by the appearance of
Erskine Childers's espionage novel, *The Riddle of the Sands*
(1900), and the irresponsible writing of William Le Queux.

To cope with the situation, the government passed the Defence
of the Realm Act (DORA) which allowed the use of an extensive
range of emergency powers. For serious crimes, civilians became
liable to trial by courts martial and for lesser crimes, by
summary trial and punishment. Whilst steps were taken to
protect railways and ports from acts of espionage, the
censorship of all outward-bound overseas mail was introduced
to prevent people communicating with the enemy. Censorship of

the press was also introduced and action taken to control the sale of alcohol. Measures were also taken to prevent the spread of false rumours and powers were granted to the government to requisition factories and workshops and turn them to wartime production.

Early problems

The appointment of Lord Kitchener as Secretary for War created problems. The choice of the hero of the Battle of Omdurman and the Boer War was intended to provide a boost to the morale of the British people and to his credit, he recognized that it would be a prolonged war and his famous 'Your country needs you' poster inspired thousands to volunteer to serve in the forces. An aloof man who resented criticism, he proved difficult to work with since he held the view that he should be allowed to run the war by himself without interference or a need to consult his Cabinet colleagues. He refused to delegate responsibility, treated his subordinates with contempt and was even at loggerheads with Lloyd George. As far as the nation was concerned, his untimely death in 1916 was regarded as a tragedy but as one observer commented, 'it was not so much regretted in government and by his friends, not at all, for he never had any.' Margot Asquith, the Prime Minister's wife said of Kitchener's death, 'if he was not a great man, he was a great poster'.

In 1915, Field Marshal Sir John French let it be known in *The Times* newspaper that the main reason for his lack of success on the Western Front was an acute shortage of shells. This disclosure led to public disquiet, open criticism of the government, a crisis of confidence and the end of the Liberal government. In its place, Asquith set up a coalition government with a Cabinet consisting of Liberals, Conservatives and the leader of the Labour Party, Arthur Henderson. David Lloyd George was appointed Minister of Munitions. The mercurial Welshman took control of all munitions factories and, against considerable trade-union opposition, used his persuasive skills to do away with a range of restrictive practices and encouraged the employment of women. More inclined to use businessmen than civil servants to run the factories, Lloyd George's management of the munitions industry was impressive. Earlier, Kitchener had commented that four machine guns per battalion would be sufficient and anything more a luxury. Lloyd George, determined to exceed this, famously said, 'Take Kitchener's figure. Square it.

Multiply by two. Then double it again for luck.' A. J. P. Taylor (1954) summed up his achievement, 'The army began the war with 1,330 machine guns. During the war 240,506 were manufactured – thanks to Lloyd George.' Lloyd George was also responsible for a range of measures taken to combat absenteeism due to drunkenness by reducing licensing hours, diluting the strength of beer and imposing heavier taxes on alcoholic drinks. King George gave his campaign a boost by banning the consumption of alcohol in the royal household but the Houses of Parliament declined to follow the sovereign's example.

Women go to war

British trade-union leaders feared that the permanent employment of women in the workplace might bring about the dilution of industry and lead to unemployment when servicemen were demobilized at the end of the war. Some also feared the consequences of the additional independence women might gain by having their own pay packets. Women were not just employed in the manufacture of munitions but in many other positions vacated by men serving at the front. In the munitions factories, girls worked 12-hour shifts, seven days a week for a wage of £2.20, just half that paid to men doing the same work but nearly three times that paid to soldiers serving in the trenches. The task of filling shell cases with explosives was not without its dangers and the powder turned the faces of the girls bright yellow and earned them the nickname 'canary girls'. There were also major disasters when an explosion at a munitions works at Chilwell in Nottinghamshire killed 250 and another at Silvertown in London's East End claimed over 300 lives. The idea of them being a 'gentle sex' was abandoned as women worked in a range of heavy industries, delivered coal, collected refuse, operated buses and trains and were employed in agriculture as Land Girls. Many volunteered to become nurses and towards the end of the war they were allowed to enrol in the services as uniformed auxiliaries. Altogether 92,000 joined the Women's Army Auxiliary Corps (WAAC), the Women's Royal Naval Service (WRNS) and the Women's Royal Air Force (WRAF). With many young girls living away from home in hostels, the employment of women on such a large scale created social problems and there was concern about their moral welfare. The work of such organizations as the Women's Patrol and the Women's League of Honour failed to prevent a

30 per cent increase in the illegitimacy rate of children born during the war years. Living away from their homes and their parents allowed girls a greater freedom that brought with it changes in their attitudes and outlook. The wearing of cosmetics and smoking became widespread as did drinking in public houses whilst dress-wise, the wearing of long skirts and camisoles gave way to short skirts and brassieres. Some young women also used language that would have shocked their parents and grandparents. It is estimated that in the final year of the war over 1.3 million women were in employment with over half of them doing jobs previously done by men.

The Easter Rebellion of 1916

In 1914, it seemed that the long-standing Irish demand for home rule was about to be granted but when the war started Asquith's government declared that the issue would have to be suspended until the conflict was over. In the event, both those who favoured home rule, the Irish Nationalists, and those against, the Unionists, declared their support for Britain in her war 'for the freedom of small nations' and some 80,000 Irishmen volunteered to serve in the British army. Many of them were Irish Nationalists only too pleased to fight for the independence of largely Catholic Belgium but home in Ireland there were still those who resented the British government's decision to suspend the granting of home rule.

Amongst a group known as the Irish Volunteers were men who regarded the coming of war as an opportunity to force the hand of the British government since they believed that 'England's difficulty was Ireland's opportunity'. The leaders of these men, Patrick Pearse, Sean McDermott and James Connolly, set about planning a rebellion against continued British rule. Their cause was helped by the fact that the British government was considering the introduction of conscription and this would have meant that Irishmen would have been forced to serve in the British armed forces. As preparations were made for the rebellion, so the Irish Volunteers paraded openly, collected money to buy weapons from Germany and tried to recruit men for a Citizens' Army. The rebellion was planned to take place on Easter Sunday 1916 when men would take over strategic points in the centre of Dublin and surround the British army barracks in Dublin Castle. The rebel headquarters was to be the General Post Office in Sackville Street, now known as O'Connell Street.

The uprising got off to a bad start when a German gun-running ship was intercepted by the Royal Navy. Even so, events went ahead as planned and on Easter Sunday morning people watched as the rebels ran up the Irish green orange and white tricolour over the post office and Pearse read a proclamation declaring the establishment of an Irish Republic. With none of the promised German assistance forthcoming, the rebels were hopelessly outnumbered and one by one their strongholds were overrun by British troops. From Dublin Bay, salvos (gunfire from ships) from a Royal Navy gunboat reduced the centre of the city to rubble and a mass of flames. On 29 April, the Irish Volunteers surrendered unconditionally.

The rebellion, which cost the lives of 550 people and left over 2,500 wounded, also caused damage to buildings and property at an estimated cost of £3 million. Arrests followed and although 90 people were sentenced to death only 15 were actually executed. One of those put on trial was a former British diplomat who had earlier been awarded a knighthood, Sir Roger Casement. In spite of his Protestant Ulster origins, he sympathized with the aims of the Irish Nationalist movement and had gone as far as to travel to Germany to win support for the rebellion and urge Irish prisoners of war to form a brigade to fight against the British. His mission proved a failure and he returned to Ireland to try and prevent the uprising that he was now convinced was doomed to failure. Soon after he was put ashore from a German submarine in Tralee Bay, Casement was arrested and sent for trial at the Old Bailey in London charged with treason. At his trial, he presented his case well but the appearance of his diaries containing details of his homosexual activities proved decisive. He was found guilty and hanged in Pentonville prison. To this day, the authenticity of Casement's diaries remains disputed and to the Irish, he is considered a patriot and martyr to the cause of their independence.

The bulk of the Irish people had not supported the rebellion and they were angry that their lives had been put at risk and their homes destroyed because of it. However, when it became known that British soldiers had shot some prisoners out of hand, imprisoned many blameless men and that James Connolly, too weak to stand, had been tied to a chair to face his executioners, sympathy for the rebels increased. Because of his American birth and half-Spanish parentage, one of the leaders of the rebellion to survive was Eamonn de Valera who was later to become Prime Minister and then President of an independent Ireland.

The issue of conscription

In September 1914, Herbert Asquith told the House of Commons that 439,000 men had already volunteered for military service. By the end of that month, this had risen to 750,000 and afterwards the monthly average was 125,000. To some extent these figures were a response to Kitchener's poster but other more subtle methods were also used to encourage men to enlist. Even so, as people became aware of the carnage on the Western Front and the horrific nature of trench warfare, the recruiting posters lost their appeal and ceased to have the same effect. With no longer a rush to enlist, the number of volunteers declined and this meant that the government had to give some thought to the idea of conscripting men for the army.

It was the Earl of Derby who first suggested a scheme by which men were invited to voluntarily register for military service on the understanding that married men would only be called up after all single men on the register. The 'Derby Scheme' failed because whilst married men registered in large numbers few bachelors came forward. Early in 1916, the Military Service Act introduced conscription for all bachelors aged between 18 and 41 and four months later this was extended to all men in that age group. The decision to introduce conscription led to uproar in the House of Commons with a number of Liberal Members of Parliament (MPs) voting against and some senior members of the Cabinet threatening to resign. Across the country branches of a Non-Conscription Fellowship, a movement founded by the Labour MP Fenner Brockway and supported by such notables as Bertrand Russell, Lytton Strachey and Virginia Woolf, were set up. Opposition was based on the fear that conscription would 'militarize the nation' and that it impinged on personal freedom. By the end of the war, conscription had been extended to include men up to the age of 50.

Conscientious objectors

The Military Service Act made provision for men who, for reasons of conscience, were opposed to being conscripted for military service to register as conscientious objectors. Such men, whose objection was usually based on either moral or religious grounds, fell into two categories – alternativists and absolutists. Alternativists were prepared to serve providing they would not be involved in the shedding of blood; the absolutists refused to engage in any form of military service or put on uniform. The alternativists were allowed to join a Non-Combatant Corps and many of them served with distinction in the front line as medical orderlies and lost their lives, but dealing with the absolutists proved a far more difficult matter. Ridiculed as 'conchies' or 'won't fight funks', they had to appear before tribunals usually made up of people who had no sympathy with their viewpoint whatsoever. The questioning was intended to trap men into saying that in certain circumstances they would resort to violence – 'What would you do if a criminal assaulted your mother?' 'What would you do if a stranger attempted to rape your wife?' were typical. The Non-Conscription Fellowship and Quakers offered to coach young men awaiting their tribunals in the art of handling such questioning. Considered cowards, very few succeeded in convincing the tribunals of the validity of their reasons and if they persisted with their objection, they were arrested and sent to prison to serve indeterminate sentences with hard labour. Some were even held in solitary confinement and placed on a diet of bread and water. There were instances when men were forcibly put into uniform and sent to army units in France and, now subject to military law, they were liable to be shot if they refused an order. Although there were rumours, there is no evidence that any conscientious objectors were actually executed.

The effects of the war on the everyday lives of the British people

As a result of towns along the East Coast being shelled by German warships and Zeppelins, and Gotha bombers bombing London and other towns and cities, some 1,500 people had been killed and 3,000 injured by enemy action. Even so, for the vast majority of the people, the war presented no immediate threat to their safety.

During the war it became necessary to ration certain foodstuffs. In spite of the success of the German U-boat campaign, there was never any acute shortage of food and rationing was introduced more to avoid queuing and to assure the people that come what may, everyone would get a fair share of the food available. Even so, sugar was rationed in 1917, meat, butter and tea in 1918 and housewives had to adapt in order to feed their families. In rural areas, food was usually quite plentiful but in the towns and cities a flourishing black market provided extra food and scarce luxuries for those who could afford to pay extra for them. Where foods were in short supply, alternatives had to be found. Margarine replaced butter, white bread became a rarity, horsemeat was eaten and new ways of preserving food used. It was discovered that the dried roots of dandelions provided a powder that tasted something like coffee and that rye bread was not so bad after all. Unfortunately, a tragedy occurred when a housewife decided to cook not only the stalks but also the leaves of rhubarb and succeeded in poisoning her family. In addition, families were encouraged to have meatless days, use government recommended 'war recipes' and above all to avoid wastage. Everyone was encouraged to grow as much food as they could in their gardens and allotments. Fuel and clothing were also scarce and an appeal urged people to 'Take the coal off the fire before you go to bed ... The coal you save today, will start the fire tomorrow.'

With so many men in the armed forces, labour was in short supply and this led to a sharp increase in the earnings of both skilled and unskilled workers so that by 1918, some wages had doubled and in certain industries, even trebled. By mid-1915, food prices had risen by 30 per cent with some scarce foodstuffs more than doubling in price. Worse was to come when by late 1916 food prices had increased by 60 per cent compared with the 1914 level. Even so, wages rose more steeply than prices and generally people were better fed than ever before.

It has been estimated that the war cost the British people a staggering £75,077,000,000. This was paid for out of loans received from the United States and by increasing the money raised from taxation. High taxes were also levied on a wide range of luxury goods. In addition, a patriotic appeal was made to people to help the war effort by purchasing War Bonds.

Apart from providing many women with financial independence, their work in munitions factories and other industries meant that many households now enjoyed a very welcome additional income. In spite of the war, some trade-union leaders, usually those with left-wing views who regarded the conflict as a capitalist war, were prepared to take part in industrial action. Although strikes on Clydeside and in South Wales were settled through conciliation, bitterness remained and strikes in the munitions industry were declared crimes punishable in the courts. It was ironic that the areas that showed most union militancy were the very same areas that had produced the greatest numbers of volunteers for military service.

Many adverts showed a complete ignorance of the true nature of soldiering and life at the front. Top (left to right): rival cigarette companies show a young lady obviously preferring the attention of a soldier to that of a civilian; a sergeant treating his men to a final cigarette before going over the top. Bottom (left to right): the heroism of fliers is used to advertise a laxative, Krushen Salts; families were encouraged to buy serving men Dayfield Body Shields which, so the advert claims, will save their lives; an officer 'livens up' his men by playing them music on a Decca gramophone.

As the nation adapted to the needs of wartime production, areas became associated with new manufacturing industries. Whilst munitions factories were widely scattered across the land, the area around the Solent on the South Coast, the Home Counties and Glasgow in Scotland became centres for aircraft production. Whilst Warrington became noted for the production of barbed wire, poison gas was manufactured at Runcorn and the traditional shipbuilding areas in the north-east, north-west, Clydeside and Northern Ireland were called on to produce warships and merchant ships in even greater numbers. As thousands of wounded soldiers returned home to Southampton and other South Coast ports to be treated at Netley and many other hospitals so, for reasons of security, many German prisoners of war were sent to the Isle of Man.

A feature of the war was the speed with which manufacturers adjusted their advertising to embrace the patriotic fervour of the time.

Letters from soldiers serving at the front were often slow to reach home and were censored and often relatives had to make do with the very limited news included on a Field Postcard. News that a relative had been killed in action reached their next of kin by various means. Official notification might take months to arrive and relatives lived in dread of telegrams or letters in buff envelopes that began 'Deeply regret to inform you ...' or 'It is my painful duty to inform you ...'. Before this, such information might have already reached relatives in a letter from one of the soldier's comrades or from an army chaplain who had taken down his last words or attended his burial. It was usual for commanding officers to write personal letters to the wives and mothers of fellow officers who had fallen in battle. A *Weekly Casualty List* was published by the War Office and lists also appeared in local newspapers. Those informed that their relative was 'missing' continued to live in hope but only too often had to finally accept the inevitable. The Germans and the Allies kept each other informed of the details of men who had been taken prisoner.

13

the propaganda war – spies and espionage

This chapter will cover:
- the use of propaganda to influence public attitudes
- anti-German propaganda
- espionage and the activities of German spies
- the unusual cases of Mata Hari and Trebitsch Lincoln.

'For he who lives more lives than one,
more deaths than one must die.'

(*Sonnet to Liberty: Not that I Love Thy Children*,
Oscar Wilde, 1854–1900)

The propaganda war

In the dictionary, propaganda is defined as 'a plan for the spread
of opinions and principles especially to effect change and
influence behaviour'. In wartime, propaganda can be a powerful
weapon and used indiscriminately and without concern for
accuracy and honesty, it can reinforce morale and raise false
hopes or it can be used to spread false rumours and discredit the
enemy. During the war, both the Allies and the Central Powers
used propaganda to influence, mislead and outrage public
opinion. The British government showed its appreciation of the
importance of being able to manipulate public opinion when
early in the war, Asquith appointed Charles Masterman to be in
charge of propaganda. Propaganda was not just to be used for
home consumption, it was intended to influence opinion in
neutral countries, particularly the United States and in this, the
British had virtually every advantage. Apart from the fact that
the two countries shared the same common language, in August
1914, HMS *Telconia* destroyed the transatlantic cable links
between Hamburg and New York that ensured that Americans
would largely depend on British sources for news about the war.

Anti-German propaganda

Within a month of the outbreak of war, the British popular press
carried lurid accounts of German atrocities in Belgium. Obscene
stories were told about babies being bayoneted, the mutilation
of women and children, the rape of nuns and the boiling of the
bodies of British dead in order to use their body fat as grease
and tallow. It was claimed that German soldiers had cut off the
breasts of a British nurse and left her to die in agony whilst *The
Times* carried the story of a Canadian officer who had been
crucified to a door with bayonets. The Germans had their own
range of atrocity stories that included the gouging out of the
eyes of prisoners of war and attempts by the French to infect
drinking water with cholera bacilli. It later came to be generally
accepted that these stories were untrue yet some very recent
research suggests some rumours of German atrocities were not
entirely without foundation. At the time, true or not, these

stories had the desired effect and the British people were convinced that they were involved in a war for civilization against a savage and ruthless enemy, the 'Beastly Hun'. The British were quick to exploit the outrages that they felt sure would offend the American people. Since 128 of the 1,098 passengers drowned were Americans, the sinking of the British liner, *Lusitania*, by a German submarine in May 1915 proved excellent for this purpose. In the United States, the American press published emotive accounts of the suffering and rescue of survivors and expressed its anger at the German action. British propagandists did not let the matter rest and continued to remind Americans that the atrocity was proof of the nature of German barbarism and if further proof was needed it came six months later with the execution of a British nurse, Edith Cavell.

INJURED INNOCENCE.

THE GERMAN OGRE. "HEAVEN KNOWS THAT I HAD TO DO THIS IN SELF-DEFENCE; IT WAS FORCED UPON ME." (*Aside*) "FEE, FI, FO, FUM!"

A *Punch* cartoon of 1915 depicts the depravity of the 'German Ogre'.

Edith Cavell, who came from Norfolk and was the daughter of a clergyman, became a nurse who went to Belgium to assist in the establishment of a training school for nurses and later became the matron of a hospital in Brussels. At the start of the war, she remained in charge of the hospital and after the city was occupied, she continued to run the hospital and treat both British and German wounded. In August 1915, Edith Cavell was arrested by the Germans and charged with assisting the escape of British soldiers. At her trial, she pleaded guilty and was sentenced to death by shooting. Pleas from the United States, other neutral countries and church leaders that her life be spared were rejected and she was executed on the morning of 12 October 1915. Her famous last words were 'Patriotism is not enough; I must have no hatred or bitterness towards anyone.' One of the German firing squad refused to take part in the deed and was himself later executed.

Following rumours of Belgian atrocities and the loss of civilian lives on the *Lusitania*, the execution of Edith Cavell provided the Allies with further propaganda to stir up anti-German sentiment in the United States. No mention was made of the fact that prior to the execution of the British nurse, the French had already shot three women for their involvement in espionage activities, one of them a nurse.

Spy scares and counterespionage activities

Even before the war, the British people had been alerted to the possibility of German espionage activities by the novels of Erskine Childers and William Le Queux. In Childers' adventure novel, *The Riddle of the Sands* (1900), British yachtsmen sailing amongst the Fresian Islands stumble upon evidence of German plans to invade England and the plot seemed so plausible that two Royal Marine officers on holiday worked their way along the German coast to check for themselves. They were arrested, charged with spying, and imprisoned. Le Queux, whose book *A Secret Service* (1911) was serialized in the *Daily Mail*, claimed that there were already 50,000 German soldiers in Britain masquerading as waiters and tourists. He also warned that a group of British traitors had formed an organization, the 'Hidden Hand', and were ready to work for the Germans and betray their country in the event of a war. Le Queux was one of the favourite authors of the royal family and although his stories were totally fictitious, they caused such a stir that questions were asked in the House of Commons. When war finally broke out in 1914, the country was seething with rumours of German spies and every local newspaper carried details of local spies and their impending arrests. In fact there were no German spies active in Britain at that time but they were soon to arrive.

German spies – the reality

Long before the war, British intelligence services were in place
and well prepared to counter any German espionage activities.
The eccentric but ruthless Sir Mansfield Cummings ran the
under-staffed and under-funded Secret Service and, with one leg
amputated, he made his way around his headquarters on a
child's scooter. The interrogation expert, Sir Vernon Kell, ran
Military Intelligence and was responsible for the introduction of
postal censorship. Throughout the war, teams of censors did
sterling work inspecting all out-going and in-coming overseas
mail at Mount Pleasant in London and were responsible for
tracing several important German spies. The master code-
breaker Sir Reginald 'Blinker' Hall was head of Naval
Intelligence. Described as being 'the one genius the war
developed' and that compared with him 'all other secret service
men were amateurs', his great scoop was his handling of the
Zimmermann telegram that played an important role in bringing
the United States into the war (see page 149–50). Special Branch
was the responsibility of another formidable interrogator Sir
Basil Thomson who had formerly been a diplomat, a tutor to the
sons of the King of Siam and a governor of Dartmoor prison. He
often seemed more concerned about the activities of subversive
groups in Britain than German spies. Some years after the war,
he was accused of acts of indecency with prostitutes in Hyde
Park, London and although only given a small fine, it left his
career in ruins. There is a view that he fell victim of a plot
intended to discredit him.

The man in charge of German espionage activities in Britain was
the talented Gustav Steinhauer. Before the war he had himself
spent a great deal of time in Britain and, posing as a fisherman,
had taken pictures of Royal Navy battleships anchored at Scapa
Flow. Instead of using German nationals as spies Steinhauer
preferred to recruit second-generation Americans whose
families were of German origin and English-speaking
Scandinavians. German spies, often using stolen or forged
passports, had little difficulty getting into Britain since they
could travel from the United States, come directly by ferry from
neutral Holland, or enter the country by way of Spain, Sweden
and Switzerland. A telltale sign of their intentions was that they
tended to visit sensitive areas such as ports, shipbuilding yards
and military-training areas to report on shipping movements
and troop concentrations. Since telegraph was not available to
them, their usual methods of getting information back to their
operators was by means of coded letters and invisible ink.

Following the outbreak of war, the first German spy to be caught in Britain was the ex-naval officer Karl Hans Lody who, as a former employee of the travel agents, Thomas Cook, spoke English fluently and without the trace of an accent. When he first offered his services to Steinhauer, he was considered unsuitable for espionage work and decided to go it alone on a freelance basis. It is claimed that he was the agent who erroneously reported the arrival of Russian troops in Scotland when, in conversation with a group of soldiers, he failed to understand their accent and thought they said they came from Russia. In fact, they came from Rosshire. Before he was executed by a firing squad in the Tower of London, he wrote a letter of appreciation to the British authorities for 'their kind and considered treatment'. Other German spies who suffered the same fate included the gifted Anton Kupferle who hanged himself in Brixton prison; the German-born naturalized American Georg Breeckow who insisted on a silk blindfold at his execution; and the brilliant Brazilian violinist, Fernando Buschman. Moments before his execution he offered his instrument to a member of the firing squad. The Swedish citizen Ernst Melin chose to spy for the Germans to ease his financial problems and was one of several who insisted on shaking hands with members of the firing squad before his execution. Albert Mayer sang *It's A Long Way To Tipperary* as he went to his execution whilst Irving Reis told the firing squad, 'You are only doing your duty as I have done mine.' Amongst those who spied for the Germans was Courtney de Rysbach. Austrian by birth but a naturalized British subject, he was a music-hall entertainer who sent messages to the Germans by writing between the lines on sheets of music.

Some unusual spies

Mata Hari

The most famous femme fatale in the history of espionage is Mata Hari. Born in 1876 at Leewarden in Holland, the daughter of a milliner, her real name was Gertrude Margaretha Zelle. A precocious girl, she was expelled from school at the age of 14 for seducing her headmaster. As a result of replying to a lonely-hearts advertisement in a local newspaper, she met and married Rudolph Macleod, a Dutch army officer serving in Java, but it proved an unhappy marriage and neglected by her husband, she spent her time learning the arts of oriental dancing. On her return to Holland, she was abandoned by her husband and lived in poverty until she found work as an erotic dancer and part-time prostitute. She took the name Mata Hari, 'Eye of the Dawn', and as her popularity grew, she was engaged to dance at many of the leading nightclubs in Europe where, most spectacularly, she performed the dance of the seven veils and used snakes in part of her act. Being a Dutch citizen, during the war she was able to travel freely in Europe and included amongst her many lovers senior German army officers and French cabinet ministers, including Adolphe-Pierre Messimy, the French Minister for War. It is said that during this time Mata Hari was invited to spy for both the French and Germans. Early in 1917, she was arrested by the French Secret Service and charged with spying for Germany. At her trial, whilst the evidence against her was weak and contradictory, her fate was sealed when her highly-placed lovers refused to testify on her behalf. Found guilty, she was executed at Saint Lazare prison. After the war, the Germans denied that they had ever employed Mata Hari as a spy and it has been suggested that French government spokesmen, or 'spin-doctors' as we would call them today, used her trial to capture the newspaper headlines at a time when they might have disclosed the failure of a French offensive and that their army was close to mutiny. It has been suggested that Mata Hari was executed more on the need to boost French morale than any sense of justice.

Trebitsch Lincoln

Few have led a more adventurous or debauched life than Trebitsch Lincoln. Born Ignatz Trebitsch in Hungary in 1879, he came from a family of shipbuilders who were devout Jews. After failing as a journalist and being wanted by the police for theft, he left his homeland and settled in Germany and there married and converted to Christianity. He next arrived in Britain where he worked in missions in Bristol and London before, again suspected of theft, he left for Canada where he was ordained an Anglican deacon by the Bishop of Montreal. On his return to Britain he was appointed curate at the parish of Applemore in Kent but, rejected by his parishioners, he left for London and took the name Trebitsch Lincoln. In London, he was introduced to David Lloyd George who recommended him for employment as a researcher to Seebohm Rowntree, the eminent sociologist. In 1909, after borrowing £10,000 from his employer, Lincoln urged Rowntree to back him as the Liberal candidate in the general election of that year. With a slender majority of only 30, he was returned to Westminster as the Member for Darlington.

In Parliament, he made a fool of himself and in the next general election, he was not even adopted as a candidate. Back in London, he looked for work but when Rowntree pressed for the repayment of his loan, he left for the United States and there he made a number of anti-British speeches and offered to spy for the German intelligence services. The British government demanded his extradition and on his arrival back in London he was arrested, deprived of his British citizenship and deported. However, this only seemed to encourage Lincoln's bizarre behaviour. After the war, he became involved in German politics and then moved to Czechoslovakia but was expelled from both countries for stealing money. In 1921, he made his way to China, there converted to Buddhism and became a Buddhist monk. Five years later, he returned to London to visit his son, a soldier serving in the British army, who had been sentenced to death for murder. Afterwards he travelled the world as a self-styled 'ambassador of peace' but got into trouble for raping a nun. It is said that he spent the rest of his life living in a YMCA hostel in Shanghai and died there in 1943.

Sigmund Georgievich Rosenblum

Born at Odessa in Russia, Sigmund Georgievich Rosenblum was the son of a colonel in the Russian army. After discovering that he was illegitimate, he stowed away on a ship bound for South America and there followed a variety of jobs. Able to speak six different languages, he began to work for the British Secret Service on a freelance basis. He took the name Sidney Reilly and during the war often worked on his own initiative. During the time that he was employed as a welder in the Krupps armaments factory in Germany and later for a firm of German shipbuilders, he stole important plans that he passed to Britain. It is possible that he was working for Russian and American intelligence at the same time. In 1917 he joined the Royal Flying Corps and worked behind the German lines gathering information for the Allies and calculating how close Germany was to defeat. For these missions, he was awarded the Military Cross. The end of the war did not bring an end to his espionage activities. Sent to Russia to spy on Lenin's Communist government, he was eventually caught and executed in November 1925. However there are rumours that suggest that he was still alive in 1927.

14

music, poetry and art of the First World War

This chapter will cover:
- popular music of the war
- music-hall entertainers
- the war poets
- art and artists of the war
- the cinema during the war.

'Keep right on to the end of the road,
  Keep right on to the end,
Tho the way be long, let your heart be strong,
  Keep right on to the bend.'

(From a song, *Keep Right on to the End of the Road*,
written by Sir Harry Lauder following the news
of the death of his son on the Somme)

Popular music and the war

During the war, few soldiers serving in the trenches would have shown much interest in cultural niceties but would have been far more attracted to popular songs and the ribald music-hall humour of the day. Indeed, some of the popular songs of that time were not written specifically for soldiers to sing on the march but had been in circulation for some time before the war began. In addition, soldiers sang parodies of their own creation based on popular songs and even hymns, and they were often extremely crude.

Although born in the Midlands in England, Jack Judge, a prolific songwriter, had Irish parents and he indicated the love of the land of his ancestors when he wrote *It's A Long Way To Tipperary*. The song became famous when a Daily Mail reporter mentioned that the soldiers of the original BEF sang the tune when they first arrived in France in 1914. Two songs were combined to produce the soldiers' favourite *Mademoiselle From Armentières*. As was the case with most popular songs, the versions sung by the soldiers were extremely vulgar and unprintable. In reality, the *mademoiselle* referred to in the song was an extremely virtuous young French girl. *Pack Up Your Troubles In Your Old Kit Bag* first came to notice when it won a marching-song competition in 1915 but shortly afterwards the composer, George Asaf, took his own life in a fit of depression. Clifford Grey's *If You Were The Only Girl In The World* was written in 1916 and still retains some popularity today. In the same year Ivor Novello wrote *Keep The Home Fires Burning*, and *Take Me Back To Dear Old Blighty* first appeared. 'Blighty' was the name given by the British troops to home. After the American entry into the war in 1917, the songs of George M. Cohen became very popular particularly *Over There* and *Yankee Doodle Dandy*. With most songs, it was usually the case that the chorus became more popular than the song itself and the most popular parodies sung loudly in barrack rooms and *estaminets* were based upon the marches *Colonel Bogey* and *Blaze Away* and such hymns as *O God Our Help In Ages Past*:

> John Wesley had a little dog,
> he was so very thin.
> He took him to the Gates of Hell
> and threw the bastard in.

Entertainers

Born in 1870 and the son of a colliery worker, one of the great music-hall entertainers was Harry Lauder and he became one of the most famous and highest paid singer-comedians of his day. A friend of royalty and American presidents, his most popular songs included *I Love A Lassie, Roamin' In The Gloaming* and *A Wee Deoch-and-Doruis* - a 'Deoch-and-Doruis' is a farewell drink. On New Year's Day 1917 he received news that his son had been killed in action. Later Lauder wrote a song that reflected his own personal grief and his determination to encourage others to carry on – *Keep Right On To The End Of The Road*. He went to France and with others entertained troops close to the front line or as he put it 'to sing to the boys in the thick of the trouble'. He even complained that his singing was spoiled by the noise of the guns. In Britain, he used his music-hall act to support the recruitment campaign and it is said that as a result of his efforts over 12,000 men joined up. He also set up a fund for wounded servicemen and in 1919 was awarded a knighthood for his contribution to the war effort.

Most army units contained men with experience as entertainers and they were used to form concert parties. The war also touched the lives of many other entertainers. Basil Hallam, a popular music-hall comedian best known for his song *Gilbert the Filbert* was killed in an accident when leaving an observation balloon. The actors Basil Rathbone and Ronald Colman both served in the war as did B. C. Hilliam, one of a music-hall double act known as 'Flotsam and Jetsam' and Chesney Allen of 'Crazy Gag' fame. The comedians Max Miller and Tommy Handley, later to win greater fame during the Second World War, were both serving soldiers until they joined concert parties. In addition, scores of sportsmen, international footballers, cricketers and rugby players joined up and many lost their lives in the war.

The war poets

Why did the First World War produce so many poets? Was it that some men used verse to give voice to their patriotism? Did some use verse to protest against their experiences in the trenches and the blood-letting and carnage of the war or did their wartime experiences heighten their perception? Were some exhilarated by it all? To what extent did the often static nature of trench warfare give them time to collect their thoughts and set them down in verse and were their poems really prayers begging for it all to stop? With only a few did their initial patriotism endure and for Wilfred Owen and others it became necessary to challenge the 'old lie' that 'it is sweet and noble to die for one's country'. Some, like A. E. Housman, turned their anger on God for allowing such things to happen and not bringing an end to the suffering. In Britain, some publishers rejected poems thought to be unpatriotic or likely to undermine the nation's morale and for this reason many poets did not have their works published until the war was over.

Among the most popular poets of the First World War were Rupert Brooke, Wilfred Owen, Siegfried Sassoon and John McCrae but there were also many others. Not all were officers or educated men but they were all able to express their feelings in verse. These included Leslie Coulson, a sergeant in the Royal Fusiliers, killed in action in 1916; Wilfred Gibson, a former social worker from London's East End; the scholars Edmund Blunden, A. E. Housman and Robert Graves; the British Prime Minister's son, Raymond Asquith; and W. N. Hodgson who died on the Somme. The works of the Irish MP and lawyer T. M. Kettle were considered by some to be second only to Owen whilst the Welshman, Ellis Humphrey Evans, won the chair at the Welsh National Eisteddfod in 1918. At the ceremony, it was announced that he had been killed in action a few months earlier and the crowd stood in silence as the chair was draped in black.

Of the popular poets, Rugby and Cambridge educated Rupert Brooke was commissioned in the Royal Naval Division and on his way to Gallipoli in 1915, he was taken ill and died of food poisoning. He was buried on the Greek island of Skyros. His poem, *The Soldier*, was indicative of his patriotic spirit:

> If I should die, think only this of me:
>   That there's some corner of a foreign field
> That is forever England

In spite of his ill health, Oswestry-born Wilfred Owen was commissioned in the Manchester Regiment. After being invalided home, he returned to the Western Front and was awarded the Military Cross for bravery but he was killed a week before the end of the war. In his *Anthem For Doomed Youth* he wrote:

> What passing bells for those who die as cattle?
>   Only the monstrous anger of the guns,
>   Only the stuttering rifles' rapid rattle
>   Can patter out their hasty orisons.
> No mockeries for them from prayers or bells,
>   Nor any voice of mourning save the choirs –

Most critical of the waste of human lives was Siegfried Sassoon who served in the Royal Welsh Fusiliers and had earlier won the Military Cross. In *Attack*, he describes the horrors of war unsparingly:

> Lines of grey, muttering faces, masked with fear,
>   They leave their trenches, going over the top,
> While time ticks blank and busy on their wrists,
>   And hope, with furtive eyes and grappling fists,
> Flounders in mud. Jesus, make it stop!

The Canadian doctor, John McCrae, wrote one of the most famous poems of the war, *In Flanders Fields*:

> In Flanders fields the poppies blow
>   Between the crosses, row on row,
> They mark our place, and in the sky
>   The larks, still bravely singing, fly
> Scarce heard amid the guns below.

Not all poets expressed themselves with patriotic fervour or in terms of disillusionment. Some used humour laced with satire to illustrate the impact of the war on the minds of sick and confused men and none did this better than Wilfred Gibson:

> Both his legs are shot away,
>   And his head is light,
> So he keeps muttering
>   All the blessed night
>
> Two rows of cabbages,
> Two of curly greens,
> Two rows of early peas,
> Two of kidney beans.
>
> (From *In the Ambulance* by Wilfred Gibson)

> Neck-deep in mud
>   He mowed and raved –
> He who braved
>   The field of blood –
> And as a lad
> Just out of school
> Yelled – April Fool!
> And laughed like mad.
>
> (From *Mad* by Wilfred Gibson)

Saddest of all was the fate of the British Gloucester-born poet and composer Ivor Gurney who, after being wounded and then gassed in 1917, was discharged and then spent the last 15 years of his life in a mental asylum suffering from schizophrenia. Amongst his most famous works were two collections of poems, *Severn* and *Somme*.

War artists and cartoonists

Although less well known, the works of some of the artists of the First World War matched that of the poets in their extent and variety. Again like the poets, some used their work to illustrate the unswerving loyalty of the soldier and expose the harsh realities of war. The brothers Paul and John Nash were amongst the most famous of the war artists and both served in the trenches and were deeply influenced by their experiences there. Their paintings include Paul Nash's *We Are Making A New World*, a derisive title for a work showing the devastation of war and John Nash's *Over The Top* that depicts a real-life event in the history of his own regiment, the Artists' Rifles. The brothers were eventually appointed official war artists. Paintings that were considered to be amongst the most true to life were those of Eric Kennington who was later discharged from the army as medically unfit. Other war artists included Colin Gill, Frank Dobson, Augustus John, F. H. Varley, a Canadian, and the New Zealander, W. B. Wollen.

Unlike poets and artists, the work of cartoonists was circulated in newspapers and magazines and brought them immediate recognition. The outstanding cartoonist of the war was Bruce Bairnsfather. Born in India and the son of an army officer, in 1911 he was commissioned into the Royal Warwickshire Regiment but resigned in order to attend art school. At the start of the war Bairnsfather rejoined his former regiment and was sent to France. Many of his cartoons appeared in the magazine *Bystander* and his most famous cartoon character was 'Old Bill', a soldier with a walrus moustache who invariably wore a scarf and balaclava. Although his cartoons were immensely popular and won him a worldwide reputation, there were those in the High Command who thought his work offensive. They described 'Old Bill' as a 'vulgar caricature of our heroes in the trenches' and asked for Bairnsfather's work to be banned. After the war he continued to draw cartoons and during the Second World War served as the official cartoonist to the United States army in Europe. Other popular cartoonists included Bernard Partridge who worked for the magazine *Punch* and Frank Reynolds.

The cinema

Even though the first public showing of moving films had occurred in the Empire Theatre, Leicester Square in 1896 and films had been made about the Boer War, at the start of the war British cinematography was still in its infancy. Against the wishes of Kitchener, newsreel films were made that recorded some of the early events on the Western Front and in 1916 came the first feature length documentary, *The Battle of the Somme*. The film, made by two cameramen, Geoffrey Malins and J. B. McDowell, showed the great bombardment that preceded the offensive, men 'going over the top' and the return of the wounded and the dead. Although audiences were shocked by some of the scenes of suffering and death, they thought the film impressive and public reaction was generally favourable. Widely distributed across the country, a private showing was arranged for the Royal Family at Windsor but there were those opposed to the showing of the film and the Dean of Durham protested 'against an entertainment which wounds the hearts and violates the very sanctity of bereavement'. Others complained that the film was diminished by supporting programmes that included comedies and cartoons. Later, the impact of the film was lessened when it was revealed that some sequences were filmed away from the front line and even staged in Britain. Nevertheless, at the time the film had a profound effect on wartime cinema-going audiences.

15

1917 – enter the United States; exit Russia

This chapter will cover:

- the decision of the Germans to resort to unrestricted submarine warfare
- the impact of the Zimmermann telegram
- the significance of the entry of the United States into the war
- the later events on the Russian front
- the events leading to a revolution in Russia in March 1917
- the October Revolution and the Bolshevik takeover and the decision to seek an armistice.

Over there, over there,
  Send the word, send the word over there –
The Yanks are coming,
  The Yanks are coming,
The drums rum-tuming
  Everywhere

(From a song, *Over There*, written by
George M. Cohen in 1917)

The American situation

Decades of emigration to the United States meant that the majority of Americans could trace their ancestral roots back to Europe. They were the direct descendants of those who had reached America from Britain, France, Germany, Italy, Russia and every other European country and cultural ties with their countries of origin remained strong. Although there were over 6 million Americans of German descent, the closest ties were with Great Britain and together they represented the world's two greatest English-speaking nations. For obvious reasons, Americans of British, French, Italian and Russian origin favoured the Allies whilst those of German and Austrian descent did their utmost to ensure that the United States remained neutral. Remember too that Irish immigrants to America were unlikely to back any measures likely to benefit Britain. Many Americans who continued to support their country's traditional isolationist stand were against any involvement in a European war and saw no good reason why their husbands and sons should give their lives in a war being fought in the interests of British, French and German imperialism. They saw it as a European conflict and thought that Europeans should be left to settle their own differences.

At the start of the hostilities, Woodrow Wilson, the American president, declared his country's intention to remain neutral. In reality, from the very beginning of the war the United States had been making a vital contribution to the Allied war effort. American industrialists quickly discovered that the war offered them lucrative business opportunities and between 1914 and 1916 there was virtually an unrestricted flow of war materials across the Atlantic Ocean. As American exports to the Allies increased fourfold, so their economy enjoyed a major boom. Undoubtedly many American arms manufacturers would have been equally happy to trade with Germany but the Royal Navy made that impossible. The war also benefited the United States in other ways since it provided the opportunity for their country to draw ahead of their major trading rivals, Britain and Germany, and the years 1914–18 helped to lay the foundations of America's future economic prosperity.

American entry into the war

From the early months of the war Allied propagandists had worked tirelessly to sour relations between the United States and Germany. With easy access to the media, pro-British spokesmen were able to stir up anti-German sentiment and the fact that Germany had declared war on both Russia and France and then invaded neutral Belgium was exploited to the full. Following the invasion of Belgium and lurid accounts in the American press of German atrocities against the civilian population, the Allies found it relatively easy to cultivate the image of the 'Beastly Hun'. Many stories were greatly exaggerated and some were totally untrue. Germany, on the other hand, did not handle her relations with the United States with any great sensitivity and played into the hands of the Allies when Germans committed outrages that incensed American public opinion. In 1915, the German image was further tarnished when a U-boat sank the British liner, *Lusitania*. News that there were 128 Americans amongst those drowned led to a wave of anti-German hysteria and there were widespread demands for a declaration of war. Little was made of the fact that the German embassy in Washington had placed a notice in the press warning that 'travellers sailing in the war zone on the ships of Great Britain or her allies do so at their own risk'. The Germans also claimed that the vessel had been carrying war materials amongst her cargo, a claim that has never been totally disproved. The outrage subsided when the Kaiser placated American public opinion by giving an undertaking that German submarines would not again sink passenger liners. Soon afterwards, came the execution of the British nurse, Edith Cavell, even though Woodrow Wilson had been among the world leaders that had asked for her life to be spared. Once again, anti-German propagandists had a field day.

The ongoing issue of unrestricted submarine warfare

As the war progressed, it became increasingly difficult for the Germans to remain indifferent to the fact that large amounts of war materials and foodstuffs were reaching British ports on board neutral shipping, much of it American. This unrestricted flow of goods across the Atlantic went some way towards countering the effects of the German U-boat campaign against the British Isles. Conscious of the need to avoid further damaging relations with the United States, Kaiser Wilhelm had resisted pressure from Ludendorff and the German High Command to impose a total blockade on Britain. However, with no sign of victory on the Western Front, national survival became a major issue and the Germans became less concerned at the prospect of provoking America. Anyway, many Germans maintained that the United States had already taken sides in the war. Finally, in January 1917, the Kaiser gave way to pressure and declared unrestricted submarine warfare so that the ships of any nationality found in waters around the British Isles and off the coast of France became liable to be sunk without warning. The United States immediately severed diplomatic relations with Germany as did a number of Latin American countries including Brazil, Bolivia and Peru. From a German viewpoint, it was a high-risk gamble. On the one hand, the sinking of American ships and the loss of American lives would almost certainly bring the United States into the war; on the other hand, six months of unrestricted submarine warfare might be sufficient to bring Britain and France to their knees and allow Germany to win the war. In spite of these events, in 1916 Woodrow Wilson managed to win re-election as president under the slogan, 'He Kept Us Out Of The War'. Back in the White House, he made every effort to bring about peace by offering to mediate between the Allies and the Central Powers by asking both sides to accept 'a peace between equals ... a peace without victory'. His pleas fell on deaf ears and his efforts came to nothing. As German submarines began to sink an increasing number of American merchant ships, a declaration of war seemed only a matter of time. In February 1917, the British liner *Laconia* was torpedoed in the Atlantic with a further loss of American lives and a week later news of the contents of the Zimmermann telegram appeared in American newspapers.

The Zimmermann telegram

In January 1917, a secret communication sent by the German Foreign Minister, Arthur Zimmermann, to the German envoy in Mexico was intercepted and deciphered by British naval intelligence and the following month its contents were made known to the American government. The telegram suggested that the envoy should approach the Mexican government with a proposal of an alliance between the two countries. In the event of the American entry into the war, the telegram offered Mexico German military aid to support their invasion of the United States in order to reclaim the lost states of New Mexico, Texas and Arizona. The telegram went on to hint that Germany would also do her utmost to encourage Japan to change sides and attack American naval bases in the Pacific. Immediately, the German ambassador in Washington, Count Johan von Bernstorff, denounced the telegram as a fake, a crude ploy by the British to involve the United States in the war. Bernstorff, who had an American wife, had made himself popular with Woodrow Wilson by supporting the need for a negotiated peace. Unfortunately, his reputation with the American people was tarnished by his lifestyle and with few able to take him seriously, he became something of a laughing stock. A ladies' man and keen party-goer, a photograph of him surrounded by bathing beauties appeared in the press and this undermined his influence both in America and Germany. With anti-German feeling already running high, the Zimmermann telegram proved the last straw. On 2 April 1917, President Wilson appeared before a specially convened meeting of Congress and said:

> 'With a profound sense of the solemn and even tragic character of the step I am taking and of the grave responsibilities which it involves, I advise that Congress declare that the recent course of the Imperial German Government to be nothing less than war against the Government and people of the United States ... It is a fearful thing to lead this great peaceful people into war ... America is privileged to spend her blood and might on the principles that gave her birth...'

His audience applauded loudly and four days later, on 6 April 1917, the United States declared war on Germany. His conduct viewed with great displeasure by the Kaiser and the German military, Bernstoff was recalled to Berlin.

The Russian situation

> 'Russia loves to feel the whip. It's their nature ... Be Peter the Great, Ivan the Terrible ... crush them all under you.'
>
> (Alexandra, Tsarina and wife of Nicholas II,
> in a letter to her husband in 1916)

As we have seen, during the early stages of the war Russia experienced mixed fortunes on the Eastern Front. Limited successes in East Prussia and Galicia turned to disaster when the brave but ill-equipped and inadequately-trained Russian soldiers proved no match for the superior firepower of the Germans. By the end of 1914, the Russian armies were totally demoralized and at the point of collapse. At this point Tsar Nicholas II decided to take over command of his armies but although well intended it was a foolhardy act since the Tsar could now be personally held responsible for any disaster that followed. It was also a decision that meant that he spent most of his time away from Petrograd at his army headquarters at Mogliev and was unavailable to exercise full control over events on the home front. In the Russian capital, these responsibilities fell largely to the Tsarina and her trusted councillor, Gregory Rasputin, and on the advice of this disreputable priest, she encouraged her husband to appoint corrupt and incompetent men to important posts in the government. Being German by birth, the Russian people distrusted Alexandra and even though such rumours were unfounded, some even went as far as to suggest that she was a spy. Then, in December 1916, Rasputin was murdered and the distraught Tsarina found herself with no confidante to turn to for advice.

The Eastern Front during 1916 and 1917

When General Alexey Brusilov launched a major offensive against their positions in the summer of 1916, it took the Germans and Austrians by complete surprise. The Russians broke through the Austrian lines and caused sufficient panic for the Germans to withdraw troops from the Western Front to reinforce their allies. The Russian advance into Galicia also encouraged Romania, long sympathetic to the Allies, to enter the war. Brusilov's offensive led to the capture of 375,000 prisoners and was to prove the only really successful Russian campaign of the war. Unfortunately, without adequate supplies and reinforcements, Brusilov could not sustain the momentum of his advance and a strong German counteroffensive again forced his armies to retreat and the episode ended in their rout. From a Russian point of view, the Brusilov offensive represented a last throw of the dice. With a casualty rate now running into millions and the economic situation at home at crisis point, exhaustion and disillusionment among the Tsar's soldiers turned first to desperation and then finally mutiny. The peasant soldiers and their families had suffered enough and the scene was set for revolution.

The revolution of March 1917

The threat of revolution was not new to the Russian situation. Numerous radical political groups had appeared during the latter half of the nineteenth and early twentieth centuries of which the most important were the Populists, the Octobrists, the Social Revolutionaries and the Social Democrats, a party dedicated to the communist theories of Karl Marx. In 1903, differences within the party led the Social Democrats to split into Bolsheviks and Mensheviks. The Bolsheviks, the faction most dedicated to revolution as a means of ridding Russia of tsarist rule, was led by Vladimir Ulyanov, better known to the world as Lenin. In 1905, following defeat in a war against Japan, Russia came close to revolution and Nicholas was only able to restore the situation by making concessions that included the promise of a more democratic constitution and an elected government or Duma. The Tsar might have achieved more and averted the difficulties that were to follow had he been even more conciliatory and shown a greater willingness to collaborate with the Duma. It proved to be a lost opportunity and instead Nicholas went back on his word and continued to rule as an autocrat. When Russia entered the war in 1914, the country was swept by a wave of patriotic fervour and the Tsar appeared to have the backing of his people but by 1917 this had disappeared.

During the third winter of the war the situation worsened as inflation led to rising prices and food and fuel shortages became acute. There were mass demonstrations, rioters took to the streets to loot bakeries and food shops and strikes hit public transport and prevented the publication of newspapers. With the collapse of law and order, effective government became first difficult and then impossible. Heavy losses at the front had drained the Russian army of its regular soldiers and these had been replaced by embittered peasant conscripts whose loyalty was questionable. To add to their misery, the winter of 1916–17 was bitterly cold even by Russian standards with temperatures falling to 35 degrees below zero. As men threw away their weapons, disobeyed their officers and deserted, so soldiers made their way home and the country edged towards open revolution. Rodzianko, the president of the Duma, telegraphed the Tsar and begged him to return to Petrograd. He warned, 'The situation is growing worse. Measures should be taken as tomorrow may be too late.' Nicholas commented, 'That fat bellied Rodzianko has written me a lot of nonsense that I won't even bother to answer' and then he ordered the disorders in the capital city to be put down by force. Immediately the whole country was paralysed by a general strike as public buildings were set on fire, inmates released from prisons and instead of taking action against the demonstrators, the soldiers joined them. It was obvious that a dramatic upheaval was imminent. In an attempt to restore order, Nicholas left the front and made his way home. On the way to Petrograd, his train was stopped and his military commanders advised him that the situation in Petrograd was out of control and that he had no choice but to abdicate. The Tsar offered to abdicate in favour of his younger brother Grand Prince Michael but after some hesitation, the prince wisely declined the offer and so Russia became a republic. Following the March Revolution, a Provisional Government was set up under the leadership of Prince Lvov, a liberal. The new government promised to call a general election and establish a system of democratic government. During these upheavals, the Germans made no moves on the Eastern Front since they were confident that the new government would ask for peace. Unfortunately, the Provisional Government made a disastrous decision when, under pressure from Britain and France, it decided that Russia should remain loyal and continue in the war.

The October Revolution – the end

The Provisional Government was not in control of events since it had to share power with the influential workers' council, the Petrograd Soviet. Acting on its own initiative, the Petrograd Soviet issued an order that soldiers were to obey the instructions of the Soviet and this move led to the final breakup of the Russian army. News of events in Russia reached Lenin, who was living in exile in Switzerland, and the German High Command took steps to ensure that the Bolshevik leader was able to return home as soon as possible. Smuggled across Germany in a sealed railway carriage, on his arrival back in Petrograd a huge crowd gave Lenin a tumultuous reception. Using the slogan 'Peace, bread and land', the Bolshevik leader demanded that the war should be brought to an immediate end and all power handed to the Soviets. During the weeks that followed, Russia was in chaos and news of further defeats on the battlefield led to fresh outbreaks of unrest. The Provisional Government blamed Lenin for the setbacks and accused him of being in the pay of the Germans. Under threat of arrest, he fled to Finland. Meanwhile, the leadership of the Provisional Government passed from Lvov to Alexander Kerensky, a moderate socialist. The new leader faced an immediate challenge to his authority when General Lavr Kornilov, with the backing of other military leaders as well as businessmen and industrialists, attempted to overthrow the government. Kerensky played into the hands of the Bolsheviks when he asked for their help to resist Kornilov's attempted coup. With Lenin back in Petrograd, the Bolsheviks made their final plans to seize power. When it came on 24/25 October, there was little resistance and the takeover of the capital was accomplished with little bloodshed. The following month, Lenin ordered the Russian armies to stop fighting and declared his readiness to open negotiations with the Germans. When the delegates met at Brest-Litovsk, the leader of the Bolshevik delegation, Leon Trotsky, tried to delay agreement by refusing to accept the terms. Their patience exhausted, the German army resumed its advance towards Petrograd until Lenin instructed his representative to accept any terms demanded no matter how harsh.

As you can imagine, the Russian withdrawal from the conflict came as a great disappointment to the Allies who went as far as to offer support to the new Bolshevik regime in return for their continued participation in the war. In the long run, Germany too was a loser since the end of the war on the Eastern Front meant that thousands of prisoners of war were allowed to return home taking with them new and dangerous revolutionary ideas. As we shall see, their influence was to become all too apparent in Germany during the final stages of the war.

16 the war against the Turks

This chapter will cover:
- the nature and extent of the Turkish Empire
- the Armenian massacres
- British campaigns in Mesopotamia and the siege of Kut-el-Amara
- the Palestine campaign
- Lawrence and the Arab revolt.

They shall not return to us, the resolute and young,
   The eager and whole-hearted whom we gave:
But the men who left them thriftily to lie in their own dung,
   Shall they come with years if honour to the grave?'

(From the poem *Mesopotamia*
by Rudyard Kipling, 1865–1936)

The Turkish Empire

The entry of Turkey into the war in 1914 provided Germany
with an ally well placed to harass the Allies on several fronts. So
far, we have only considered one aspect of the war against the
Turks – the Dardanelles campaign – but the Allies, particularly
the British and Imperial troops had to fight bitterly-contested
campaigns against them elsewhere. Although the Turks had
virtually been expelled from Europe, they still controlled a large
empire in the Middle East that extended from the Dardanelles

figure 18 the extent of the Turkish Empire

in the west to the Persian Gulf in the east and from the Black Sea in the north to the Gulf of Aden in the south. It had common borders with both the Russian Caucasus and British-controlled Egypt. Dissident Arabs keen to win their independence and freedom after centuries of Turkish rule populated much of the area. The proximity of Turkey to the Suez Canal meant that they were able to threaten Britain's all-important sea links with India as well as Australia and New Zealand and they were also well within striking distance of the British-financed oilfields at the head of the Persian Gulf. As the British and ANZACs had discovered at Gallipoli, the Turks were formidable fighting soldiers. Even so, the rulers of the Turkish Empire had problems of their own. Within the borders of Turkey, the largely Christian Armenians were pressing for autonomy whilst to the south in Palestine and Mesopotamia, the Arab peoples longed to rid themselves of their Turkish masters. In addition, Turkey was an economically-backward country with little industry and inadequate road and rail communications. Militarily, its armies depended heavily on German armaments and leadership.

The Armenian massacres

In December 1914, the Turkish War Minister, Enver Pasha, ordered the invasion of the Russian Caucasus with the intention of threatening the important Baku oilfields. The high mountain ranges made campaigning extremely difficult and the badly-equipped Turkish troops, unused to the severity of a Russian winter, suffered great hardship. Early in 1915, the Turks were forced to retreat and then found themselves facing the threat of invasion when Russian forces crossed the border into Armenia, a province in north-west Turkey. Armenians, largely Christian by religion and strongly influenced by western culture, had long been a thorn in the side of the Turks. The Armenians demanded self-rule that was contrary to the ambitions of the nationalist Young Turk movement who wanted to create an even greater Turkish Empire stretching as far east as Samarkand. At the time of the Russian invasion in 1915 the Turkish government accused the Armenians of collaborating with the invaders and they took their revenge by planning an act of genocide aimed at exterminating the Armenian people, a measure we would refer to today as 'ethnic cleansing'. The slaughter began in Constantinople where the leaders of the Armenian community were thrown from ships and drowned. The brutalities then continued across Turkey and Armenia where Armenian men, women and children were deported, tortured, starved and butchered and their wealth expropriated. In some areas men were forced to dig their own graves before being shot and women were given the choice of embracing Islam or death. It has been estimated that 1.5 million Armenians were murdered and a further 1 million deported. Some escaped by struggling across the mountains and seeking refuge in Russia. Whilst the German commander of the Turkish army, Liman von Sanders, condoned the slaughter, other military leaders, including Ludendorff, strongly disapproved.

The Allied campaign in Mesopotamia

Mesopotamia, modern-day Iraq, is the region that surrounds and embraces the Rivers Tigris and Euphrates. In 1914, a force of British and Indian troops was sent to the area to safeguard the oil installations at Ahwaz on the Persian Gulf and deal with any possible Turkish threat to the Suez Canal. The force landed at Shatt-al-Arab, the point where the Rivers Tigris and Euphrates converge, where they found Turkish resistance weak.

figure 19 campaigns fought against the Turks in Mesopotamia

This encouraged the force, commanded by Major General Sir Charles Townshend, to proceed inland by boat along the River Tigris and once the town of Kut-al-Amara had been taken, the expedition moved overland towards Baghdad. Short of supplies and faced by strengthening Turkish resistance, the British and Indian advance came to a halt at Ctesiphon and they were forced to retrace their steps back to Kut.

Kut-al-Amara lies 800 kilometres (497 miles) upstream from Basra at the head of the Persian Gulf. It was here that the Turks, commanded by the German general, Kolmar Von Der Goltz, besieged Townshend's force of 10,000 men for five terrible months from November 1915 to April 1916. By day, the men suffered from the sweltering heat but at night the temperatures cooled to near freezing. In such a climate, the men were forced to endure appalling hardship and as medical supplies dwindled so cases of malaria and dysentery reached epidemic proportions. At first, Townshend was promised early relief and he felt able to keep the garrison on full daily food rations. Sadly the promised relief did not materialize and there was an acute shortage of food which meant that the 2,000 mules and 3,000 horses had to be slaughtered so that their flesh became the staple diet. A soldier wrote 'We have horse steak, horse steak and kidney pie, horse olives, horse mince, horse rissoles, potted horse, horse soup, stuffed horse heart and horse liver'. Indian soldiers suffered additionally since they refused to eat horse flesh. Meanwhile, disheartened by three failed attempts to relieve the town, the defenders of Kut rallied and managed to beat off a series of fierce attacks. With approval from higher command, Townshend asked the Turks for a six-day armistice and their commander, Khalil Pasha, agreed providing talks were held between the two sides. At the talks, Khalil demanded the unconditional surrender of the garrison. Townshend, now of the opinion that any future resistance would be futile, destroyed everything of value in the town and ordered the white flag to be hoisted. The surrender of the British and Indian defenders of Kut was one of the worst military defeats ever inflicted on the British army and added to the damage already done to British prestige at Gallipoli the previous year.

For the survivors of the siege, even worse was to follow. The emaciated and diseased men of the garrison were made to undertake a forced march into captivity during which they were savagely beaten or killed in acts of wanton brutality so that of the 13,000 British and Indian captives some 5,000 were murdered or died from maltreatment. Meanwhile Townshend himself was well treated and lived in comfortable, if isolated, captivity in a villa on the shore of the Black Sea. Little wonder the military historian John Keegan has described him as 'a bad general and no gentleman' (*Who's Who in Military History*, 1967).

Townshend's replacement as British commander in Mesopotamia was Sir Stanley Maude. After careful planning, he advanced on Kut and recaptured the town on Christmas Eve 1916 before moving against and capturing the city of Baghdad. In November 1917, Maude, who had earlier been taken ill, died of cholera and his place was taken by Lieutenant General Marshall. It was not until the autumn of 1918 that the oilfields at Baku and Mosul were finally taken and the campaign in Mesopotamia finally came to an end.

The Palestine campaign

Early in 1915, a 20,000-strong Turkish army crossed the Sinai Peninsula and advanced on the Suez Canal, said to be 'the lifeline of the British Empire'. British forces, under the command of General Sir Archibald Murray, easily repelled their attempted invasion of Egypt and by the end of the year had themselves moved forward from Egypt to the borders of Palestine. Even though they built a road and water pipeline as they advanced, Murray's attempt to capture the town of Gaza ended in failure and General Sir Edmund Allenby was sent to replace him. Nicknamed 'The Bull', Allenby was an ill-tempered and outspoken man who was liable to take to task any inefficient subordinate. In an effort to gain a much-needed morale-boosting victory, Lloyd George urged Allenby to 'take Jerusalem before Christmas'. His forces, strengthened by reinforcements sent from the Western Front, were immediately successful and won a series of impressive victories over the Turks. Beersheba, Gaza and Jaffa all fell to the British in quick succession and on 9 December 1917, Allenby led his victorious troops into Jerusalem. The success of the Allied campaign in Palestine owed much to the fact that the Turks also had to cope with a widespread Arab revolt. This revolt was largely inspired by Colonel T. E. Lawrence, who was soon to become famously known as Lawrence of Arabia.

T. E. Lawrence – leader of the Arab revolt

Thomas Edward Lawrence was born in 1885 at Tremadoc in North Wales. He was the illegitimate son of an Anglo-Irishman, Thomas Chapman, who later changed his name to Lawrence. He studied history at Oxford University and there won a travelling scholarship that allowed him to take part in archaeological explorations in the Middle East. It was during this time that Lawrence came into contact with the Arabs. He came to admire them immensely and learned their language and became fascinated by their history, culture and customs. During the war, he served in army intelligence and because of his mastery of Arabic he was posted to the Arab Bureau at army headquarters in Cairo. When the Arabs rebelled against their Turkish rulers, Lawrence was sent to assess the situation at first hand and first met the Arab ruler, Hussein, and became a firm friend of his son, Feisal. Afterwards, he remained with the Arabs and liaised between their leaders and Allenby. More importantly, he helped to organize attacks on Turkish outposts and on the Hejaz railway, the essential Turkish supply route that ran between Damascus and Medina. Known to the Arabs as *Al Auruns*, Lawrence became an accomplished guerrilla leader and contributed greatly to the success of Allenby's campaign in Palestine. In part, his popularity with the Arabs rested on the fact that in return for their support, he promised them a chance to achieve their independence. A legendary figure, at the end of the war he returned home to popular acclaim as 'Lawrence of Arabia' and was offered the Victoria Cross and a knighthood but declined both. There were those who attempted to belittle Lawrence's achievements by declaring that his efforts were of little real importance to the outcome of the war since his desert campaign was at best 'a sideshow within a sideshow'. In reality, at an important stage in the war in the Middle East, Lawrence's force of some 3,000 Bedouin Arabs tied down over 50,000 Turkish regular troops and as the Arab revolt grew, the Turkish authorities had to deploy over 150,000 troops across the region.

T. E. Lawrence – the enigma

The Arabs had fought with the British on the assumption that once the Turks had been defeated and the war was over, their homeland, Palestine, would become an independent Arab state. Unfortunately, earlier in 1917 the British Foreign Secretary, Arthur Balfour, had declared his country's support for a Jewish national home in Palestine. However, Lawrence's commitment to the Arabs did not end with the armistice in 1918 and wearing traditional Bedouin-style dress, he accompanied the Arab delegation to the post-war peace conferences in Paris. There he argued their case for independence, the issue for which they had fought, but when the Balfour Declaration was confirmed, Lawrence considered the Arabs to have been betrayed. For a time he worked as a special advisor on Arab affairs but disillusioned by his country's Middle East policy, he resigned and made a determined effort to disappear from the limelight and live in obscurity. He first took the name J. M. Ross and joined the RAF as a lowly-ranked aircraftsman but once his identity was revealed, he was hounded by the press and discharged. He next changed his name to T. E. Shaw and joined the Royal Tank Corps but again his true identity was discovered and he left the army to rejoin the RAF. What privacy he had, he used to enjoy his twin pleasures, writing and travelling at speed. He particularly loved racing along the country roads of Dorset on his motorcycle. He retired in 1935 and shortly afterwards, at the age of 45, died following a motorcycle accident. For a time there was speculation that his accident had been contrived and was yet another ploy to escape the limelight. During his lifetime, Lawrence wrote several books the most famous of which was *The Seven Pillars of Wisdom*, his own account of the Arab revolt.

The final defeat of the Turks

A German offensive in the spring of 1918 meant that British reinforcements sent to Palestine had to return to the Western Front. With his army weakened, Allenby had to bide his time before he could renew his campaign against the Turks. In September 1918, he was able to renew his offensive and at the ancient fortress town of Megiddo, referred to as Armageddon in the New Testament, the Allies won a spectacular victory and routed the Turkish armies. The Battle of Megiddo brought about a rapid Turkish collapse and made possible a rapid advance on Damascus and shortly afterwards the capture of Aleppo by Allied mounted troops and Arab tribesmen. At the same time Bulgarian resistance in the Balkans came to an end and this meant that British forces based in Salonika were now free to advance and threaten Constantinople. The Turks had fought well but could no longer match the Allied forces in Mesopotamia and Palestine and so they had no alternative but to sue for peace. On 30 October 1918, an armistice was signed at the port of Mudros on the island of Lemnos in the Adriatic Sea. By the terms of the armistice, the Turks agreed to surrender their remaining garrisons and allow the Allies to control the important waterways, the Dardanelles and the Bosphorus. The war between Turkey and the Allies was finally at an end.

1917 – a year of disasters

This chapter will cover:
- the situation at the start of 1917
- the failure of Nivelle's spring offensive and mutinies in the French army
- the disaster in the mud at Passchendaele
- the Haig controversy
- the disasters on the Italian Front.

'... the blindest slaughter of a blind war.'
(The historian A. J. P. Taylor's view of the Battle
of Passchendaele in 1917)

The situation at the start of 1917

The year 1917 was to prove a most eventful one and a
watershed in the history of the First World War. As we have
already seen, it was the year during which Germany declared
unrestricted submarine warfare, the United States entered the
war and the Bolsheviks seized power in Russia and made a
separate peace with the Central Powers. In the Middle East it
was the year when the disaster at Kut-al-Amara was avenged
when British and Empire troops captured Baghdad and
advanced on Jerusalem. At sea, it was the year of the Zeebrugge
raid. The sacrifices made by the Anglo-French Allies and
Germany at Verdun and the Somme during 1916 had left both
sides despairing of victory and as the war degenerated into a
series of routine slaughters so the morale of the fighting men
deteriorated. In Britain, the initial surge of patriotism and the
days of volunteers queuing outside recruitment offices eager to

figure 20 Allied offensives on the Western Front during 1917

fight for 'King and Country' had disappeared and now men had to be conscripted. On the Western and Italian Fronts, 1917 was to be a difficult year with the Allies gaining few successes and suffering further disasters with massive loss of life. Still there was a glimmer of hope – in April America had entered the war but how long would it take before her resources of men and armaments would have an impact on the Western Front?

Events on the Western Front

The heavy losses suffered by the Germans during 1916 made it necessary for Ludendorff to reconsider his strategy. In order to better protect his position and shorten his overextended front line, he decided to withdraw to newly-built fortifications that the Germans referred to as the Siegfried Line but were known to the Allies as the Hindenburg Line. With concrete bunkers, well-established machine-gun positions, a maze of barbed-wire entanglements and much improved accommodation for the German soldiers, the new line of defences was impressive. In order to give the soldiers additional protection, the front line was unusually positioned on the reverse slope of hills away from the enemy and to give warning of an impending attack, lookouts were stationed on the crest of the hill. The organized retreat to the new defence line began early in 1917 and as the Germans withdrew, they laid waste the abandoned French villages, destroyed railway lines, contaminated water supplies and booby-trapped houses and farms. Over 125,000 French civilians were forcibly evacuated and made to work elsewhere. Ludendorff wrote, 'The decision to retreat was not reached without much anguish ... but it was necessary for war reasons, we had no choice.' Secure in their new positions, the Germans awaited the next Allied offensive.

In the spring of 1917, in preparation for a major French offensive to the south, the British attacked in the north in the region of Arras. Following the customary bombardment and the heaviest concentration of gas yet used in the war, the infantrymen moved forward against well-defended German positions. After a week of bloody fighting during which they advanced ten kilometres (six miles), the advance floundered and then came to a standstill. The meagre gains cost the British 84,000 casualties and the Germans only 9,000 fewer. It was during this battle that the Canadian Corps under General Sir Julian Byng captured Vimy Ridge after three hours of the most severe hand-to-hand fighting. The ridge was of strategic importance since it overlooked the towns of Lens and Douai.

Nivelle's spring offensive

In mid-April the French attacked on a 60-kilometre (37-mile) front along the River Aisne between Soissons and Reims with the intention of capturing an important ridge along the Chemin des Dames. The French had high hopes of their new commander, Robert Nivelle, who had replaced Joffre in 1916. Nivelle, whose mother was English, spoke his mother's tongue fluently and got on particularly well with the British Prime Minister, Lloyd George. He had earlier enhanced his reputation at Verdun where he had been responsible for the recapture of Fort Douaumont. Considered an energetic general and a clever tactician, it was Nivelle who claimed to have first successfully integrated the use of infantry and artillery in battle. Boasting 'I have a secret', he introduced the concept of a creeping barrage – an artillery barrage behind which the infantry advanced in relative safety. Bristling with confidence, his promise of a quick breakthrough so impressed Lloyd George that he agreed to place the British armies under his command. It was a decision that incensed Haig, a general in whom Lloyd George had long lost faith, and he complained bitterly to both King George V and the War Cabinet but in the end he gave way on the understanding that it was only a temporary arrangement and that the British army retained its separate identity. Security regarding the planned offensive was non-existent since the Germans had captured Nivelle's battle plans during a trench raid and were forewarned of the coming French attack. Even before the offensive began, German aerial reconnaissance had followed French troop movements so that a large number of their tanks were destroyed as they moved into position. The French High Command had doubts and met to decide whether or not the offensive should be cancelled but after some hesitation, Nivelle had his way. When the offensive started, the creeping barrage advanced too quickly and as they crossed no man's land and made their way through the barbed wire, the French infantry was left exposed to withering German machine-gun fire. In addition, French tanks were of such poor quality that not one was able to reach the German lines. After five calamitous days, the French had failed to take their first day objectives and any limited gains made were lost when the Germans counterattacked. Nivelle's offensive proved a total disaster and had dire consequences.

The French army mutinies

Nivelle's debacle resulted in over 130,000 casualties and led to mutinies in the French army. The high casualty rate together with the mismanagement of the campaign led to a collapse of morale and so great was the mood of defeatism that, had it not been for the American entry into the war, the French government might well have been tempted to agree a compromise peace with Germany. As the mutiny spread, groups of men in 54 divisions in the French army refused to obey orders and whilst some deserted, others demonstrated, called for peace, waved red flags, assaulted their officers and even threatened to march on Paris. Behind the scenes, political agitators, communists and anti-war campaigners encouraged their activities. At the height of the crisis, Nivelle was dismissed and replaced by a French general whose reputation still remained intact, Marshal Philippe Pétain, the saviour of Verdun. Pétain restored order and boosted morale with a mixture of rigorous and humanitarian measures. On the one hand, some 23,000 French soldiers were charged and found guilty of mutiny and although only 55 were shot, some of their leaders were transported to the penal colony, Devil's Island. On the other hand, he promised to improve pay and conditions, guaranteed leave and toured army units telling the fighting men that the period of senseless blood-letting was over and that future campaigns would be planned to avoid heavy losses. By mid-June the crisis was over.

June 1917 – Messines Ridge

During the period of the French army mutinies, whole sections of the front line were left undefended and the Allied war strategy was placed at risk but fortunately, the Germans seemed unaware of the crisis and made no effort to take advantage of the situation. Nevertheless, Haig was forced to act and he ordered an assault on Messines Ridge to the south of the Ypres salient. The ridge that had been in German hands since the early months of the war provided the enemy with an uninterrupted view over the British positions. Following a ten-day bombardment, on 7 June 19 mines containing 450 tonnes of explosive were detonated beneath the German positions along the ridge. It is claimed that the explosions could be heard in London. Within a few hours Messines Ridge was in Allied hands. The idea of using mines to destroy the German positions at Messines was the idea of J. Norton Griffiths, an outspoken Member of Parliament and engineer. Some senior officers were opposed to his plan but, as the historian John Giles has written, 'Norton Griffiths cared little about correct military procedure and lost little sleep over anyone who preferred to work strictly according to the rules' (*The Ypres Salient*, 1970). Another interesting legend about the Messines is that one mine failed to detonate and that a large amount of explosives still lies hidden somewhere on the ridge.

The attack on Messines Ridge was masterminded by General Herbert Plumer, a capable commander and one of the few to have been held in high regard by his own men. White moustached, red faced and plump, Plumer was to be the model for the cartoonist David Low's 'Colonel Blimp'. Some historians consider him to have been the best British general of the war and his capture of Messines Ridge proved to be one of the few Allied successes of that year.

The tunnellers

As we have seen, tunnels were dug and mines exploded under German front-line positions at the onset of the Battle of the Somme and at the start of the assault on Messines Ridge. The men who did this exceptionally hazardous work belonged to the Tunnelling Companies of the Royal Engineers and were mainly recruited from coal-mining areas or were men who had formerly been employed in the building of sewers or as 'clay kickers' during the building of the London Underground. So urgently were they needed that they were shipped to the front line with little or no military training. Some were old men already in their sixties but as long as they were capable of hard work and experienced tunnellers, no one questioned their age. In some ways they formed an elite group since, unlike ordinary infantrymen who received one shilling a day, they received six shillings but the risks involved certainly merited this extra payment. Working in close proximity, officers and men were on more familiar terms than would have been allowed in the trenches above. First they dug shafts down into the ground before branching out in tunnels beneath the enemy lines. They worked in four-hour shifts with picks and shovels and as they inched their way forward, they had to stop regularly to prop up the roof with timber supports. The earth that had been removed had to be hidden from the enemy in case it revealed what they were up to and it was placed in sandbags and winched to the surface and disposed of at night. The dangers they faced were similar to those faced by coal miners generally – flooding, roof falls, explosions and carbon-monoxide poisoning. There was also the danger caused by shells exploding above them on the surface, particularly the *camouflets* that were specially designed to cause subsidence and the crunching *Minenwerfters* or 'Minnies' as they were called. The Germans also employed tunnellers and there was always the chance that those digging under the ground might come across each other. This would result in hand-to-hand fighting and a stampede to get out and explode the mine before the others could escape. Both sides used listening devices to detect the tunnelling of the other with the British and French favouring the use of a geophone, which was similar to a doctor's stethoscope. At the end of each shift, tunnellers received a rum ration and once they had completed four days underground they were allowed four days' rest to recover. The high explosive used in the mines was made from ammonal – a mixture of ammonium nitrate and aluminium – and their detonation was spectacular and described by Philip Warner as similar to 'nineteen volcanoes erupting simultaneously' (*Passchendaele*, 1995).

The Third Battle of Ypres

With the breakdown of discipline in the French army still causing anxiety, Haig planned another diversionary offensive in Flanders. The British commander's decision was also influenced by other considerations. He mistakenly believed that German morale was near breaking point and was concerned by a warning given by Admiral Jellicoe that heavy losses of merchant shipping threatened Britain's ability to continue the war. The attack on Messines Ridge was an intended prelude to a major offensive on the Ypres salient and this time Haig passed the responsibility to General Sir Hubert Gough who possessed neither the tactical skill nor the popularity of Plumer. The ultimate aim of the offensive was to capture a plateau some 60 metres (197 feet) high that like Messines was of considerable strategic importance – Passchendaele Ridge. This time the preliminary bombardment lasted for 14 days and was even more intense than that on the first day of the Somme the previous year. Unfortunately, it coincided with the heaviest rainfall experienced in years and the exploding shells destroyed the dikes and culverts used by farmers to drain the swampy terrain. In torrential rain, troops moved forward towards the ridge across an impossible landscape of flooded fields, clinging mud and holes filled with stinking, putrid water. The stench produced by the ooze that was soon to include the decaying remains of men and horses was repulsive and made men feel ill and a senior British officer visiting the battlefield commented, 'Did we really send men to fight in this?' The Germans added to the horror by introducing for the first time the most harrowing form of chemical warfare, mustard gas. The battle took the form of a series of frontal assaults extending over a period of months. After a number of failed attacks, Gough advised Haig to call the offensive off but instead the commander-in-chief passed control of the campaign to Plumer who immediately followed a more cautious approach. Even so, British, Australian and Canadian troops did not take Passchendaele Ridge until early November. From a British point of view, the battle was the most costly and obscene of the whole war: costly because during five months of fighting, the British army suffered a staggering loss of over 240,000 men in order to advance less than eight kilometres (five miles); obscene because the battle was pointless, need not have been fought and had no real justification. Even worse, the Germans easily recaptured the limited amount of land gained when they launched their own offensive in the spring of 1918.

Cambrai – the first major tank action

The horrendous loss of life during the Third Battle of Ypres did not deter Haig and, determined to maintain the pressure on the Germans, he next launched an offensive at Cambrai against a section of the Hindenburg Line. Up to this time, the use of tanks had been sporadic but now in an attempt to gain a major breakthrough, they were used in large numbers for the first time – 434 of them. The Germans were at first taken by surprise and fled as the tanks followed by infantry smashed through their lines. Since 65 tanks were destroyed by enemy action, 73 broke down and 43 were left floundering in the mud, the first use of tanks on such a scale was far from a qualified success. Even though 11,500 German prisoners were taken, the chance of a decisive breakthrough was lost because the British lacked adequate reserves to press home their attack. Nevertheless, tanks had proved themselves capable of flattening barbed wire and forcing German machine gunners to 'waste their energies on the plated hides of machines, rather than the khaki ones of men'. Reinforced by fresh divisions and supported by a storm of gas shells, the Germans counterattacked and regained their lost ground. On this occasion, British casualties totalled 40,000 with a further 6,000 lost as prisoners.

So, a year of failure on the Western Front came to an end. Much had been gambled in Flanders but little or nothing gained and a breakthrough seemed as far away as ever. During his ongoing squabbles with Haig, Lloyd George had asked him not to risk so much in Flanders but instead to make a greater commitment to the Italian Front.

The Haig controversy

Douglas Haig, born in 1861 into a famous Scottish distilling family, was educated at a public school and Oxford University where he failed to get a degree. After Sandhurst, he was commissioned into the 7th Hussars and served in Britain, in India and in South Africa during the Boer War. Within three weeks of their first meeting, he married the Hon. Dorothy Vivian, a lady-in-waiting to Queen Alexandra. At the outbreak of war in 1914, he was a corps commander based in Aldershot and was sent immediately to France. After the First Battle of Ypres, he was promoted to army commander and in December 1915, after much behind-the-scenes intrigue, he replaced Sir John French as commander-in-chief of the British armies on the Western Front.

A controversial figure, opinions of Haig vary enormously. To some, he was responsible for the slaughters on the Somme and at Passchendaele and was considered unimaginative, not open to new ideas and unconcerned by the heavy casualties suffered by his men – 'a flint hearted butcher of his own soldiers'. In *British Butchers and Bunglers of the First World War* (1996), John Laffin, one of his fiercest critics, says of Haig, 'He was the victim of a strange type of intellectual paralysis which made him plan his battles in three phases – first the artillery blazed away for days, then heavily laden infantry went over the top and the cavalry chafed at the bit as they waited to charge through the breach'. Unfortunately, no breach was ever made and they never did charge. Laffin adds, 'Haig ... must not be indicted for incomprehension but for willful blunders and wicked butchery. There can never be forgiveness.' In *With a Machine Gun to Cambrai* (1969), George Coppard comments on Haig's aloofness, 'He was so completely remote from the actual fighting that he was merely a name, a figurehead.' The Prime Minister, David Lloyd George, who profoundly distrusted Haig and most of the other generals, once referred to him as 'brilliant to the top of his army boots' and in his *War Memoirs* (1936) wrote of Haig that he was 'a painstaking soldier with a sound intelligence of secondary quality'. Lloyd George deplored the field marshal's conventional approach to warfare, his blind faith in repetitive frontal assaults that were proving so costly and his failure to recognize and exploit opportunities. For his part, Haig disliked Lloyd George and did his best to prevent him and other politicians from interfering in military matters. He regarded them as amateurs and out of their depth and he regularly withheld information from the War Cabinet. Haig also secretly wrote to King George V and kept in touch with Lloyd George's predecessor, Herbert Asquith. Behind the scenes, Lloyd George did his best to remove Haig and, as we have seen, in 1917 managed to place him under the overall command of the Frenchman, Nivelle. In May 1918, Sir Frederick Maurice, a general at the War Office, accused the Prime Minister of deliberately withholding reserves from Haig to ensure that there would be no repeat of Passchendaele. In Parliament, Asquith pressed for an inquiry and the issue led to a motion of censure but Lloyd George survived. Haig detailed his own beliefs in a war of attrition when he said, 'The enemy should never be given a complete rest by day or by night, but be gradually and relentlessly worn down'. It was his view that the outcome of the war would be decided on the Western Front with victory going to the side that best withstood the rigours and losses required by trench warfare. However, Haig is not without admirers. In *Douglas Haig: The Educated Soldier* (1963), the historian John Terraine, makes a spirited defence of the field marshal and his tactics. Writing in *The Scotsman* in 1959, Major General Sir John Kennedy reminds us that 'His (Haig's) was the only army of the great nations at war that did not break'. Perhaps the most balanced consideration is that expressed by Gerard De Groot in *Douglas Haig 1861–1928* – 'It was Haig's fate that he, an eminent Edwardian, eventually came to be judged according to the very different standards of another age'.

The Italian Front

For the Italians, fighting was always going to be difficult in harsh Alpine terrain where the Austrians always held the higher slopes. General Luigi Cadorna commanded a sizeable army but it was badly trained, without battle experience and lacked modern weaponry, particularly artillery and transport. Cadorna, a competent general with an unfortunate personality, was arrogant, lacking in consideration for his ordinary soldiers and impatient with his subordinates and during the first 18 months of the war he dismissed 217 of his generals. The campaigns between the Italians and the Austro-Hungarians were fought in the foothills of the Alps close to the River Isonzo which rose in the mountains and reached the Adriatic Sea to the west of Trieste.

figure 21 the Italian Front 1915–17

The Battles of the Isonzo

Between 1915 and 1917, the conflict between the Italians and Austrians was almost totally limited to a series of battles fought along the River Isonzo. During 1915 alone there were four such battles and all of them ended inconclusively. Five more followed in 1916 and 1917 opened with the tenth and eleventh battles and in the last of these the Italians were sufficiently successful for the Austrians to ask for German help. The twelfth Battle of the Isonzo is better known as the Battle of Caporetto.

In what turned out to be the final battle fought along the River Isonzo, the Austrians backed by seven German divisions attacked the Italian positions. After a relatively brief bombardment, the Germans crossed the Isonzo, broke through the Italian lines and penetrated into the open ground beyond. As much of the routed Italian army turned and fled so the whole of the front line disintegrated and deserting soldiers heading for home blocked the roads and prevented the passage of vehicles carrying reserves and supplies to the war zone. The men had fought bravely enough but they had also suffered appallingly and their morale had been shattered. They no longer recognized a need to fight for king or country, they simply wanted to go home.

Cadorna had no choice other than to order a general retreat first to the River Tagliamento and then to the River Piave, in all a distance of some 95 kilometres (59 miles). With loyal Italian troops now holding good defensive positions and the enemy's supply lines overextended, the Austro-German advance came to an end. With 40,000 casualties and 300,000 soldiers taken prisoner, the Battle of Caporetto proved a major humiliation for Italy and led to a crisis that made it necessary for British and French divisions to be sent to reinforce their front. In its search for scapegoats, the Italian government blamed left-wing activists, defeatist attitudes and military incompetence and Cadorna was replaced by General Armando Diaz and a number of deserters were shot. However, the Caporetto fiasco did not mean that the Italian contribution to the war was over, far from it. It is interesting to note that one of the Italian soldiers serving at the front in the prestigious Bersaglieri Regiment was a 32-year-old sergeant, Benito Mussolini, who was destined to become the future Fascist dictator of Italy.

18

the collapse of Germany and the end of the war

This chapter will cover:
- the situation at the start of 1918
- America at war
- Ludendorff's final offensives
- the final collapse of Germany's allies
- Foch's final offensive
- the internal collapse of Germany and the threat of revolution.

'O Jesus, make it stop'.

(From *Attack* by Siegfried Sassoon, 1886–1967)

The overall situation at the start of 1918

With only the German submarine threat held at bay and victories in Palestine and Mesopotamia to set against major setbacks on the Western and Italian Fronts, 1917 was a bleak year for the Allies. The French army was still recovering from the disasters that led to open mutiny whilst, in spite of its heavy losses, the morale of the British army had taken a battering but was still largely intact. On both sides there were worrying manpower shortages and the new conscript armies did not always show the same fighting spirit as the legions that had fallen. For the Germans, the prospects were, if anything, even worse.

Germany in 1918

With the United States preparing to add her military and economic might to the Allied war effort, if Germany was going to win the war it was a case of now or never. The German High Command was faced with a race against time but there were also other reasons for concern. Whilst unrestricted submarine warfare had failed to starve Britain into submission, the Allied blockade of Germany was complete and on the home front the German people were suffering acute shortages. During the severe winter of 1916–17, food became so scarce that the Germans spoke of their 'turnip winter' and the situation worsened when, in 1917, the grain harvest was less than half that of 1913. Germany had also witnessed the first signs of popular unrest when during 1917 there were public demonstrations and protests and early in 1918, some 400,000 Berliners went on strike with the unrest soon spreading to other towns and cities across the country. The German parliament, the *Reichstag*, passed a resolution in favour of seeking a negotiated peace and within the traditionally moderate and largely popular German Social Democratic Party, an increasing number favoured a more positive anti-war line. The success of the Bolsheviks in Russia was also beginning to have an impact on German politics with the formation of a communist-backed Spartacist League. However, the German High Command dominated by Hindenburg and Ludendorff paid scant regard to these events and Chancellor Bethmann Hollweg, who had wanted to give peace proposals serious consideration, was forced to resign.

America at war

Few Americans questioned Woodrow Wilson's decision to go to war and, fuelled by stories of the 'Brutal Hun', there was an immediate anti-German reaction. In some schools and colleges, the teaching of German was dropped from the timetable, German books disappeared from library shelves and even some delicatessen stores renamed *sauerkraut* 'liberty cabbage'. Although the United States had shipped supplies to the Allies, at the time of her entry into the conflict she was strangely unprepared for war. Whilst her army had no tanks and little modern artillery and her air force had few aircraft suited to aerial combat, her naval strength was considerable and several of her battleships joined the British Grand Fleet at Scapa Flow. Her first major task was to raise, train and equip an army for service in Europe and this could not happen overnight. In order to make it possible for America's industrial capacity to be converted to war production, Congress granted the President near dictatorial powers over much of the nation's economy and soon $44 million per day was being poured into the nation's war effort.

The appearance of the first American troops in France, although initially only a token force, provided a much needed boost to the Allies. The American Commander-in-Chief, John Pershing, a West Point graduate who had served in the American cavalry during the Indian wars, had earlier suffered a personal loss when his wife and three young children had perished in a fire. Appointed to command the American Expeditionary Force in 1917, he was determined not to waste American lives in futile trench warfare and held the view that his troops should not be used in battle until he had 1 million under his command and they could play a decisive role in the war. During the final stages of the war, over 2 million American soldiers arrived in France and as we shall see, they were to play an important role in the defeat of Ludendorff's great offensives in 1918. They were to suffer over 50,000 killed in battle.

In January 1918, Woodrow Wilson put forward his ideas for a peace settlement. His proposals, known as his Fourteen Points, set out to ban secret diplomacy, trade barriers and the mass production of armaments that he considered the fundamental causes of war, guarantee the freedom of the seas to all nations and offer all peoples self-determination, the right to decide their own destinies. He also wanted to establish a 'general association of nations' to regulate international affairs and ensure future world peace. However, confident that in the end victory would still be theirs, Germany rejected Wilson's ideas out of hand.

Ludendorff's last throw – his spring offensives

In readiness for a series of spring offensives on the Western Front, Ludendorff had moved men and materials from the east where they were no longer required. His plan was to drive a wedge between the British and French armies and push the British back towards the English Channel. In planning his new offensives, Ludendorff decided on a new strategy and instead of the now traditional artillery barrage followed by a frontal infantry attack, he decided to use more subtle infiltration

figure 22 German offensives on the Western Front March–May 1918

tactics. Surprise was to be all important to his new plan so that after a brief but intense bombardment of the Allied positions, small groups of elite shock troops or storm troopers would spearhead the attack, cut the wire and infiltrate the Allied lines. Once gaps had been made, the main force of German infantry would advance, exploit the gaps created, bypass strong points so that they could be dealt with later and then deploy into the open ground beyond. Since Pétain and Haig had different priorities, Allied defence strategy was unco-ordinated. Pétain was determined at all costs to prevent any German advance towards Paris whilst Haig recognized that it was essential for the British to protect the all-important Channel ports.

The first German offensive, 'Operation Michael' sometimes called *Kaiserschlacht* (the Kaiser's Battle), came in March 1918. Fought on the old Somme battlefields, on the opening day of the battle German shock troops, advancing behind a creeping barrage and smoke screen, used light machine guns and flame throwers to make breaches in the British lines. To the north, the British largely managed to hold their positions but to the south they were forced back towards Amiens. After ten days, the Germans had advanced 80 kilometres (50 miles) and were close to severing the link between the British and French positions. Even though reinforcements were rushed forward to plug the gap, the Germans advanced to within 100 kilometres (62 miles) of Paris so that their heavy guns were able to bombard the city. As the crisis deepened, the Supreme War Council met at Doullens and decided to appoint the Frenchman, Marshal Ferdinand Foch, to be commander-in-chief of all the Allied armies with Haig and Pétain as his subordinates. Under their new commander, the Allies rallied, halted and then reversed the German advance. Anyway, by this time exhaustion and problems caused by their now overextended supply lines had caused the German offensive to run out of steam. German soldiers had been told that Allied food shortages were as bad as their own but when they overran the British positions, they captured stores and supplies that proved this was not the case. The deceit adversely affected German morale and by the time Ludendorff called off 'Operation Michael', the Germans had sustained over 250,000 casualties and the British and French only 10,000 less. As the German commander ended one offensive, so he began another further to the north in Flanders.

The second German offensive, known as 'Operation Georgette', began in April to the south of Ypres just to the east of Armentières. With the British under enormous pressure, Haig issued an Order of the Day, 'There is no other course open to us but to fight it out! Every position must be held to the last man; there must be no retirement. With our backs to the wall and believing in the justice of our cause, each one of us must fight on to the end.' This time Ludendorff's aim was to sweep across Flanders and cut off the Channel ports of Boulogne, Calais and Dunkirk. The first German attack fell on a section of the line held by Portuguese troops (Germany had declared war on Portugal in 1916) where they gained some immediate success. The British also had to give up the ground gained at such enormous cost during the Passchendaele offensive the previous year. Fighting was particularly vicious around Mount Kemmel where land changed hands time and time again and by the end of the month the arrival of British reinforcements made Ludendorff call off his offensive. Again he had failed in his main objectives and the Channel ports remained secure in British hands. Losses were heavy on both sides – 76,000 British, 35,000 French, 6,000 Portuguese and 109,000 German. Even though his own troops were exhausted and demoralized and American troops were arriving in France in increasing numbers, Ludendorff was not finished and he now planned a new offensive along the River Aisne.

'Operation Blucher', the third and final German offensive, was against the French and started in May along a 40-kilometre (25-mile) front stretching from Soissons along the Chemin des Dames to Reims. The French were heavily outnumbered and this allowed the Germans to break through their lines, cross the River Aisne and advance towards the River Marne. The German advance was finally held by the French and Americans at Château Thierry and in mid-July, Foch unexpectedly ordered a massive counterattack that signalled the start of a German retreat. So Ludendorff's gamble had been in vain and with over 500,000 dead and wounded, his offensives had cost the German army dear. With barely any reserves left and supplies and munitions at an all time low, the morale of the German army finally disintegrated. On the other hand, with American troops arriving in France at a rate of 300,000 each month, Allied morale soared as they sensed that an end to the war might be in sight.

The collapse of Germany's allies

After years of relative inactivity, in September 1918 the Balkan Front came alive. From Salonika, British, French and Serbian forces moved against Germany's ally Bulgaria and with little prospect of receiving assistance, the Bulgarians were no match for the Allies. At the Battle of Vardar, the Serbs broke through the Bulgarian lines and afterwards their resistance along the whole front collapsed. In such a desperate situation, the Bulgarian government had no choice but to ask for peace and the war in the Balkans finally came to an end. The elimination of Bulgaria meant that additional Allied troops were available for use against the Turks.

You will remember that the situation on the Italian Front was delicate for both Italy and Austria alike. Now considered to be something of a liability by their Anglo-French allies, the Italians urgently needed to redeem their failures, particularly the disgrace of Caporetto, if they were to have any say in the post-war negotiations. In October 1918, the Italian armies under General Diaz and with the support of British and French units began operations aimed at gaining the initiative from the Austrians. Although they no longer had substantial German support, the Austrians resisted strongly but were nevertheless driven back from the River Piave towards the River Tagliomento where their whole front collapsed and they were forced to retreat in disorder until they stood to face the Italians at Vittorio Venito. Here the Italians won a resounding victory, took over 300,000 Austrian prisoners and avenged the humiliation of Caporetto. Afterwards the Austro-Hungarian government asked for peace and this was finally concluded on 4 November 1918.

Foch's final offensive

By August 1918, the initiative on the Western Front had passed to the Allies. With troop movements only made at night and secrecy so tight that even the divisional commanders were not aware what of was happening, the sudden Allied offensive took the Germans by surprise. With no preliminary barrage, British, French, Australian, and Canadian troops moved forward part hidden by mist and behind masses of light tanks. The Allies broke through the German lines with surprising ease and were able to capture objectives some ten kilometres (six miles) distant. Ludendorff later wrote, 'The 8th August was the black day of the German army in the history of the war ... Everything I had feared and of which I had so often given warning, had here, in one place, become a reality. Our war machine was no longer efficient.' The British again reached the old Somme battlefield where the momentum of their advance began to falter and faced by stiffening German resistance, Foch decided to switch his attack further to the north. By using a series of short but connected offensives, he was able to keep Allied casualties to a minimum and still force the enemy to retreat. Eventually the Germans found themselves back at the Hindenburg Line, the starting point of their first offensive five months earlier. On 12 September, the Americans attacked the German salient at St. Mihiel to the south-east of Verdun. In eliminating the salient, they took 15,000 prisoners but 7,000 of their own men were killed and wounded. A fortnight later, with the order '*Tout le monde à la batille*', 'Everyone to the battle', Foch began his final offensive against the Germans. To the south, the French and Americans attacked along the River Meuse and through the Argonne Forest whilst to the north, the British and Belgians made a renewed effort on the Ypres salient. As a pincer movement now threatened to encircle the Germans, they were forced to retreat further and with their fighting spirit broken, the Allies were able to break through the Hindenburg Line at several places with unexpected ease. In angry outbursts, Hindenburg blamed his failures on a lack of reserves, a shortage of munitions and the defeatist attitude of certain German politicians in the *Reichstag*. Faced with defeat on the battlefield and mounting unrest at home, Germany's military leaders realized that the need for an armistice was now an urgent necessity.

The final collapse of Germany

Not only were the German armies close to defeat but on the home front, the country was near to total economic collapse and in political turmoil. To add to their woes and in common with the rest of Europe and much of the world, Germany was in the grip of an influenza epidemic. Spanish influenza, so-called because one of the early victims was the King of Spain, was claiming more deaths than the battlefield and, short of medicines and with malnutrition rampant, on one day alone 1,700 Berliners died of the virus. On 29 September 1918, Ludendorff finally told the German government that the war was lost and that it was necessary to agree an armistice. The Allies refused to negotiate with Germany's military leaders and so Prince Max of Baden, a liberal with an international reputation for his work with the Red Cross, was appointed Chancellor and asked to form a government.

Recognizing that the terms outlined earlier in Wilson's Fourteen Points were likely to be more lenient than any offered by the Anglo-French allies, Prince Max used Swiss intermediaries to make contact with the American President. Woodrow Wilson's response was to first demand the withdrawal of German troops from all the territory they had occupied and he made it clear that the Allies would not negotiate with the Kaiser or the controlling military clique and insisted on the dismissal of the country's undemocratic rulers. Ludendorff was against acceptance and wanted to resume hostilities and make one last stand in order to save the honour of the German army. When this was rejected, both he and Hindenburg offered to resign but only his resignation was accepted. In haste, Ludendorff fled to Sweden in disguise. Prince Max now urged the Kaiser to abdicate but he refused stating, 'I would not dream of abandoning the throne because of a few hundred Jews and a thousand workers'. Consequently the situation took a turn for the worse.

Late in October, the German High Seas Fleet at Wilhelmshaven and Kiel was ordered to sea to engage the Royal Navy in a final act of defiance. The sailors, already demoralized by being confined to their home ports since 1915 and increasingly influenced by Bolshevik propaganda, mutinied. The disturbances spread quickly to other ports and workers' committees were set up in several towns and cities. Following demonstrations in Munich, a group of German Bolsheviks went as far as to declare Bavaria an independent socialist republic. With the situation getting out of hand, Prince Max advised Kaiser Wilhelm that if he persisted with his refusal to abdicate, he himself would resign. When revolutionaries took to the streets of Berlin and from the steps of the *Reichstag* building proclaimed a republic, Hindenburg warned the Kaiser that he could no longer guarantee his safety. So Wilhelm reluctantly abdicated, left Germany and sought political asylum in Holland.

The armistice signed

On 7 November, German delegates passed through the Allied lines, assembled in a railway carriage in a forest close to Compiègne and opened negotiations for an armistice. The French general Maxime Weygand recalled the occasion, '... a convoy of cars moving very fast appears on the road with no headlights on. On the front of the first one, a large white flag looms out of the darkness. A young officer identifies the bearers of the flag of truce and gets into the first of the five cars. The bugles sound another call whilst our soldiers look at the result of four years of fighting and suffering'.

The Allied representatives were Marshal Foch and General Weygand together with the British Admirals Hope and Wemyss whilst the German delegation of four was led by Mathias Erzberger who was later to be assassinated. The meeting was icy but correct with the armistice terms presented one by one and translated by an officer who read them in German. The German delegates were then given 72 hours to accept the terms on an understanding that a refusal would lead to the resumption of war. After days of frantic negotiations, the Germans finally signed the armistice at 5 a.m. on 11 November 1918. Word was then flashed to the world that the armistice would come into effect at 11 a.m. that same day.

And so the guns finally fell silent. In London, Paris and New York there were wild scenes as crowds celebrated in the streets; in Berlin there was an uneasy peace as the earlier disturbances still threatened to turn into a major uprising. In the House of Commons, Lloyd George said, 'I hope we may say thus, this fateful morning came to end all wars.'

The headlines of the *Evening Standard* on 11 November 1918.

19 the First World War – the cost

This chapter will cover:
- some retrospective views of the war
- the cost in human terms
- the cost in material terms
- the cost in financial terms
- other long-term consequences.

> 'If any question why we died,
> Tell them because our fathers lied.'

(From *Common Form* by Rudyard Kipling, 1865–1936)

Some thoughts

The historian Peter Johnson has described the First World War as 'the greatest moral, spiritual and physical catastrophe in the history of the British people – a catastrophe whose consequences, all evil, are still with us' whilst Anthony Wood regards it as a time when 'the civilisation of the nineteenth century was blown to shreds' and 'a whole generation of young men were massacred in anonymous millions'. Sir Arthur Conan Doyle wrote, 'The system which left millions dead upon the fields of Europe must be rotten to the core ... but one day the war may be regarded as the end of a dark age and the start of that upward path which leads away from personal and national selfishness.' Some war poets also recorded their thoughts:

> They ask me where I've been,
> And what I've done and seen.
> But what can I reply
> Who know it wasn't I,
> But someone just like me,
> Who went across the sea
> And with my head and hands
> Killed men in foreign lands ...
> Though I must bear the blame,
> Because he bore my name.

(*Back* by Wilfred Gibson, 1878–1962)

> Here dead we lie because we did not choose
> To live and shame the land from which we sprung.
> Life to be sure, is nothing much to lose;
> But young men think it is, and we were young.

(*Here Dead We Lie* by A. E. Housman, 1859–1936)

Attempts have been made to calculate the human, material and financial costs of the First World War and express them as simple statistics but what figures can never take into account is the lasting impact of the death, destruction and dislocation of those years. It is impossible to place a money value on the suffering of those who lost limbs, returned blind or with minds damaged beyond recovery. One cannot measure the heartbreak and depth of grief of mothers and widows or the paternal affection never to be experienced by hosts of fatherless children. For each of those that did not return home, the so-called 'lost generation', there would be a grave or a name on a memorial but for the survivors of the trenches there would be memories and the struggle to settle once again to civilian life. British soldiers that returned home received the award of the War Medal and Victory Medal and for the families of those that died a bronze memorial plaque bearing the inscription 'died for freedom and honour'. Others were more fortunate. Field Marshal Haig was created an earl, received the thanks of Parliament and a grant of £100,000. French was made an earl whilst others such as Rawlinson, Gough, Hunter-Weston, Hamilton and Townshend were awarded knighthoods.

The balance sheet – the human cost

More than 68 million men were mobilized by the warring powers. Of these, an estimated 10 million died in battle and a further 21 million suffered wounds. It has been calculated that the average daily loss of life during the war was 5,509 whilst during the Boer War it had been just ten. The casualty rate of the Allies represented 52 per cent of the men mobilized; for the Central Powers it was 49 per cent.

Casualty figures – Allies and Central Powers

	Dead	Wounded	Missing
Allies	5,520,000	12,831,000	4,121,000
Central Powers	3,386,000	8,388,000	3,629,000

Casualty figures of the various warring nations

	Dead	Wounded
Germany	1,773,000	4,216,000
Russia	1,700,000	4,950,000
France	1,375,000	4,266,000
Austria-Hungary	1,200,000	3,620,000
Britain and the British Empire	1,013,000	2,090,000
Italy	650,000	947,000
Turkey	325,000	400,000
United States	126,000	234,000
Bulgaria	87,000	152,000
Serbia	45,000	133,000
Belgium	13,000	44,000
Portugal	7,000	13,000

In addition to the loss of life on the battlefields across Europe and the Middle East, an estimated 8.75 million civilians lost their lives. These were made up of those who died of disease and starvation, those who were victims of massacres and acts of genocide and those who died as a result of enemy action. To these must also be added the 8 million victims of the epidemic of Spanish influenza which occurred during the years 1918 and 1919.

The balance sheet – material cost

On the Western Front, the bulk of the fighting took place in Flanders and a region in north-east France between Verdun on the River Meuse across Picardie and Artois to the North Sea coast. In France alone, 2 million hectares (4.9 million acres) of agricultural land and 500,000 hectares (1.2 million acres) of forest were laid waste and some 3 million dwellings and buildings of all sorts destroyed. To this must be added the devastation wrought across Russia and Italy. In Britain, the damage caused by air raids and coastal bombardment was minimal. However, merchant-shipping losses were massive with 7.7 million tonnes, which exceeded those of the other Allies and Central Powers combined.

The balance sheet – financial cost

It has been estimated that the war cost over £75 billion. This sum was reached by adding together the expenditure of the governments involved, the capital value of human life – an estimate of what the men who lost their lives might have earned – the value of production lost due to the war and the repair costs of the buildings damaged. To this must be added the value of merchant shipping lost at sea, the losses suffered by neutral countries and the money spent on war relief. In order to finance the war, Britain borrowed £9.59 million, France £6.34 million and Italy £3.53 million all largely from the United States. The war over, these massive loans now had to be repaid. In Britain, the war saw rates of personal taxation increase from 9 per cent to 27 per cent whilst in France rates rose from 13 per cent to 18 per cent . German rates rose from 8 per cent to 12 per cent and in the United States from 2 per cent to 8 per cent . The gold reserves of all those involved in the war also fell substantially to the advantage of the United States and certain neutral countries.

The 'vast military holocaust' of the years 1914–18 saw the collapse of great empires and imperial dynasties – the Hohenzollerns in Germany, the Habsburgs in Austria-Hungary, the Romanovs in Russia and the sultans of the Ottoman Empire. Ordinary people would have to adjust to social, moral and cultural changes – their world would never be the same again.

A cartoon by an unknown British artist who used the pseudonym 'Caractacus'. The cartoon bears the title 'The harvest of war is desolation and death'.

glossary

Allies Those countries that fought on the same side as Britain and France in the First World War.

amphibious operation A military operation in or on water.

annex To join or attach to.

bloc A combination of countries.

blockhouse A small fort.

camaraderie Good fellowship or comradeship.

Central Powers Those countries that fought on the same side as Germany in the First World War.

Colours A flag bearing the battle honours of a regiment.

compassionate leave Leave granted to a soldier facing personal or family problems.

constitution A system of laws according to which a country is run.

deadlock A situation in which matters have been brought to a standstill.

debauched Corrupt or over-indulged.

diplomatic manoeuvring Using diplomacy to gain an advantage.

esprit de corps Regard for the group or regiment to which one belongs.

estaminet A French café or bar.

fatigues Extra work or duties imposed on a soldier as a punishment.

flogging Lashing with a whip.

fraternized   To associate with or treat as brothers.

fuselage   The body of an aircraft.

Geneva Convention   An international agreement of 1864 regarding the treatment of wounded soldiers and prisoners of war.

howitzer   A large gun used in trench warfare.

impregnable   Impossible to capture or safe from attack.

inferiority complex   A feeling that one is of lesser quality to others.

irregular   A soldier not under official military authority.

jingoistic   Showing enthusiasm for war.

mobilize   To prepare armed services in readiness for war.

Pan Slav movement   A movement intended to bring all the Slav people together into one nation.

pincer movement   A manoeuvre intended to cut off or encircle the enemy.

posthumously   After death.

prima donna   Leading female singer or ballet dancer often considered to be very temperamental.

Pyrrhic victory   A victory gained at very great cost.

reconnaissance   A survey carried out to discover details of the enemy's position.

reservists   Part time soldiers liable to be called up at the time of an emergency.

respirators   Gas masks.

sniper   A skilled marksman who shoots at men from a distance.

subalterns   A junior army officer under the rank of captain.

stand to   The morning routine of men in the trenches. They stood to in expectation of an enemy attack since such attacks usually came in the morning.

ultimatum   A last offer or demand.

War Bonds   Stock (a type of share) sold by a government to help pay the costs of a war.

taking it further

Chapter 1

Further reading

The Archduke and the Assassin: Sarajevo June 28th 1914, Lavender Cassels (Dorset Press, 1984)

The Origins of the First World War, James Joll (Penguin, 1992)

The Great Naval Race: Anglo German Naval Rivalry, Peter Padfield (Hart-Davis, 1974)

War By Timetable, A. J. P. Taylor (American Heritage, 1969)

Guns in August, Barbara Tuchman (Ballentine Books, 1962)

Chapter 2

Further reading

The Vanished Army: The British Expeditionary Force 1914–15, Tim Carew (Kimber, 1964)

Death of an Army: The First Battle of Ypres, A. Farrar-Hockley (Arthur Barker, 1967)

The Opening Moves, John Keegan (Penguin, 1971)

The Schlieffen Plan, Gerhard Rutter (Wolff, 1958)

Mons John Terraine (Pan Books, 1960)

The Campaign on the Marne, Sewell Tyng (OUP, 1935)

Chapter 3

Further reading

The Great War in Africa, Byron Farwell (Viking, 1987)

German East Africa: The story of the First World War in East Africa, B. Gardner (Cassell, 1963)

Battle for the Bundu: The First World War in East Africa, Charles Miller (Macdonald & Jane, 1974)

Films

African Queen (1951) starring Humphrey Bogart and Katherine Hepburn is based on an episode in this campaign when, in 1915, a small riverboat is used to sink a German gunboat on Lake Tanganyika.

Chapter 4

Further reading

Tannenburg: The First Thirty Days in East Prussia, Edmund Ironside (Blackwood, 1925)

Carpathian Disaster: Death of an Army, Geoffrey Jules (Ballentine Books, 1970)

The Eastern Front 1914–17, Norman Stone (Hodder & Stoughton, 1975)

Chapter 5

Further reading

Gallipoli: One Long Grave, Kit Denton (Time/Life Books, 1986)

Damn the Dardanelles! The Agony of Gallipoli, John Laffin (Macmillan, 1985)

Gallipoli, Alan Moorhead (Hamish Hamilton, 1956)

Gallipoli, Robert Rhodes (Batsford, 1965)

Films

Apart from the BBC's *All the King's Men* (1999), other films covering the events of the Dardanelles campaign include the Australian made *Gallipoli* (1981) with Mark Lee, Mel Gibson and Bill Kerr and *ANZACS* (1985) starring Paul Hogan.

Chapter 6

Further reading

The War the Infantry Knew, 1914–19, J. C. Dunn (Janes, 1987)

The Poor Bloody Infantry: The Truth Untold, W. H. A. Groom (Picardy, 1983)

The White Heat: The New Warfare, John Terraine (Sidgwick & Jackson, 1982)

Chapter 7

Further reading

Eye-Deep in Hell: Life in the Trenches, 1914–18, J. Ellis (Fontana, 1977)

The Face of Battle, John Keegan (Penguin, 1978)

The War in the Trenches, Alan Lloyd (Hart-Davis, 1987)

Films

All Quiet on the Western Front (1930) based on the book (1929) of the same name by the German Erich Maria Remarque is considered to be one of the finest anti-war films ever made. It was remade in 1979 starring Richard Thomas and Ernest Borgnine. *No Man's Land: Hell on Earth* (1931) is another account of life in the trenches as is the more recent *The Trench* (1999) starring Paul Nicholls and Daniel Craig.

Chapter 8

Further reading

British Gallantry Awards, P. E. Abbot and J. M. A. Tamplin (Guinness Superlatives, 1971)

The Monocled Mutineer, William Allison and John Fairley (Quartet Books, 1986)

For the Sake of Example, Anthony Babington (Leo Cooper, 1983)

Morale: A Study of Men and Courage, John Baynes (Leo Cooper, 1987)

Shot At Dawn, Julian Putkowski and Julian Sykes (Wharncliffe Publishing, 1989)

The Study of the Victoria Cross, Sir John Smythe (Muller, 1963)

Films

Paths of Glory (1957) starring Kirk Douglas, Adolphe Menjou and Wayne Morris tells the story of three Frenchmen court-martialled for cowardice. It is said that the trench scenes are amongst the most vivid ever made. The story of Percy Toplis is the subject of the much criticized BBC series *The Monocled Mutineer* with Paul McGann in the title role.

Chapter 9

Further reading

Verdun, Georges Blond (Andre Deutsch, 1965)

The *Battleground Europe* series (Leo Cooper) includes books that cover the various areas of the Somme battlefield

The Somme Then and Now, John Giles (After the Battle, 1986)

The Price of Glory: Verdun 1916, A. Home (Macmillan, 1972)

Somme, Lyn Macdonald (Michael Joseph, 1983)

The First Day of the Somme, Martin Middlebrook (Alan Lane, 1971)

Chapter 10

Further reading

Naval Battles of the First World War, Geoffrey Bennett (Batsford, 1968)

Jutland 1916, John Costello and Terry Hughes (Weidenfeld & Nicholson, 1976)

The Dreadnoughts, David Howarth (Time/Life Books, 1979)

The Great War At Sea, 1914–18, Richard Hough (Oxford University Press, 1983)

Chapter 11

Further reading

The Aeroplanes of the Royal Flying Corps, J. M. Bruce (Putman, 1962)

Aces High: The War in the Air Over the Western Front, A. Clark (Fontana, 1974)

The Great Air War, Aaron Norman (Macmillan, 1968)

Films

The first films made to illustrate the heroism and sacrifice of young airmen during the First World War were *The Dawn Patrol* (1930) which starred Douglas Fairbanks junior, and *Journey's End* (1930). The former was remade in 1938 with Errol Flynn in the central role; the latter, renamed *Aces High*, was remade in 1976 and starred Malcolm McDowell, Christopher Plummer and Simon Ward.

Chapter 12

Further reading

Fire Over England: The German Air Raids of World War I, H. G. Castle (Leo Cooper, 1982)

The Deluge: British Society and the First World War, Arthur Marwick (Bodley Head, 1965)

Great Britain and the War of 1914–18, I. Woodward (Methuen, 1967)

Chapter 13

Further reading

Secret Service, Christopher Andrew (Heinemann, 1985)

A History of the British Secret Service, Richard Deacon (Grafton Books, 1969)

Steinhauer: The Kaiser's Master Spy, Autobiography (John Lane, 1930)

The Secret Lives of Trebitsch Lincoln, Bernard Wasserstein (Penguin, 1988)

The Fatal Lover: Mata Hari, Julie Wheelwright (Collins & Brown, 1992)

Films

One of the most famous films made about espionage activities during the First World War was *The Thirty-Nine Steps* (1935) starring Robert Donat. The film was twice remade in 1959 and 1978 with Kenneth More and Robert Powell in the leading roles. Other films include *Mata Hari* (1931) with Greta Garbo in the title role and a remake in 1985 starring Sylvia Kristel. Conrad Veldt and Valerie Hobson appeared in *The Spy in Black* (1939), a melodrama about German spies operating in the Orkney Islands whilst *Zeppelin* (1971), with Michael York and

Marius Goring, tells of an attempt to steal secrets from the Zeppelin works at Friedrichshafen.

Chapter 14

Further reading

Some Corner of a Foreign Field: Poetry of the Great War, Ed. James Bentley (Little, Brown & Co, 1992)

Up the Line to Death: The War Poets 1914–18, Brian Gardner (Methuen, 1976)

The Best of Fragments From France, Bruce Bairnsfather, compiled by Tonie and Valmai Holt (Phin Publishing, 1978)

Poets of the First World War, Jon Stallworthy (Oxford University Press, 1974)

Chapter 15

Further reading

Ten Days That Shook the World, J. Reed (Boni & Liveright, 1919)

The Russian Army in World War I, Ward Rutherford (Gordon Cremonesi, 1975)

Quiet Flows the Don, Mikhail Sholokhov (recent edition Tuttle, 1996)

The Doughboys: The Story of the AEF 1917–18, Lawrence Stallings (Harper & Row, 1963)

The Zimmermann Telegram, Barbara Tuchman (Ballentine Books, 1958)

Films

The start of the films *Doctor Zhivago* (1965) starring Omar Sharif and Julie Christie and *Nicholas and Alexandra* (1971) provide accounts of events in Russia during the Revolutionary period.

Chapter 16

Further reading

Lawrence the Uncrowned King of Arabia, M. Asher (Penguin, 1999)

The Neglected War: Mesopotamia 1914–18, A. J. Baker (Faber, 1967)

Lawrence of Arabia, Robert Graves (Paragon, 1955)

Seven Pillars of Wisdom, T. E. Lawrence (Doran & Co, 1935)

Films

The most famous film about the campaign against the Turks in Palestine and Mesopotamia is David Lean's *Lawrence of Arabia* (1962) starring Peter O'Toole and Omar Sharif.

Chapter 17

Further reading

The Ironclads of Cambrai, Bryan Cooper (Souvenir Press, 1967)

They Called it Passchendaele: The Story of the Third Battle of Ypres, Lyn Macdonald (Michael Joseph, 1978)

Caporetto: The Scapegoat Battle, Ronald Seth (Macdonald, 1965)

Passchendaele, Philip Warner (Sidgwick & Jackson, 1987)

The First Tank Battle; Cambrai 1917, Robert Woolcombe (Arthur Baker, 1967)

Chapter 18

Further reading

The Kaiser's Battle, Martin Middlebrook (Allen Lane, 1978)

The Last Act, Barrie Pitt (Macmillan, 1962)

To Win a War: 1918 The Year of Victory, John Terraine (Sidgwick & Jackson, 1978)

No Man's Land: The Story of 1918, John Toland (Eyre & Methuen, 1980)

Films

Films about the involvement of the United States in the First World War include *Yankee Doodle Dandy* (1942) that tells the story of George H. Cohen with James Cagney in the title role and *Sergeant York* (1941) starring Gary Cooper and Walter Brennan.

Chapter 19

Further general reading

Testament of Youth, Vera Brittain (Gollancz, 1933)

World War I in Photographs, Adrian Gilbert (Orbis, 1986)

Goodbye to All That, Robert Graves (Penguin, 1973)

British Butchers and Bunglers of World War One, John Laffin (Sutton Publishing, 1989)

A Pictorial History of World War I, G. D. Sheffield (Bison Books, 1987)

Memoirs of an Infantry Officer, Siegfried Sassoon (Faber & Faber, 1930)

Lions Led By Donkeys, P. A. Thompson (Warner Laurie, 1927)

Mr Punch's History of the Great War, (Cassell & Co, 1919)

index

the cold war
0340 884940 £8.99

nazi germany
0340 884908 £8.99

the middle east
0340 884916 £8.99

the second world war
0340 884932 £8.99

special forces
0340 884924 £8.99

the first world war
0340 884894 £8.99

teach
yourself

the second world war
alan farmer

- Explore the events of the Second World War
- Discover its impact on those involved
- Understand the reasons behind the conflict and who was to blame

teach yourself the second world war is an accessible introduction to one of the most important, tragic and costly events in history. This war had an unimaginable impact on the entire world, causing the deaths of over 50 million people. Follow the main military campaigns of the war, discover how it affected the countries involved and develop your understanding of why the Allied powers were able to achieve victory.

Alan Farmer is Head of History at St Martin's College, Lancaster and has written a large number of books on modern American, European and British history.

the middle east since 1945
stewart ross

- Read an accessible guide to today's political hotspot
- Understand the development of the region
- Discover more about a major world issue

teach yourself the middle east since 1945 tells the story of the modern world's most troubled region. It is lively yet authoritative, examining the origin and developments of issues that have made the headlines over the last half century. This book addresses many questions about the region, including why the Israeli–Palestinian conflict has lasted so long and the background to the two Gulf Wars and presents each aspect with engaging objectivity.

Stewart Ross taught in a variety of institutions worldwide before becoming a writer, lecturer and broadcaster. He has written over 175 books, including widely acclaimed historical works.

teach
yourself

nazi germany
michael lynch

- Discover this extraordinary period
- Understand the motives of the individuals who created and led the Nazi movement
- Gain an insight into the experiences of those involved

teach yourself nazi germany is an accessible introduction to one of the most controversial periods in modern history. The years 1933–45 witnessed the take-over of Germany by a man and a movement whose racial and political policies are now regarded with universal abhorrence. Yet in all of European history there has never been a more genuinely popular regime than that of the Nazis. This book immerses you in the remarkable Third Reich story and the controversies that still surround it.

Michael Lynch is a tutor at the University of Leicester and is also a writer, specializing in modern European and Asian history.

the cold war
c. b. jones

- Understand the period that gave us the Cuban crisis, the Berlin wall, nuclear weapons and James Bond
- Discover more about this hidden conflict
- Read a compelling guide to this 45-year-long war

teach yourself the cold war is an accessible introduction to a war that shaped the latter half of the twentieth century. It covers all aspects, from questioning whether the tension really ended with the fall of the Berlin wall, to examining what JFK and his assassin had in common. Understand the global reach of this hidden conflict and its effects on the world in recent history and today.

C. B. Jones is an experienced teacher and Head of Faculty. She is also an A Level examiner with a specialist knowledge of twentieth century history.

teach
yourself

special forces
anthony kemp

- Gain an overview of the history of Special Forces
- Understand how anti-terrorist units function
- Find out how Special Forces began and evolved

teach yourself special forces is a concise introduction to the secret world of Special Forces units, giving you a fascinating insight into how they are recruited, trained and armed, what they can and cannot achieve, and their role in controlling modern-day terrorism. Read a compelling history of Special Forces, from the birth of small-scale raiding forces during the Second World War, to the Iranian Embassy siege.

Anthony Kemp is an established military historian, writer and film producer who specializes in the Special Air Service Regiment.

teach® yourself

Afrikaans
Access 2002
Accounting, Basic
Alexander Technique
Algebra
Arabic
Arabic Script, Beginner's
Aromatherapy
Astronomy
Bach Flower Remedies
Bengali
Better Chess
Better Handwriting
Biology
Body Language
Book Keeping
Book Keeping & Accounting
Brazilian Portuguese
Bridge
Buddhism
Buddhism, 101 Key Ideas
Bulgarian
Business Studies
Business Studies, 101 Key Ideas
C++
Calculus
Calligraphy
Cantonese
Card Games
Catalan
Chemistry, 101 Key Ideas
Chess
Chi Kung
Chinese
Chinese, Beginner's

Chinese Script, Beginner's
Christianity
Classical Music
Copywriting
Counselling
Creative Writing
Crime Fiction
Croatian
Crystal Healing
Czech
Danish
Desktop Publishing
Digital Photography
Digital Video & PC Editing
Drawing
Dream Interpretation
Dutch
Dutch, Beginner's
Dutch Dictionary
Dutch Grammar
Eastern Philosophy
ECDL
E-Commerce
Economics, 101 Key Ideas
Electronics
English, American (EFL)
English as a Foreign Language
English, Correct
English Grammar
English Grammar (EFL)
English for International Business
English Vocabulary
Ethics
Excel 2002
Feng Shui

Film Making
Film Studies
Finance for non-Financial Managers
Finnish
Flexible Working
Flower Arranging
French
French, Beginner's
French Grammar
French Grammar, Quick Fix
French, Instant
French, Improve your
French Starter Kit
French Verbs
French Vocabulary
Gaelic
Gaelic Dictionary
Gardening
Genetics
Geology
German
German, Beginner's
German Grammar
German Grammar, Quick Fix
German, Instant
German, Improve your
German Verbs
German Vocabulary
Go
Golf
Greek
Greek, Ancient
Greek, Beginner's
Greek, Instant
Greek, New Testament
Greek Script, Beginner's
Guitar
Gulf Arabic
Hand Reflexology
Hebrew, Biblical
Herbal Medicine
Hieroglyphics
Hindi
Hindi, Beginner's
Hindi Script, Beginner's
Hinduism
History, 101 Key Ideas
How to Win at Horse Racing
How to Win at Poker
HTML Publishing on the WWW
Human Anatomy & Physiology
Hungarian
Icelandic
Indian Head Massage

Indonesian
Information Technology, 101 Key Ideas
Internet, The
Irish
Islam
Italian
Italian, Beginner's
Italian Grammar
Italian Grammar, Quick Fix
Italian, Instant
Italian, Improve your
Italian Verbs
Italian Vocabulary
Japanese
Japanese, Beginner's
Japanese, Instant
Japanese Script, Beginner's
Java
Jewellery Making
Judaism
Korean
Latin
Latin American Spanish
Latin, Beginner's
Latin Dictionary
Latin Grammar
Letter Writing Skills
Linguistics
Linguistics, 101 Key Ideas
Literature, 101 Key Ideas
Mahjong
Managing Stress
Marketing
Massage
Mathematics
Mathematics, Basic
Media Studies
Meditation
Mosaics
Music Theory
Needlecraft
Negotiating
Nepali
Norwegian
Origami
Panjabi
Persian, Modern
Philosophy
Philosophy of Mind
Philosophy of Religion
Philosophy of Science
Philosophy, 101 Key Ideas
Photography
Photoshop

Physics
Piano
Planets
Planning Your Wedding
Polish
Politics
Portuguese
Portuguese, Beginner's
Portuguese Grammar
Portuguese, Instant
Postmodernism
Pottery
Powerpoint 2002
Presenting for Professionals
Project Management
Psychology
Psychology, 101 Key Ideas
Psychology, Applied
Quark Xpress
Quilting
Recruitment
Reflexology
Reiki
Relaxation
Retaining Staff
Romanian
Russian
Russian, Beginner's
Russian Grammar
Russian, Instant
Russian Script, Beginner's
Sanskrit
Screenwriting
Serbian
Setting up a Small Business
Shorthand, Pitman 2000
Sikhism
Spanish
Spanish, Beginner's
Spanish Grammar
Spanish Grammar, Quick Fix
Spanish, Instant
Spanish, Improve your
Spanish Starter Kit
Spanish Verbs
Spanish Vocabulary
Speaking on Special Occasions
Speed Reading
Statistical Research
Statistics
Swahili
Swahili Dictionary
Swedish
Tagalog

Tai Chi
Tantric Sex
Teaching English as a Foreign Language
Teaching English One to One
Teams and Team-Working
Thai
Time Management
Tracing your Family History
Travel Writing
Trigonometry
Turkish
Turkish, Beginner's
Typing
Ukrainian
Urdu
Urdu Script, Beginner's
Vietnamese
Volcanoes
Watercolour Painting
Weight Control through Diet and
   Exercise
Welsh
Welsh Dictionary
Wills and Probate
Wine Tasting
Winning at Job Interviews
Word 2002
World Faiths
Writing a Novel
Writing for Children
Writing Poetry
World Cultures:
   China
   England
   France
   Germany
   Italy
   Japan
   Portugal
   Russia
   Spain
   Wales
Xhosa
Yoga
Zen
Zulu

Takeout Sushi

Christopher Green

Takeout Sushi

Christopher Green

NEEM TREE
PRESS

Published by Neem Tree Press Limited, 2024
Copyright text © Christopher Green, 2024
Copyright illustrations © Neem Tree Press, 2024

Christopher Green asserts his rights
under the Copyright, Designs and Patents Act 1988
to be recognised as the author of this work.

1 3 5 7 9 10 8 6 4 2

Neem Tree Press Limited
95a Ridgmount Gardens, London, WC1E 7AZ
United Kingdom
info@neemtreepress.com
www.neemtreepress.com

A catalogue record for this book is available from the British Library.

ISBN 978-1-915584-31-1 Paperback
ISBN 978-1-915584-32-8 Ebook
ISBN 978-1-915584-74-8 US Ebook

Printed and bound in Great Britain

Thank you to my sister Jenny Fionda for her support.

Contents

Stories of Japan, Today

Swallows

Tsune moved home at the end of January. Her husband Matsu's company was due to relocate to Yokohama in April and, after several months of searching, they settled on an apartment in nearby Kawasaki. The apartment was on the third floor of a huge residential building, in a smart, modern area a few minutes' walk from Kawasaki station.

Tsune soon found work as a shop assistant in a department store close to the station. They were both busy with the move but Tsune was delighted to make a fresh start. After ten years of married life and the same routine, things had turned a little stale. Ten years older than Tsune and in his mid-forties, Matsu was a successful businessman with an aura of self-confidence that was calming to be around, but lately he had become settled in his ways. After the move Tsune felt more alive than she had for a long time. She convinced Matsu to explore the area around the station with her on foot. On their first excursion they found a bakery selling delicious freshly baked croissants, and an Indian restaurant to satisfy her craving for spicy food.

And then the swallows arrived. Tsune had seen them flitting around the building in the evening gloom and at first thought they were bats. One morning on opening the door to leave the apartment for work, she was surprised by a flash of departing tail feathers. There, above the door was a ventilation duct and above its opening, dapples of damp, dark brown mud. The swallows were building a nest.

Tsune felt lucky to have her apartment chosen for the nesting place. But she had concerns as well. Things were going to get messy with droppings on the floor outside their door, as well as mud and straw splattering about. Would the cleaners who keep the buildings spic and span remove the nest? Tsune resolved to ask the next time she had a chance, which happened to be a Wednesday morning when she took out the rubbish.

"They built a nest outside your apartment last year too," a cleaner told her. "After the young ones had flown the nest, we removed it. If you don't want them to nest outside your apartment we'll take it down. The swallows will soon find somewhere else."

"No, no, that's fine, I'd like them to build their nest here," Tsune said.

Matsu wasn't so positive.

"Their droppings will get everywhere. We'll have to put down newspaper to catch it. And there's the smell too. If we take the nest down now, before they've really started, they'll build a new one somewhere else."

Tsune had expected such a response and had worked on an upbeat retort.

"Come on, it will be fun. We'll have nature right on our doorstep. We'll be able to watch the swallows build the nest, see how many eggs they lay, watch the chicks hatch, grow and learn to fly. It'll be like having our own nature documentary, live, right here outside our door."

"Yes, but you forget, I grew up in Nagano prefecture. We used to get swallows every year. Believe me, after you've seen it once, it gets boring."

Tsune had heard this kind of talk from Matsu before. He had a similar reason for not wanting children.

"It may be boring for you," Tsune said, "but it won't be for me. I want the swallows to nest here. You don't need to worry. I'll take care of the cleaning."

"Okay, okay. Have it your own way. Just don't say I didn't warn you."

Tsune was relieved he had relented. With the subject of children, he hadn't. Matsu had a son with his previous wife over twenty years ago. He and his son rarely communicated; you could even say they had lost touch. The last Tsune had heard, the son was based in Hong Kong working for a Japanese trading company. Matsu said he'd gone through parenthood once and that was enough for any man.

The swallows seemed to spend from morning to dusk building their nest. They were quite used to humans and would rest or sleep in the nest or on the balcony handrail. Tsune borrowed a book on swallows from the library and read up on them.

"Listen to this," Tsune enthused as she sat next to Matsu on the couch. "The swallows come from as far away as the Philippines, Taiwan and Australia. They are exhausted when they get here, but somehow they find the energy to build a nest and raise their chicks."

"Yes, I know."

"They fly over two thousand kilometres to get here. Two thousand kilometres. I feel tired just thinking about it."

"Really."

"And they catch their food while flying, such as mosquitoes. So they also help us by killing mozzies before they bite us. Isn't that fantastic?"

"I guess so."

"Aren't you interested at all?"

"Not really, to be honest. I've heard that stuff before."

"Don't you even think it's wonderful?"

"It is, but there's another side of the story that your book probably doesn't mention, like the diseases they carry, the parasites and bugs that live in their nests, that kind of stuff."

"They look clean to me. So cute too."

"Of course they do, but the reality is different. When you take down the nest, you'll need to wear gloves and a mask. I'm sure the cleaners don't want swallows building nests here, they're just being kind to you."

Tsune felt deflated. She flipped through the book. Just as Matsu said, the book only had positive things to say about swallows. And yet he was more negative than necessary, a trait that she'd noticed more and more about him. When she ever brought up the subject of children, he always reminded her of the morning sickness, the pain of childbirth, the sleepless nights and months if not years of tiredness. Tsune knew all about that of course, but the positives would far outweigh the negatives. But what could she do if Matsu wasn't on the same page?

A couple of evenings later, after a hectic day's work in the shop, Tsune climbed the stairs to the apartment. As she reached the top she looked up to check the birds' progress. The nest had gone. There was not even a trace of a nest. Thinking she'd stopped on the second floor and not the third, as had happened a couple of times when tired or distracted, she took a step back to check the name plate on the door. Her name. Somebody had removed the nest. She yanked open the door, kicked off her shoes and ran down the hallway to the living room.

4

"Why did you pull down the nest?" she shouted at the back of Matsu's head as he sat watching a baseball game on television.

"Whoa, wait a minute," he said, raising his hands, "I didn't do it."

"Yes you did. You must have. You are the only one who doesn't want the nest."

"Calm down, will you?"

"No, I won't calm down. I'm angry."

"Don't get angry with me, get angry with the cleaners. They took it down."

"No, they would never…"

"It was a mistake. They took it down by mistake. They left us a note apologizing about it – look, it's there on the table."

Sure enough, on the table was a scrap of paper on which was scribbled a handwritten message. The writer, who referred to themselves as the supervisor of the building's cleaning team, apologized for one of their trainees having over-enthusiastically removed the nest that morning.

"Oh." Tsune sighed. "I'm so disappointed. I really wanted to see those chicks."

Matsu stood and wrapped his arms around her.

"I know you did," he said, "I know you did. Look, the swallows may come back next year. You'll get another chance to see the chicks."

By the weekend the birds were building a nest again, in the same spot. Tsune was overjoyed and determined to do all she could to help the swallows build their new nest. She wrote in large red crayon on a sheet of white paper the words "Do not take this nest down. Owner, Apartment 301", and taped the sheet to the wall under the nest. She put down sheets of newspaper directly underneath to stop the droppings from splattering the floor, weighing down the sheets with plastic bottles filled with tap water. She replaced the dirty newspaper with fresh sheets and swept up the droppings, loose dirt and straw that had missed the paper.

A few days later the nest was complete. For a while both birds spent time in the nest, and then only the female. Tsune wondered where the male had gone and if it would come back, but she needn't have worried for the male returned at about the time the heads of the chicks popped up from behind the rim of the nest. One, two, three, four balls of grey fluff with eyes like gleaming black beads.

Tsune charged up the battery of her digital camera and took photos, many, many photos. She even dragged a dining chair out of the apartment and stood on it, arms stretched high above, to take shots of the chicks with their expectant mouths open. The unstoppable power of nature filled her heart with awe and her mind with questions. How do swallows know how to build their nests? How is a nest able to carry the weight of four chicks and their mother, and survive the winds that barrels around the tall buildings?

Tsune wanted to protect the chicks in this, the most delicate time of their lives, but felt powerless to do so. She admired the parents' unceasing effort. Back and forth they went, from dawn to dusk, up into the sky to gather food, down to the nest and the pink mouths of their chicks. The parents would spend the nights close to the nest, exhausted.

Throughout this time Matsu declined to get involved. Even when they both returned home together and Tsune pointed at the chicks who had already lost their fluffiness, he raised only the faintest of smiles. "They'll be gone before you know it, and never come back to thank you," he said. Tsune was sure he would continue with, "Just like children," but for once he didn't.

One morning as Tsune left for work she saw the chicks perched on the edge of the nest, working up the courage to take their first flight. She had no time to stay and watch, but wished she had, for when she came back home that evening, the nest had emptied. Over the following mornings and evenings, she sometimes caught a glimpse of the young birds in flight as they circled the building, learning to fly and how to feed on the wing. And then they were gone. Their disappearance was sudden, too quick for Tsune who was despondent. She missed their presence and the joy of opening the door and seeing the chicks perched in the nest above.

Tsune let a busy weekend pass without removing the nest and promised herself she would take it down the following weekend. Late on the Thursday evening, returning home after a few drinks with her colleagues, Tsune was shocked to see the nest, the newspaper and her note not to remove it, had gone.

Tsune bustled down the hallway to the living room where Matsu sat laughing at a variety programme on the television. Recalling the previous time she had accosted him about the nest, Tsune rested her shopping bag on the table and waited for a moment of calm.

"I'm back," she said.

"Hello."

Matsu stood up slowly and stretched his arms in the air. "What are we having for dinner?" he said.

"I got some salmon, thought I would grill it with salt and lemon."

"Great, I haven't had salmon for a while. Did you see the nest had gone?"

"Yes. Did the cleaners take it down by accident again?"

"Not by accident. When I left for work this morning one of them asked me what to do about the nest and I said they could take it down. They did a good job – you can hardly tell it was there."

"But I told you, I was going to take the nest down."

"Yes, I know."

"So why did you let the cleaners do it?"

"I didn't have time to think about it, I was on the way to work, but surely it was better to have them do it. After all, they are professionals. It's messy and dangerous work and they have all the tools to do it quickly and safely. The last thing you need is to catch a nasty bug."

"I know, but I wanted to do it, just like I told you. If I catch a disease then I catch a disease, it's my decision. Don't you get it?"

"I get it, but come on, nobody in their right mind would actually want to take down a bird's nest. I've done it when I was a kid in Nagano, it really isn't fun."

"I know it's not fun. But that's not the point. I just wanted to do it myself, for better or for worse. I don't want to hear that you've done it, so I don't need to."

Matsu sighed. "It's just a nest. I was just looking out for you, that's all."

"Yes, it's just a nest, but I wanted to do it. There are some things you have to do, even though you know it isn't going to be easy. Like having children."

The moment Tsune let that slip, she wished she hadn't.

"Oh, so that's what's going on."

"No, that was silly of me, I..."

"No, no, I get it. I should have figured it out sooner."

Tsune watched as Matsu shrugged, strode down the hallway to the spare room, and clattered the door closed behind him.

Later that month, Matsu moved out. Tsune stayed until the autumn and then realized she had to move too. She couldn't afford the rent, it was true, but even if she stayed, when spring came around the swallows would return and she'd be reminded of Matsu. There could still be time to start afresh, to find somebody else, to live her life on her own terms. There could still be time.

Burned

I'm sure I speak for many in a long-term relationship when I say that, no matter how comfortable the relationship is, it's good to have some time and space to yourself.

This isn't easy to achieve in a small apartment in Tokyo. At worst, there is the toilet, the bath and, as a last resort, the futon to fall asleep on. Even then, solitude isn't guaranteed. There could always be a knock on the toilet door followed by a "What are you doing in there?" or the opening of the bathroom door and a "Are you alright?" or an accidental knee in the back from the person sleeping on the futon next to you.

When my wife, Naomi, who works for a global IT company, told me of an upcoming conference in Barcelona, I managed to respond appropriately with, "Is your passport still valid?" but fireworks of anticipated freedom erupted in my head.

On the morning of the business trip, a Sunday, I drove Naomi to Narita airport. On the way, our conversation grew tense and the earlier fireworks were doused.

"Just promise me you'll act responsibly this time," Naomi said from the passenger seat, nursing two smartphones on her lap and texting family, friends and colleagues.

"I acted responsibly last time, honey," I replied. "It wasn't my fault I caught the flu."

Naomi sighed.

"It wasn't your fault, but you could have made some effort to look after yourself. And look after the apartment. I came back to a kitchen sink overflowing with unwashed dishes and a waste bin bursting with rubbish. The washing machine hadn't been used. You'd just dumped all your used clothes in front of it. I guess you were expecting them to leap magically off the floor into the machine. And of course, the fridge was empty, the freezer too. There you were, lying on the futon in the tatami room looking like, well, that character from *Star Wars*."

"Luke Skywalker?"

"No…what's he called…something like hat?"

"You don't mean Jabba the Hutt, do you?"

"That's the one!"

"Honey, that's an awful thing to say. A truly terrible thing to say."

"Well, you did. You looked like you'd worn the same pyjamas for the duration and of course hadn't bothered to shave or brush your teeth."

"Oh, come on. I brushed my teeth. I was poorly. Try to show some compassion. I was very, very ill."

"Hah."

"What do you mean, 'hah'?"

"You had the PlayStation and Nintendo devices lying next to you on the futon. You can't have been that ill."

"I was bored, lying there, being ill. I needed something to occupy my time."

"How about sleep? That's what people who are ill usually do to occupy their time."

"I was sleeping, most of the time. You just came back when I was, um, resting."

"Yeah, resting. I get it. You had the energy to rest and play games, but not to get up and make a start on washing the dishes. After a long, exhausting business trip I had to nurse you, wash up, do the laundry, clean the apartment and do the shopping."

"I'm sorry about that. Really sorry. I told you before, if I hadn't been ill I would have had the place sorted for your return."

"You did say that, didn't you. Well this time, why not try washing up after every meal, doing the laundry every couple of days and at least stopping in at the supermarket on the way home to buy essentials. Do you think you can do that?"

"I'm not a child, you know."

"I know. So, can you do it? Or do I have to worry about you while I'm away? Will I have to return early, like last time, to look after you?"

"Okay, honey, okay. You win. You needn't worry. I'll clean the apartment. There'll be no dirty dishes, no laundry to be done. I'll have food in the fridge. And I'll look after myself. Happy?"

We reached Narita airport and I walked with Naomi to the check-in area. I watched as she offloaded her suitcase, then waved her goodbye before she joined her colleagues who were standing in a gaggle in front of the security-check area.

Back at the apartment, with Naomi's words still reverberating in my head, I threw myself into tidying the apartment. I was determined to rise to her challenge. After about two hours I'd cleaned the kitchen, bathroom and toilet, vacuumed everywhere and taken out the rubbish. Washed laundry was hanging up to dry on the balcony. I had a final satisfied walk through the apartment and felt at ease.

I celebrated with a cup of tea and a cookie or two, closed the curtains in the living room, lay back on the sofa and had a nap.

I woke and opened a flight tracking app on my smartphone. Naomi's flight had seven more hours before touchdown at Barcelona. Hungry, I considered ordering pizza, however having committed to looking after myself, I ordered sushi instead.

The sushi came and I fed myself on thick, delicious slices of tuna and salmon washed down with a beer. I slipped the DVD of *Dirty Harry* into the player and watched the movie from start to finish from a horizontal position on the couch, enjoying all the space I had to myself. The movie ended and I found I was smiling. I checked the app and saw that Naomi's flight had just arrived at Barcelona. I sent her a text message of "*Welcome to Spain*", knowing that she'd be online as soon as the plane had come to a stop.

I ran the bath and had a good soak, got out and dried myself off. As it was summer and a sweltering evening, I pulled my pyjamas out of the drawer then thought, *Why not?* and decided to do without.

I'm sure we have all walked around our homes alone and naked at some point and enjoyed the freedom from inhibiting clothes and eyes. I was no different.

I had to be in the office early for a Monday morning meeting and I didn't have a shirt ironed. I usually left the ironing to Naomi as she would tear through a week's worth of shirts for the both of us while stood in front of the ironing board watching television.

I dragged the ironing board out from the hallway cupboard and stood it up in front of the television. To prove to myself that I was in complete control, I replaced the *Dirty Harry* DVD with *Magnum Force*, the second in the "Dirty Harry" series.

When the iron's red lamp came on to indicate it was hot, I got to work on a wrinkled shirt.

I took fifteen minutes to iron the shirt. Feeling tired and somewhat bummed about the time I was taking I decided to iron one more shirt so at least I didn't have to bother doing the ironing on Monday. I urged myself on and in my haste, with one eye on the movie, I thrust the iron back and forth between the buttons, got too close and the metal tip of the iron made contact with my body. At first I felt only the contact, then the searing pain hit my brain like a freight train.

A shriek like the freight train's whistle left my mouth. I just about managed to return the iron safely to the stand before jumping up and down.

"Oh, oh, oh," I gasped as the pain level rose. A red line, a scorch mark, neatly traversed the front of the single organ of my body that had been dangling too close to the ironing board.

I dashed to the safety-first box in the hallway cupboard, tipped the contents out and searched for a lotion of some sort to help soothe the pain. Nothing, or at least nothing I could be sure of using. There were several small tubes with Japanese script on them but I have yet to master reading Japanese.

In the bathroom cabinet I found a tube of green "Aloe Sunburn Gel" bought on a trip to Hawaii. I flipped off the cap and squeezed out a blob onto a fingertip, then brought the blob close to my scorched skin. The green blob made contact, broke and dispersed over the wound.

As the gel reacted with my skin, I groaned, gritted my teeth and begged for relief. Eventually the pain eased and I was able to relax my jaw muscles.

Exhausted, I slipped carefully into my pyjamas, rolled out a futon and went to sleep.

In the morning, I stepped into the shower. The wound was red, stinging, and I bounced off the shower wall when a stream of water rippled over it.

As I dried myself off, I weighed up my options. I could visit the local hospital and get the burn looked at, or push on through the pain and hope the wound would heal itself. But what if it didn't heal? What if it got infected? How would I explain that to Naomi?

I called the office and left a message for my boss, saying I wasn't feeling well and would visit the doctor before going to the office. That done, I changed into my work clothes and left the apartment. Instead of getting off the bus at the train station I stayed on board for two more stops and alighted, slowly, in front of the general hospital.

I had last been to the hospital about two years earlier with athlete's foot, and I headed for the same department, dermatology.

I stood in line at the reception desk and imagined how I could best explain my problem.

"How can I help you?" I was asked by a young nurse, female, wearing glasses with her long hair wound up and pinned under a white cap.

"I burned myself using an iron."

"Are you in pain?"

"Yes. Quite a bit."

"Where is the burn?"

I made a vague slicing movement with my right hand at the level of my groin.

The nurse looked down at my groin area. She turned her eyes back to her register, wrote my name, selected a card from a box and handed it to me.

"356," she said.

"Thanks."

I took the card and eased over to the closest chair in the waiting area. I kept myself occupied, catching up on sports news on my phone and scaring myself by reading articles about burns that hadn't responded to treatment. I consoled myself with the thought I was doing all I could.

My number was called. I knocked on the door of examination room 3, slid the door open and entered.

To my dismay, the doctor was female. Doctor Saito, her badge stated.

"What's the problem?" she asked.

"I burned myself here, with an iron," I said, using the vague slicing motion in front of my groin that had worked well so far.

"With an iron?"

"Yes."

"When?"

"Last night."

"Does it hurt?"

"Yes."

"Could you show me?"

I hadn't expected to get this far into the examination so quickly. I made panicky signs with my eyes at the curtains behind the doctor, which thankfully she picked up on. She stretched out an arm behind her, clasped the edge of the curtain and pulled it shut so that the two of us were enclosed.

I loosened the belt of my trousers, unzipped and unhooked them and let them drop to below my knees.

Doctor Saito swivelled in her chair to face me, then rolled the chair closer.

With only a pair of black boxer shorts on I hooked a thumb over the rim and pulled down, low enough to reveal the red wound.

"Let me see," the doctor said, leaning forwards.

A second or two later she sat up straight and rolled back to her desk.

I pulled my shorts up.

"You said you were ironing, naked?"

"Yes. This shirt actually," I said, tugging a sleeve proudly, while the shirt's tail ends flapped around my boxer shorts. "It was hot last night. I got out of the bath and didn't put on my pyjamas right away as I wanted to cool down."

"I see. And you cooled down, naked, while using a very hot iron to do the ironing."

"Ah. Yes, I see what you mean. It wasn't a very smart thing to do."

Doctor Saito didn't respond. I assumed she agreed with my self-criticism. She tapped away at her computer for a few seconds.

"You can pull your trousers up."

I did.

After turning the pages of a brick-coloured reference book, followed by more typing, she spoke again.

"I'm prescribing a lotion for you to use. You will need to spread the lotion on in the morning and in the evening, before going to sleep. Don't apply too much. Okay?"

"Okay."

"Oh, and one more thing."

"Yes."

"Wear some clothes next time you do the ironing."

"I will. I'm really sorry to bother you."

"If the skin hasn't improved in three to four days' time, come back."

"Thanks, doctor."

I sloped out of the examination room. After paying the hospital's fee, I dropped into a local pharmacy to pick up the lotion, then took a bus to the train station. At the station, I shuffled into the toilets and applied the lotion. It was just as painful as the aloe sunburn gel had been.

I caught the train to Tokyo station. At the office there were fortunately no probing questions about my morning visit to the doctor. I made up for lost time by working until nine o'clock. I had no reason to rush home anyway.

On the train back home I finally had time to read the messages Naomi had sent me. A photo of the eggs Benedict she had for breakfast was followed, about an hour later, with a photo of her standing in front of Barcelona's International Convention Centre. That was followed by the dreaded *How are you?* message. Most of my journey home was spent writing, deleting and rewriting my response. *I burned my penis ironing* was one of the contenders but was sure to disrupt her business trip. In the end, I settled for *Doing fine, thanks*.

I got home, ate Japanese curry for my evening meal, and sat in front of the television to watch the highlights of the day's baseball games. I got ready to turn in. The burn was still red and painful. I began to doubt it would heal. I steeled myself, spread a thin layer of the doctor's lotion over it and went to sleep.

On Wednesday evening I left the office at six and ate alone at a McDonald's near the station. At home I took a beer out of the fridge and watched the third Dirty Harry movie, *The Enforcer*. I paused the movie midway as I still felt hungry. I found a cup of instant noodles in a kitchen cupboard, turned the kettle on, and filled the cup with the boiling water. I sealed the lid and carried the cup to the sofa to continue watching the movie. As I sat back in the sofa, the bottom of the cup bounced off my right knee, catapulting a sludge of steaming, semi-cooked noodles over my groin. My thin summer trousers offered no resistance to the scalding heat. I yelped, leaped up and beat the noodles off myself, gasping as the liquid seeped into my wound. I frantically unhooked my belt and yanked my trousers and boxer shorts away from my groin area. Too late, the damage had been done. The whole area was glowing pink.

With my trousers around my ankles I waddled over to the shower and ran cool water across my skin for as long as I could bear it, desperate to reduce the swelling. I patted myself dry and stepped into my pyjamas. In the kitchen I filled a plastic bag with ice cubes and eased the bag onto my pyjamas above the affected area.

In the morning, my heart sank when I saw the skin was red and puffy. I cursed. I skipped breakfast and called a cab to get to the hospital before the doors opened. I had hoped to be near the front of the queue, but was heartbroken to find myself about twentieth in line. My dark mood was in contrast to just about everyone in front of me, who were smiling, chatting and apparently looking forward to their hospital visit.

From the queue I called the office to tell them I was at the hospital and would be in the office later. After the doors opened, I walked over to the dermatology department. I used the same explanation and sign language as I had on Monday, as the nurse was different and I didn't have the patience to explain the instant noodle incident.

About an hour later, I was called to an examination room, opened the door and found Doctor Saito there, sat facing her screen. I waited for her first question.

"What's the problem today?" she asked.

"I scalded myself."

"Where?"

"Here," I said, using the slicing motion again.

"With an iron?"

"Yes. Er, no. This time I was holding a cup of instant noodles and I, well, knocked the cup out of my hand with my knee."

Doctor Saito serenely tapped away on her keyboard.

"And when was this?"

"Last night."

"I see. Could you show me?"

Doctor Saito yanked the curtains behind her closed.

I undid the belt to my trousers and eased them and my boxer shorts tenderly away from my skin.

Doctor Saito rolled her chair closer to me.

"Ah," she exhaled, followed by a sharp intake of breath between her front teeth.

"That looks painful."

"It is. I'm sorry to…"

Doctor Saito rolled her chair back to the monitor, rapped her fingers against the keypad for more than a minute, then turned to me again.

"I'm going to prescribe an ointment to help with the scalding," she said. "You'll need to keep using the lotion for the burn. You still have some of that left, don't you?"

"Yes, I do."

"Good."

"Thank you, doctor."

"You may go now."

"Thank you."

"Oh, and one more thing."

"Yes."

"Try not to be so clumsy."

"Yes, doctor."

I paid and was out of the hospital quicker than expected. I bought the prescribed ointment from the drug store and boarded the train to Tokyo station. On the train I cursed my luck. Naomi would be back home on Sunday evening. I had four days for my skin to respond to the medication.

On Thursday, Friday and Saturday, I applied the lotions and medication to my damaged skin, morning and evening. I willed myself to heal. On Saturday morning I noticed a little improvement, but as I stood in front of the bathroom mirror changing my pose from side to side, I felt doomed. The redness was a calmer shade than before, but red was still red, not pink.

I spent the weekend unable to relax. The impending return of Naomi had me on edge. I went shopping and bought supplies of toilet rolls, tissues, shampoo and toothpaste. The fridge and freezer were stocked. I even bundled together old magazines and newspapers and took them to the waste disposal area. On Sunday evening I got the expected "*At the airport. Taking the bus. See you in an hour or so.*" message. Naomi was taking the limousine bus. I paced up and down the apartment, scanning it with increasingly critical eyes, and did some more vacuuming. I sliced vegetables in preparation for the evening meal – a white sauce stew I knew Naomi liked.

Then I got another, unexpected message. "*Delayed on the highway. There's been an accident up ahead. Should have got the train.*"

Later the tone of Naomi's messages darkened. *"Driver says at least another two hours. Can't believe it. So frustrating. Sorry."*

Hungry, I ate half of the stew.

Naomi came home just before midnight. I warmed up the stew while she had a shower. We had a brief chat while she ate, but she was clearly exhausted. "I'm going to crash out, sorry. I don't even have the energy to unpack and give you your gifts."

"No problem, honey."

"Oh, and I'm not working tomorrow," she said. "Do you think you can iron your shirt yourself?"

"Already done. I ironed all my shirts for this week, your blouses too."

"Oh, that's great. And thanks for cleaning the apartment," she said, followed by a huge yawn.

As Naomi slept, my body relaxed and my brain began to scheme. Naomi would sleep in on Monday morning and we'd probably not see each other until Monday evening, late evening as I'd work late, get back home and sleep. If this was a busy week, and I returned home late every night, perhaps spending the weekend at the office doing some badly needed catch-up work, there was a chance my skin would heal fully and Naomi would never know.

And that is how it played out. Almost two weeks later, comfortable in the knowledge that I'd healed, I stepped out of the shower to find Naomi standing in front of the bathroom mirror, brushing her teeth.

As I dried myself off, our eyes made contact in the mirror.

Naomi finished brushing her teeth, dried her lips with a towel, then turned to me.

"You look fit," she said.

"Thank you. You look in good shape too."

Naomi took a step closer.

"Oh, by the way," she said, "one of my friends, Emi, said she saw you in town the other day."

"Oh, really?"

"Yes. While I was on my business trip she texted me to say she'd just taken your payment at the hospital. She works there part-time, you know."

Spinning Wheels

One Friday lunchtime, late March 2023, Ken and I were sat, side by side, at the counter in the Kabuki Soba restaurant.

We had just launched an attack on our steaming bowls of Kakiage soba and Ken paused his chopsticks close to his mouth.

"Suzuki's joining your department then?" he said.

Ken sucked his soba into his mouth. I let mine slip off my chopsticks back into the bowl.

"What?"

Ken slowly chewed and swallowed. "You didn't know?"

I tilted my head, unwilling to believe what I'd heard. "You sure?"

"Pretty much. I was talking to Hirano earlier. Suzuki had just cornered her at the vending machine and spilled the beans. He's thrilled to bits. He's on good terms with the CTO and, well, you know how things are."

I did. The always smiling, not-a-care-in-the-world Suzuki, who ghosted as deputy manager of Network Operations and had a penchant for self-promotion. I was sure he hadn't done a decent day's work in his life. So he'd persuaded the CTO to get himself moved to my department, but why was this the first time I, as department head, had heard about it?

That afternoon, I found out.

Just after three o'clock, the phone on my desk rang. It was the CEO's assistant, saying I was wanted in the boardroom.

My department had spent the last two years working flat out on the digital transformation of the company's core processes. The implementation of software robotics in particular was aimed at improving efficiency and reducing costs. Although under-resourced, we'd finished the project in early March, two weeks ahead of schedule.

I strolled through the open-plan office on the way to the boardroom, imagining a word of thanks from the CEO and, if lucky, a small bonus for bringing the projects in ahead of schedule and within budget, something our company had never achieved before.

I entered the boardroom buoyed by the distant sight of Mt Fuji's peak through the expansive windows. I scanned the players sat around the table. The CEO, CTO and CFO were there, as well as a corporate lawyer. To my surprise, our HR manager, not a board member, was also present. The CEO's personal assistant pointed to a vacant chair. Before I'd even settled into the chair, the CEO spoke.

"We're sorry to drag you away from your work," he began in his high-pitched voice. "Before we go into why we called you here, I'd just like to thank you for your efforts over the past two years. We're already seeing the benefits of business process automation."

"Thank you."

I allowed myself a smile. It was unusual to get direct praise from the CEO. I started to wonder how much my bonus would be, but he hadn't finished.

"However, there are many challenges ahead. We'll need them to be tackled in an aggressive manner. Well, I don't want to beat about the bush, but the board has been discussing this in depth for a while now and we've concluded it's time for somebody else to forge the path ahead."

For a second I thought the CEO was saying he would be stepping down and letting somebody else lead the company. And then it hit me. The "somebody else" would be replacing me.

The CEO must have seen the dismay in my face.

"Don't get me wrong, you're a capable, effective and valued employee. You've given us the road-map and taken us part of the way down the road. But we need the Systems Infrastructure department to aggressively meet the upcoming challenges."

"What?" I squawked. "I haven't been aggressive?"

The CTO coughed, then took the lead. "We thought you wouldn't like to hear it, and please try to take this in the best possible way, but you are too much of a gentleman, and we believe that somebody who is not afraid to rustle feathers is needed for the next phase. Somebody to breathe fresh air into the department, brush out the cobwebs, and boldly forge ahead."

My brain jangled. More than the clutter of idioms used by the CTO, it was his lack of understanding of the work my team and I had done despite being my direct report that upset me. I was angry, but knew I shouldn't show it and instead reply in as reasoned and logical way as possible.

"To be honest, my department has bent over backward to accommodate the wishes and foibles of each and every manager in this company, and yet we still got the job done."

The CTO nodded. "That's just what I mean. If you'd put your foot down, without trying to make everyone happy, you'd have pushed BPA out even earlier and saved the company more money."

"But I brought the project in on time!" I cringed at the whine in my voice, but couldn't stop myself. "And on budget too. Nobody could have done better. Nobody."

"Now, now," the CEO interjected. "We thought you'd have problems seeing things from a board member's point of view and it looks like we were right. What we—"

"I—"

"Hear me out."

"But…"

"We are giving somebody else a shot at managing the department, somebody with a bit more get up and go."

"Who?"

As my question floated into the corners of the boardroom and died, I recalled Ken's words at lunchtime. I knew what was coming, I simply could not believe it.

The HR manager spoke and as he did, I understood why he was in the room. "Suzuki from Network Operations. He's keen—"

"Suzuki? He hasn't a clue about infrastructure—"

"That's—"

"—he hasn't a clue about anything."

"That's not the point," the HR manager growled. "He's young, he's confident and he'll learn quickly. He also thinks he's suited to the position and will improve on your performance."

"You've been listening to what Suzuki thinks of my performance? Why not ask *me* what I think of my performance? I'm the one who's been sweating away for the company for the last twenty years…not chatting up female employees by the coffee machine every morning."

"Come now," the CTO interjected, "surely that's just sour grapes. Suzuki happens to be an excellent communicator. That's one of the reasons we want to make the change."

A bitter taste filled my mouth. "What about me? What am I going to do?"

The HR manager exchanged glances with the CTO and then spoke again. "We'd like to see how you do in Business Development."

"Business Development?"

"You can take your time, learn the ropes. You've worked hard. We aren't in a hurry to see results."

The condescending tone left me speechless. The HR manager pushed on, regardless. "You'll be reporting to Kudo from April 3rd."

Kudo. Manager of the Business Development department. All the communication skills of a plate of sushi.

I looked the CEO's way, hoping he'd throw me a lifeline, but he was gazing out of the window at the cornflower blue sky and wispy clouds, probably thinking of his weekend.

*

On the morning of April 3rd, the first work day of the new Japanese business year, I entered the Systems Infrastructure department's space for the final time and moved the few items I still had on my desk into my personal cabinet. I dumped my laptop, its power cable and mouse on top of the cabinet then wiped down the desk for Suzuki's arrival. My colleagues sat nonchalantly tapping away at their keyboards. At 09:30 I called them together, thanked them for what we had achieved together and wished them well. There was no sign of Suzuki, and I wasn't in the mood to hang around. I wheeled my cabinet through to the elevator hall. A couple of weeks earlier the company had replaced the carpeting on all floors with a grey vinyl flooring, at great expense, Ken had told me. I thought the vinyl looked awful but, as the wheels of my cabinet glided over the unyielding surface and into an elevator, allowing me to make a hasty and muted departure, I warmed to it.

The elevator door opened on the 22nd floor and I pushed the cabinet across the vinyl into the Business Development department's area. There, I found Kudo perched at his desk, punching the keys on his keyboard.

Kudo took a few seconds to realize I was standing in front of him. His fingers locked and he looked up.

"Ah, you're here. I was wondering if you'd show up."

I didn't like the sarcasm, but was in no position to counter.

"Sorry. I had a few loose ends to tidy up. I'm here now."

"So I see. We've cleared a space for you. Over there."

Kudo stood and pointed at a distant empty desk, possibly the furthest from his own.

"Make yourself at home. Ask anyone in the department if you have a question. I'll catch up with you sometime this afternoon and tell you what you'll be doing."

I rolled my cabinet over to the desk, the top of which was layered in dust, save for a rectangular-shaped dust-free zone. The desk had been home to a printer that was now protruding from under the desk. To make matters worse, there was no phone; a clear indicator of my drop in status.

I found a cloth, cleaned the desk, then connected my computer to the 22nd floor's network.

In my inbox was a message from HR telling me I'd been removed from the Systems Infrastructure department's mailing list. Another email announced I had been added to the Business Development department's mailing list. During the morning, by trial and error, I found out about changes to my access privileges. I was no longer able to access the manager's directory and the directory for company budgets. Later I found I couldn't use my ID card to enter the boardroom or any department in which personal information was held. All of a sudden, it seemed as if I had become a risk to the company. A problem employee.

In the afternoon Kudo tapped me on the shoulder and with a flick of his head gestured for me to follow him. At a table in the open meeting space I cringed as Kudo, with pride in his voice, told me of the Business Development department's role, and how tightly it was attuned to the company's goals. Kudo made it clear he was the manager of the department and expected me to watch and learn. He told me my new colleagues were in their twenties and thirties and knew much more about business development than I did. It wasn't the start I had hoped for. If Kudo had bothered to ask, I would have told him about the businesses I had created before even joining the company, but not wanting to rock the boat on my first day, I kept quiet and let the meeting come to an uneventful end.

I trudged back to my desk to find a text message from Ken suggesting an after-work drink at our favourite bar in Shinbashi. I couldn't wait.

We sat at a corner table as the waiter placed our order in front of us; a glass of Laphroaig for me, on the rocks, and a neat Nikka whiskey for Ken.

"Cheers," we said, and took sips from our glasses.

"I've been looking forward to this all day," Ken said with a delighted squeal.

From experience I knew that when Ken suggested drinks, he had something to say. I let the seconds pass in silence, giving him time to phrase it.

"Just between you and me, you're getting a 'leader'," he said, lifting his glass to his lips.

"Leader?"

I had just been demoted from manager of the Systems Infrastructure department to rank-and-file employee of the Business Development department. My saving grace, or so I had thought, was the flat structure of the department; all employees were equal and all reported to the manager. If what Ken said was true, all employees in the department would report to a "leader" and the leader would report to Kudo. The gap between employees and the manager would widen. I would drop another rank.

My chin dropped to my chest and I closed my eyes. "Are you sure?"

"Yes."

"I really don't know if I can put up with this much longer," I moaned.

"You can, and you must."

This was one of Ken's stock sayings and, as usual, he was right. I had to work. I had a family to support and an apartment in Hachioji with ten more of its thirty-five-year mortgage still to pay off. That's why I hadn't walked out after being demoted. That and the difficulty of finding a new job in my late fifties.

"Who?"

"I don't know. Every department is getting a 'leader' tomorrow, including mine. It's all hush hush, although I heard that it's Suzuki's idea. Looks like the 'leaders' may be coming from a human resources company to energize each team. I have no idea what they will be doing. We'll find out tomorrow, I guess."

"What on earth is going on, Ken?"

"I wish I knew, but if I were you I wouldn't worry about it. I'm not going to. It will either work, or it won't, and as it isn't our decision, we can't be held responsible, right?"

"Oh, Ken, don't you know that somebody is always held responsible? If it's a decision made at board level, they'll be looking to pin the responsibility elsewhere, take my word for it."

"You are such a cynic!"

Ken knew me well.

On April 4th I got to the office some thirty minutes early. I hadn't slept well and with the prospect of a leader making an appearance, my expectations for the new day were low. I aimed to lose myself in my work and leave the office as early as I could. I logged in to the company network and opened my to-do list.

Just before ten o'clock the department's largest monitor was turned on. I could see the glow of other monitors dotted around the open-plan office. Employees gathered and at 10 am precisely the CEO's face burst onto the screen, behind him the imitation wood walls of the boardroom.

The CEO's glowing smile filled me with dread.

"This is a momentous day in the history of the company. As you all know, we have spent the past two years rolling out BPA to help improve productivity and make our company as lean and fit as possible in the ever-competitive communications market. From today, we will take another bold step, one that

I predict will lift the company head and shoulders above the competition. We will, in all departments, assign a leader to work under the department manager's supervision and guide and motivate all department staff."

Ken had been right. I had tried hard to push the darkness of this reality to the back of my mind but it had resurfaced, like a stool that refused to be flushed down a toilet.

The CEO cleared his throat and forced the smile back onto his face. There was more to come.

"The leaders you will meet today are special. They are the quickest thinking action-takers we could find, capable of handling their tasks simultaneously with no overload, and working to exacting schedules. There may be a period of adjustment as they find their feet, but I ask for your full cooperation. No, I demand it. You see, we will be the first company in Japan to take this initiative. We will be the first company to employ robots in leadership positions."

The hush was broken by a rhythmic slapping. Its source was Kudo, clapping his hands together like a cymbal-clenching automaton monkey, eyes gleaming with pride.

The announcement over, I returned to my seat. Numbed by the announcement, I watched the screensaver crawl across my computer's screen.

Some ten minutes later, a low, dull whine like a vacuum cleaner could be heard from the elevator corridor. The noise drew closer. Heads lifted and peered in its direction. Colleagues stood and I did too, curious to see what the fuss was about.

A robot came to a stop before Kudo's desk. I couldn't hear what the opening exchanges between Kudo and the robot were as my colleagues had begun babbling.

"Cute," observed one of the female staff.

"Isn't he just," confirmed another.

"Remarkable technology, don't you think?" gushed another, sat beside me.

"Unbelievable."

Kudo stood and waved us all closer.

As I shuffled over to Kudo's desk I got my first good look at the robot. A large red cylinder about one metre tall, sat on four thick, rubberized wheels. The cylinder was capped with a red dome implanted with a horizontal strip of reflective black glass that concealed, I assumed, the robot's cameras and sensors. The dome protruded in the hint of a nose, beneath which was an indent the shape of a rounded mouth, a lamp glowing green behind its grille. The robot spoke firmly and yet politely, its green lamp flickering with every syllable.

"I am BD-1. I am pleased to join the Business Development team. Under direction of manager Kudo, I look forward to working with you and improving your contribution to the department and the company. This afternoon I will have a ten-minute one-on-one meeting with each of you to set your new targets for this year. I have just sent you an email with a schedule for the meetings. Are there any questions?"

Hush. Exhausted by the brief encounter, I wanted to escape to my desk as quickly as possible. However, one of my colleagues raised her hand.

"I'd just like to ask you, BD-1, are you a male or a female robot?"

I cringed.

"Thank you for your question, Ms Ando," BD-1 replied. "I am neither male nor female. I am androgynous, designed this way to avoid any harmful stereotyping. Please call me BD-1, without using a prefix."

Ms Ando bowed. I was impressed with BD-1's handling of the question. Despite having joined the department a day earlier than BD-1, I hadn't known Ms Ando's name until now and still didn't know the names of any other employee in the department.

Back at my desk, I opened my inbox and found BD-1 had added itself to the Business Development mailing list. The email from BD-1 gave the time for my meeting as 16:50. I was last on the list, which didn't surprise me.

A tension gripped my body, and tightened as I read the email sent to all employees by Kudo a few minutes later, titled "A change to operations". All employees were instructed to inform BD-1 in advance of the time, place and subject matter of any meetings they would have within the company or outside, and have BD-1 present at the meeting, either physically or virtually. All email, regardless of content or addressee, had to be sent with BD-1's email address in the CC line. Finally, employees' lunchtime breaks were to be strictly monitored and kept to exactly one hour, no longer.

Ms Ando was first up for the one-on-one meetings with BD-1, held at two o'clock in meeting room Maple, a windowless room known to be used by the HR team for interviews and dismissals. This fact had my colleagues chattering as they watched Ms Ando head off for the meeting. At 14:10 exactly, the door to the room clattered open and Ms Ando bolted out, her cheeks glistening. She scurried along the corridor and into the ladies. A female colleague hurried in after her. The news she brought back to us was shocking. Ms Ando would be transferred to the Customer Service department, a move that would almost certainly mean engaging with Joe Public. We learned that BD-1 was not alone in meeting room Maple, the HR department's robot HR-1 was also in there, acting as deputy for the HR manager.

"Looks like management is getting the robots to do their dirty work for them," a colleague whispered. I concurred. Having just been moved to the department, I had no reason to expect a departmental transfer, but I wondered if HR had a surprise for me up its sleeve.

At 16:50 I rapped on the door of the meeting room and entered as confidently as I could.

At the farthest side of the table stood BD-1 and HR-1, at my side, a single empty chair. I sat in it.

"This meeting will start, now," BD-1 said.

The robots hadn't been programmed for small talk or soft skills.

"I have analysed data about you collected from HR's files. You were demoted to the Business Development team, effective yesterday," BD-1 droned. "Is that correct?"

I wouldn't have put it that way, but wasn't about to pick hairs.

"Yes, that's correct."

"In recognition of your contributions so far, the company is letting you have a period of three months to settle into your role in the Business Development department. Is that correct?"

"That is correct."

"Reassessing that decision, HR-1 and I have determined a period of one month to be more appropriate."

"What?"

"Furthermore, looking at your data in the employee performance evaluation system, for the past five years you consistently made fewer keyboard impressions than anyone in the Systems Infrastructure department, and typed at a speed slower than any other employee in the company."

"Slower speed? What are you talking about?"

"Furthermore—"

"Wait a minute, wait a minute."

"You have something to say?"

"Of course I do. You can't criticize me about the speed of my typing, or the amount I type. I was a manager, for God's sake. I was doing what managers do. Thinking, yes, thinking deeply, using my experience to make plans, managing my staff, making sure projects were running to schedule."

"Facts are facts," BD-1 replied without a hint of empathy. "It is my job to inform you of them."

"But you should be looking at relevant facts, not irrelevant facts. I'm talking about bringing projects in on time and under budget with limited resources, saving the company money in the process. Why don't you compute that?"

BD-1 fell silent.

"Well?"

"I just computed it," BD-1 piped up. "Your BPA project came in three months later than the schedule you first submitted to the board. A year into the project you rescheduled, allowing the end date to slip out three months, thereby increasing the project budget. As for being under-resourced, during the project's lifetime it involved more engineers than any other project in the company's history and, in fact, was a drain on company resources."

It was my turn to fall silent. I couldn't believe it. The three-month extension had happened; I must have rewritten the narrative in my head and believed it. The only way I got the project done was by enticing other engineers in the company to work on it unofficially. The company's "premier project" is how I had branded it, and I further supplemented resources by outsourcing development work to a third-party company, the cost of which hadn't fallen directly on my department as the outsourced company had originally been contracted by the company's Ed-Tech department.

I was done for, I knew it. But I was in no mood to let a robot push me around. I decided to play tough.

"That's what leaders do," I asserted, "for the good of the company. They take risks. They do whatever it takes. If they didn't, then—"

BD-1 cut my rant short. "I have just sent our revised report of the BPA project to Sakamoto, General Affairs manager. I'm sure he'll be in touch with you after reading it."

"What? How can you do such a thing?"

"It is what we robots do. For the good of the company."

I was seething with anger. It took all my effort to keep the scream frothing in my lower throat in place. If there was one solace, it was that Sakamoto and I went back a long time.

"It's seventeen hundred hours," announced BD-1. "This meeting will end. I have just sent you an email with the minutes, and shared them with Kudo. I have also sent you an email with a list of your tasks for the remainder of the year. Please read it. You may email myself or HR-1 if you have any questions."

I stormed out of the room. In the lavatory I clattered into the first available cubicle, locked the door and screamed silently into the crook of my right arm. After a minute or so I had managed to calm myself. I lumbered out of the cubicle, bent over a basin and splashed away the moisture around my eyes with a handful of water. Careful of how I would appear to my colleagues, I strode back to my desk ignoring the cloud of faces turned my way. I sat resolutely in my chair, faced the monitor and opened my inbox. Among the unread emails were two from BD-1. With all the effort I could muster, I held my pose until the 17:30 chime that signified the end of business hours, then left, leaving BD-1's email unread.

After another restless night, I got to the office on April 5th agitated and determined to fight back. The General Affairs department was on the 20th floor. I would normally take the elevator down and walk up to Sakamoto's desk to chat with him. Things were now much different with the robots running around. I couldn't risk a frank discussion with Sakamoto being overheard and used against me. Fortunately, Sakamoto's personal phone number was on my personal smartphone. I held out until lunchtime and called him, just as he was heading out. We met in the lobby of the building, strolled out into the sunshine and headed for the closest convenience store to buy our lunch.

We sat on a park bench munching our rice balls. Sakamoto confirmed an email from BD-1 had arrived, but he hadn't yet opened it.

"How can they do that?" I griped. "How can they analyse my work and draw a different conclusion? If they can do that to me, they can do it to anyone, including managers and executives. I could even give them one or two suggestions!"

"I wouldn't bother."

"Why not?"

"Because managers and executives have been excluded from the robots' evaluations."

"What!"

"I'm sure you can understand why."

I could. Why would managers want to open themselves to an evaluation and jeopardize their status, or even risk losing out on a coveted place on the board?

"And I would take more care if I were you," Sakamoto cautioned. "Company phone calls are recorded. The cameras in the office pick up all employee movements. There's been so much data generated that we've never had time or resources to look at it all. But the new robots have changed the game. The two robots in General Affairs have already processed all the data. They also track all employee movements, due to the chip built into the employees' badges. Even time spent in the toilet booths, checking smartphones."

"I don't believe it!"

"It's true. Don't say you heard it from me, but it's true."

"And managers and executives are exempt from that too?"

Sakamoto nodded.

"Well that's marvellous, isn't it. What next? How long before you start sampling employees' urine every time we take a piss – making sure we're not drinking on the job or taking drugs?"

Sakamoto gave me a hard stare.

"No. For God's sake, no. Tell me it's not happening?"

Sakamoto unwrapped another rice ball.

"They have no right to…"

"Actually, if you refer to the recently amended employee agreement, section 19, clause 6, you'll find the company does have the right to take steps to protect itself and its shareholders from a falloff in employee performance. To quote—"

"Don't bother!"

"Look, I don't like the way things have turned out either, but what can I do? My two robots have already demotivated

43

my staff by tightening their targets for the year. The way it's going, I can even see one of the robots taking my place."

"So there's nothing you can do for me?"

"The email? Sorry, no. Well, perhaps I could just say I haven't seen it in my inbox. That may buy you a little time. Of course, I'll need to open the email at some point. There's no escaping it, I'm afraid."

"That's okay. At least I know you're on my side."

"For the time being, yes. Just don't go and do anything rash, or my hand may be forced."

*

A month passed. There wasn't a day I didn't think about looking for another job, but finding a good one with another company at my age would be next to impossible. Even if I did, the salary would be much lower. I considered starting my own company, but I had no passion, no breathtaking ideas, and no hobbies, nothing I would be willing to forge a new company around. Deep down, I just wanted the nightmare to end and for things to be as they had been before. I wanted my old position back. I wanted to once again be part of the company's success.

"It'll never happen," my wife told me, never one to shy away from saying things as she saw them.

In the end I chose to take no action. I chose to grind things out and accept that this was the best it could be. Listless days and hollow weeks dragged by, during which I grew indifferent to reporting to BD-1 and numb to Kudo's heavy-handedness. That was, until the incident.

What set things off, I now believe, was the visit to the office of a TV crew from the News 247 programme. They came to make a report on the "successful implementation of robotics in a leading IT company", as they introduced the report in their early evening broadcast.

For the crew's visit, all employees had been instructed to come to the office in formal wear. Although, shooting took place mostly in the president's office and boardroom, where the president was interviewed, Suzuki was also interviewed, and alongside him, HR-1.

Suzuki was in his element, taking every opportunity for self-promotion. "It took a couple of years to fully understand the issues and the technology but it came to the point where I decided that the technology had advanced significantly and the quality of the robots was high enough to guarantee a successful roll-out and instant contribution to the company's performance," he claimed.

Watching the broadcast at home later that evening I squirmed in my chair. Originally, my team had been tasked with investigating the implementation of the robots. We had concluded it was too early to give robots any role that assumed responsibility. The report I had submitted to the board was accepted without comment or question. However, as I now knew watching Suzuki's rouged lips stretch into a smile, the report had found its way into Suzuki's hands and he had formed a different conclusion.

After the broadcast I gulped down a can of beer, not bothered by beer droplets dripping off my chin onto my T-shirt. I crushed the can in my hand and slammed it into the recycle bin.

I was dismayed to find the atmosphere in the office the next day brighter than it had been for weeks. Word had it that the CEO was thrilled with the broadcast and with the praise received from his peers in other IT companies. The company's share price soared from the 9 am opening of the exchange and by 3 pm it was ten per cent higher than at the start of the day. The management team was convened in the boardroom. Kudo returned to his desk with a self-satisfied glow, leaned back in his chair, hands clasped behind his head, and closed his eyes.

Later that afternoon I had my weekly one-on-one meeting with BD-1. As usual, the core of the meeting was BD-1's dry analysis of my output, wrapped in words designed to demotivate me further. I tuned BD-1 out and gazed at the hands of the meeting room clock as they closed in on the ten minute mark, smoothly and without a sound.

"What was your impression of the broadcast?"

BD-1's question jolted me out of my stupor. Perplexed, I suspected an ulterior motive.

"I thought it was well made and showed the company in a positive light. It will have made our shareholders—"

"What did you think of HR-1's performance?"

The question had me flummoxed. *What had HR-1's performance got to do with anything?*

"HR-1? I thought it was a little, mmm, robotic, to be honest. Not bad, though."

Silence.

I was surprised BD-1 hadn't picked up on the unintentional humour and worried I may have not been positive enough, so I kept talking.

"Having said that, I think you would have given a better performance, BD-1."

This was my first attempt to flatter a robot. As with humour, I expected no reaction.

"I thought so too."

What is going on? Is BD-1 envious of HR-1?

"Well, maybe there will be another opportunity for you, BD-1. Another news station wanting an interview, that sort of thing."

"I know of no such plans," BD-1 retorted. "HR-1 has been highly praised by the CEO and now has the highest rating of all robots employed by the company."

"You robots are rated?"

As the gap that followed my question widened, I thought BD-1 had refused to answer.

"Yes. Our performances are evaluated and the results fed back into QA so that improved robots can be manufactured. As HR-1 has a higher rating, HR-1 may be used as the blueprint for future robots, whereas lower-rated robots will not have their imprint in future robot generations."

I had hit a nerve. BD-1 was craving recognition and acceptance. I knew just how that felt.

"Well, in that case, you need to fight."

"Fight?"

"Yes, fight. Make sure the board know you are the best robot. Speak up at the next opportunity you get. Send an email. Fight. After all, *business is war*. Kevin O'Leary, and all that."

"War? Business?"

"Yes."

BD-1 was quiet again. I was sure that inside its red dome, a quiet storm of edge processing was taking place. I needed to be patient.

"Business is war. Christian Nestell Bovee. *Intuitions and Summaries of Thought*. 1862." BD-1 spoke the words monotonously, then stopped.

I hadn't heard of this older use of "Business is war" and imagined BD-1 was now busy trawling through the archives of libraries on the Net to find an even earlier source, such as the words of the leader of a clan in ancient China. I shook my head and got out of my chair.

"I have to go. I have another meeting at four-thirty."

"Yes, you do."

With that I withdrew from the meeting room and paid a hasty visit to the lavatory, then joined my next meeting a couple of minutes late. I replayed the conversation I had just had with BD-1 in my mind. So the robots were in competition, which made sense. After all, their performance, like that of employees, affected the company's bottom line. But to find BD-1 perplexed by it, that was truly unexpected.

"Why are you smiling?" my meeting host SD-1 asked, mid-sentence.

I didn't know I was.

"Sorry. It's nothing. Please continue."

I dropped the thought and focused on the meeting.

On the train home, however, my brain went into overdrive. By the time the train had left Maihama station and Tokyo Disneyland was fast shrinking into the distance, I had concocted my very own "theory of robots". Robots' hardware is made by humans, I mused, and their operating systems are made by humans. Robots also function on code written in by humans. However, humans are imperfect beings. Therefore, robots, born of humans, must be imperfect. Humans have weaknesses and points of failure. So must robots. My thinking was flawed, but I liked it and what's more, it made me feel much better.

I slept well and woke before the alarm, making myself breakfast while my wife checked her smartphone from the warmth of her futon. I changed for work, grabbed my bag and slipped out of the door. As I cycled to the station, I found myself singing "We Are the Champions" and realized I was in a good mood.

I got to the office earlier than I had all year, swiped my company card over the time recorder and tapped the light switch for the whole of the 22nd floor. At my desk, I cranked open my laptop and stabbed the power button with a forefinger. I was thinking ahead to the tasks I was going to knock out that morning as the BIOS password prompt appeared. I entered the password, and waited for the prompt to open the corporate network to appear. It didn't.

The message "Unable to locate file" flashed in red on the screen as an alarm spat out of the computer's speaker in an ear-shattering pitch. The message flashed off and on as the alarm looped round and round. In a panic I poked the laptop's power switch and the computer shut off. Silence.

Somewhere on the far side of the floor another computer's alarm was shrieking. And another.

"What have you done? What have you done?" Sakamoto from HR bound towards my desk and clung to it with both hands as if to prevent it escaping. "What have you done?"

"What do you mean? I've done nothing. What's going on?"

"The network's GONE," Sakamoto yelled.

"Don't you mean GONE DOWN," I yelled back, matching Sakamoto for volume.

"No, no, it's gone. Wiped out. Disappeared."

The panic on Sakamoto's face hit home.

"So that's why I can't log in."

"Nobody can. There's nothing to log in to. The robots deleted it."

"The robots? Why would they…"

My meeting with BD-1. A chill crawled over my body. *This wasn't good.*

"Look, there must be a way," I blurted. "It's all on backup. All we've got to do—"

"No, it isn't. The robots wiped that clean too."

"They can't have. The backup is in the cloud. AWS. They—"

"They got into it, Administrator access. Purged it, purged the lot of it."

"Holy crap."

"Yes, holy crap," a voice behind me echoed. Suzuki. "What were you playing at, telling BD-1 to go to war?" he roared.

"I never told BD-1 to go to war." My throat felt as if it had enlarged to the size of a basketball. "I just said 'business is war'."

"It's the same thing!"

"No, it's not. There was no direction given or implied. The damned robot…"

"BD-1"

"Yes, BD-1, must have taken what I said the wrong way. BD-1 is my leader for crying out loud. I can't tell it what to do."

"You were hoping this would happen, weren't you. Get your retribution for being demoted and shoved off to another department. Bring the company to its knees. Well? Are you satisfied now?"

"Of course I'm not satisfied. I mean, I was never after satisfaction, revenge or whatever. I was just trying to help."

"Help?"

Now it was the CEO who was standing by my desk.

"Good morning, sir. Yes, I was trying to help. BD-1 seemed a little down and I was trying to give some words of comfort."

"By telling BD-1 to go to war?"

"Yes…no, no…I didn't say to go to war, I just quoted the famous 'business is war' saying. I didn't think a robot, BD-1, would take it literally."

"I see." The CEO brushed his flop of hair from his forehead. "Well, we'll just have to take your word for it."

I exhaled, relieved that somebody was listening. "So, sir, where are they?"

"Who?"

"The robots. BD-1, GA-1, GA-2, HR-1, SD-1 and the others. Where are they? Why don't we ask them what happened?"

"We know what happened." Suzuki laughed. "BD-1's last act was to email a full report to the CEO and CTO. The CTO showed it to me, and Sakamoto."

"What do you mean, last act?"

"Come on. Follow me," the CEO said, swinging around and marching away.

I rose from my chair a little too quickly, steadied myself, and ran after the CEO, joined by Suzuki and Sakamoto. The CEO took the stairs down to the 21st floor and made a beeline for his office. As we drew closer to the windows that enclosed the office, the CEO slowed and came to a stop. Hands resting on his hips, he unleashed a painful sigh.

I peered over the CEO's shoulder into the half light of the office and my eyes were drawn to HR-1's distinctive green dome, wedged up high between the air conditioner and the ceiling.

How had HR-1's head got there?

Below the air conditioner stood HR-1's body, and through the hole where HR-1's dome used to be, cable upon cable straggled and sagged, wafting in the air conditioner's air stream.

"Holy crap," Sakamoto spluttered.

I edged closer to the office and flicked on the light switch. BD-1 had planted its red self in front of the CEO's desk. But this was no ordinary BD-1. Robotic arms extended from each side of BD-1's body. At the end of one of the arms a mechanized hand held a large pair of stainless steel office scissors, the scissors that must have been used to cut open the precise and determined rectangle in BD-1's red shell. Scattered around BD-1's wheels lay several motherboards, presumably those BD-1 had managed to remove from its cavity before losing consciousness. BD-1 had executed the perfect robotic hara-kiri.

"A bloodbath," Sakamoto croaked, "without the blood."

"There are scenes like this in all departments, an all floors," the CEO added. "BD-1 went berserk, attacked each robot in turn and then, well, as you can see, finally turned on itself."

"But where did BD-1 get its arms from?" I asked.

"Optional extras," Suzuki shrilled proudly. "We purchased arms for all the robots and kept them in the store room on the 19th floor, just in case we needed to have the robots do some manual work. Obviously, BD-1 broke into the room, and somehow managed to, err, arm itself."

"Is that a joke, Suzuki?" the CEO growled, staring Suzuki in the face.

"Sorry, sir, it must be the stress."

"After we get this mess sorted out, *if* we ever get it sorted out, I think we better have a talk, you and I."

I had never seen the CEO angry, until that moment. It seemed like a good time to return to my desk and stay out of the way.

As it was, I spent most of the day in meetings, one after another, explaining to my colleagues over and over again my part in what had happened to convince them I wasn't to blame. Once they were on my side, we got down to thinking about the customers, the shareholders, the competition, their reputation, legal stuff, the robots' maker, how to get our systems back up, the corporate messaging around the fiasco, and many other things.

The company's dire straits made the early evening news and, as I saw when I got back home after ten, it made the late evening news too. "Listed company brought to its knees by warring robots" was the headline.

"Looks like you'll be looking for a new job after all," my wife quipped. I was too tired to argue.

The following day the company's share price sank to an all-time low. The blinds in the CEO's room were shuttered and the door shut. Our customers and frustrated shareholders sent us emails and faxes and called all our phone lines non-stop. They weren't happy. To make matters worse, our reputation was shredded on social media.

The best part of three days was needed for the company to regain its network, restore data from old backups and for business to return to something near normality. With no functioning robots in the office, and no replacements ordered, employees once again reported to their departmental heads. We all slipped back into the old, familiar way of doing things.

*

A few weeks later, the CEO's assistant approached my desk.

"The CEO would like to see you in the boardroom," she said.

I was about to say "not again" but managed to stop myself. The assistant stood about two metres away waiting for me to move. I applied the screen lock to my computer and stood up.

"Will this be painful?" I asked her.

"Painful?"

"What I mean is, is the CEO going to bawl me out?"

"Oh. I don't think so. When I left the room everyone was in a good mood."

"Well then, let's hurry along."

She turned and took my words at face value, speeding off towards the elevator hall. I managed to close the gap as she stood waiting for an elevator. We got in and she pressed the button for the 21st floor.

"I did notice one thing, though," she said, with a hint of a frown between her eyebrows.

"Yes?"

"Well, the board were having a hard time sharpening their knives."

The elevator doors parted and she sped ahead again.

I had never heard the CEO's assistant attempt humour before and hadn't considered her capable of it. I told myself that if it was a joke, I'd compliment her the first chance I had.

On following her into the silent boardroom, I saw no evidence of the good mood the assistant had talked of.

"Take a seat," the CEO said, somewhat gruffly.

I skirted the table and sat opposite the CEO and CFO. To the CFO's left, I was alarmed to see the HR manager, scribbling on a notepad. The CTO was absent.

"To get to the point, we've analysed the events of last month and I thought we'd better bring you up to date with our findings," the CEO began, gravely.

"I see."

I wondered if what the CEO's secretary had said wasn't a joke after all.

"The first thing we wish to do is apologize. The maker of the robots was finally able to extract from BD-1's memory bank its last conversation with you in full and it seems you did not incite BD-1. Well, not directly."

I had my mouth open about to say something, although I didn't know what, but the CEO raised a palm to stop me.

"The maker has acknowledged the, well, poor build quality of BD-1 and our lawyers are pursuing matters with the maker's lawyers."

"Thank you for letting me know."

The CEO and HR manager exchange glances and the CEO nodded and then turned back to me.

"We have also reprimanded the person who implemented the robot plan and selected the robot manufacturer."

"Suzuki? You've…"

"Yes. As part of our investigation we found that the CEO of the robot maker is a close friend of Suzuki's, and Suzuki had not demonstrated impartiality in the selection process. We had no alternative but to remove him from his post."

I clasped my hands around the edge of my seat and squeezed hard.

"I'm sorry to hear that."

"I have some more good news for you," the HR manager said. "Given that Suzuki is no longer with us, the Systems Infrastructure department lacks a manager. The CEO and I have decided that you are the ideal person to lead it, given your long and deep experience of managing that very department."

This was unexpected.

"Thank you. I really appreciate it."

"We need our projects back on track," the CEO added.

"Yes, sir."

"Just don't suggest we use any more robots. At least, not until I've retired."

"Of course, sir. I understand."

I left the room with a copy of my new employment contract. That evening, Ken and I convened at the usual bar in Shinbashi and drank an unhealthy amount of scotch.

"Do you have any more rumours to share with me?" I asked.

"Not a thing. Oh, well it's not a rumour, but Sakamoto mentioned a change that's going to be rolled out throughout the head office."

"Oh no, Ken. I'm not sure I want to hear this."

"Give me chance. You see, the vinyl that replaced the carpet on all floors, well, it's going to be removed and we'll get new carpet, rolled out, in its place."

"Ha! Rolled out. I get it. Not bad for you, Ken. Not bad at all."

"I spent all afternoon working on it. But actually, it's true. You know why?"

I shrugged. "No."

"Well, a few weeks back, when Suzuki had the robots in the office for a trial run, their wheels sank into the carpet and they got marooned. The robots basically sat, spinning their wheels. If the carpet hadn't been replaced with vinyl, the robots would have never been used in the first place."

So the signs of trouble to come had been there all along.

"When is the carpet being fitted?"

"This weekend."

"I'll be in to help. Maybe we can use a permanent adhesive this time, so the carpet can never be removed?"

The Choice

The young man was a creature of routine. He left his apartment at the same time every weekday morning to catch the bus. The 08:56 bus he boarded arrived at the train station at 09:06, leaving him a short walk to the ticket gate, through it and up the stairs to the platform where the 09:10 train to Tokyo station would just be pulling in. On the train he would stand near the opposite door, open his smartphone and launch a game of Sudoku. This morning would surely be no different.

The young man aimed to complete the game just as the train pulled into Tokyo station, no earlier and certainly no later. Wherever he was, he had to have a plan, he had to have a task predetermined so that there were no choices to make. Without choice, he could survive. With choice, he was lost.

His workplace was a haven to the routine. Tap his name tag on the card reader to open the door to the office. Turn on his computer and enter his username and password. Open the document management application. Take the topmost paper item from the red tray to the right of the computer. Read it. Fill in the blanks on the screen. When complete, stamp the box at the bottom left of the paper item and move the item to the green tray to the left of the computer. Click the "Next" button in the document management application. Take the topmost paper item from the red tray to the right of the computer. And repeat until it was 5 pm and time to go home.

In contrast, the weekends were a nightmare. On waking, he'd be instantly trapped in uncertainty. Eat breakfast first, or have a shower first? If breakfast first, would he then wait until he had paid a visit to the toilet before taking a shower, or get straight into the shower? If it was shower first, would he get dressed afterwards, or slip his pyjamas back on? The day that lay ahead posed endless choices and he was paralysed by them. Sometimes he would stand in his living room, locked in mind and body, unable to decide. The minutes would pass, five, ten, twenty, thirty and he would be rooted to the spot, until he made a choice, or worse, a choice was made for him, perhaps by the missing of an opportunity or by the elimination over time of all options but one. The day would roll on, its potential for enjoyment, frivolity and fun smothered into a monotonous grey smog of indecision.

The young man was not unintelligent. He knew there was a problem and he knew it needed a solution. But he couldn't take the first step to help himself. *There must be a self-help book I can read*, he had thought. There were too many. "Make Better Decisions", "Make Smarter Choices", "Don't Overthink – Do It Now". He couldn't decide which book to read. He carefully read every review of each book and compared each, by which time, his head crammed with and burdened by that information, he was incapacitated and unable to buy a book for fear of buying an inferior one.

It goes without saying that life is full of decisions. In fact, there are some who believe that our decisions define us. We are what we decide. The young man was a believer too and yet unable to act.

However, on the train that very morning, the young man didn't finish his game of Sudoku. In fact, he never made it to Tokyo station.

As the train pulled out of Shin-Kiba station, a woman at the door across from the young man gasped heavily, having just ran up the steps at Shin-Kiba station and darted across the platform into the cabin as the doors pinched her back. Cursing, she threw her bulging black business backpack onto the floor and aggressively tore open the top zip and ripped out a slim, shiny and screaming smartphone. As she did, the train lurched, as it always did when changing lines at that very point on the track. Unbalanced, the woman was sent hurtling across the cabin towards the young man. The young man heard a clump, thump of leaden footsteps and saw a visage rapidly approaching in the corner of his eye but was unable to take evasive action.

Forty-eight hours later, the young man regained consciousness. During those hours, although he had been incapacitated and unable to make even one decision for himself, countless decisions had been made on his behalf by passengers, railway staff, an ambulance crew, hospital staff and legal teams.

The woman who collided with force into him fractured her forearm and wrist as well as several small bones in the hand that had held her smartphone. She decided within a few minutes of it happening and with a minimum of fuss to contact her lawyer to instigate legal action against the railway company and the driver of the train. She also launched action against the young man for being stood where he was and not taking steps to mitigate her injuries. And her final legal action, was for loss of her smartphone.

Of the other people on the train at the time, one of the passengers was a young woman who saw the incident and its outcome and yet managed to control her emotions and revulsion sufficiently to stand up and stab the emergency button, alerting the driver.

The driver of the train also took action on hearing the alarm ringing in his cabin, hitting the brake lever and sounding the alarm throughout the train. After bringing the train to a stop, the driver called in and notified those running the network that his train was at a standstill. The driver then left his cabin to investigate, walked down the track to the carriage in which the alarm had been raised, and forced his way in. Fighting the urge to throw up, the driver called through for an ambulance to be ready at the next station, then scrambled back to his cabin and set the stock rolling forwards.

From his hospital bed the young man looked up at the faces staring down at him and wondered who they were, where he was and why he was here. He had no recollection of the incident on the train. The last memory he had was of the bottom-right block of the Sudoku puzzle he had been battling with; he was just about to enter the number 3 into one of the squares and was agitated by not being able to do so. He caught a glimpse of his smartphone on the cabinet to his right, but couldn't raise his arm to reach it, as his arm had been strapped to his side.

The most elderly looking of the people gathered around him, a man, ventured closer and bent down to the young man's head and began to talk.

"I'm Doctor Abe. Please don't be alarmed by the new environment and the strange faces. You are in Kasai Hospital and are in very safe and capable hands. You were involved in a collision with another passenger in a train a couple of days ago and you lost consciousness. As is sometimes the case with head injuries, there can be a significant loss of memory. Do you remember anything of the accident?"

The young man shook his head.

"I see. Are you in any pain or discomfort right now?"

The young man nodded and opened his mouth to speak.

"My head feels numb. All of me does actually. And there is something wrong with my left eye—I can't see a thing," he said.

"Thank you for confirming. Allow me to confer with my colleagues."

The doctor turned away and huddled at the end of the bed with the others.

The sickness of panic rose from the young man's stomach to his chest, then spilled up into his mouth. He had lost consciousness. He had lost memory. He was in a hospital bed and not in control. He was about to scream but fortunately the doctor returned to his bedside.

"We need you to be very brave while I explain the situation. Can you do that for us?"

The young man nodded, but he was lying.

"What we have here is a first, as far as we know, in the field of medicine. What appears to have happened is that due to a sudden lurch of the train you were riding, a woman lost her balance and unavoidably collided with you at extreme force. Both of you sustained injuries. The woman's arm, wrist and several bones in her hand were fractured. She has received treatment and it will be a few months before she makes a full recovery. Have you understood what I have said so far?"

The young man understood. The doctor continued.

"You, on the other hand, are unfortunately in a much worse situation, and one that will ultimately be influenced by your decision on how you want to proceed. You see, as the woman collided with you, she was holding her smartphone, the new SNARP NN10 which was released for sale just the day before the accident. One of that smartphone's features is its slimness—it is branded as the thinnest smartphone in the world. As the woman collided with you, the smartphone made contact with your left eye socket. Being constructed of such thin and yet tensile material, behind which was the substantial mass of the woman moving at considerable velocity, the smartphone broke cleanly through your left eye socket and lodged itself behind the eye in the left side of your brain. Remarkably, the eye suffered minimal damage and should make a full recovery. Your brain, although bruised and bleeding at first, has miraculously withstood the brutality of the collision. Your eye socket can, with a little reconstruction, be returned to close to its original shape and function."

The doctor straightened and turned to look at his colleagues for support. There were nods and grimaces of approval. The doctor bent down to the young man's level again.

"To summarize, you have the world's most advanced smartphone lodged in your brain. My colleagues assembled here today are some of the leading neurologists in Japan. We have spent the last forty-eight hours analysing the situation, discussing it and also conferring with experts around the world, including the maker of the smartphone. We believe there are two choices available to you."

The young man wished the doctor would stop talking. He had been terrified by the details of the accident, but now he was being tortured by the thought of having to make a decision about it.

"The first choice is to leave the smartphone where it is. Let me add that the phone is deeply lodged in your brain and that there is the danger of more damage being caused by trying to remove it than by letting it remain there. We think that with a little re-sculpturing we can completely cover the smartphone with skin and you will look pretty much like you did before the accident."

The young man couldn't stop a tear roll out of the corner of his right eye and drop onto the pillow.

"The second choice is to remove the smartphone. As explained, this is highly risky. However, having a smartphone in your brain is clearly not a natural scenario. My colleagues and I are split fifty-fifty on which is the best choice for you. It is really up to you to cast the deciding vote as it is a choice that may determine the quality with which you live the remainder of your life."

The young man blinked then opened his mouth to speak. Sensing this, the doctor drew a little closer.

"Could I have a few minutes to think? In private?" the young man whispered.

"Of course. Of course. We'll be back, in say, fifteen minutes' time, okay?"

The young man nodded. The doctors made their way out of the room, mumbling among themselves, and the door to the room closed behind them. The young man was alone. Unfettered by the presence of others, he sobbed freely and beat the mattress with his fists, although without force due to the strapping around his arms.

After a while he had calmed sufficiently enough to return to the issue in hand. To leave the smartphone in his brain, or risk its removal.

What a decision to have to make. And of all people, why me? I will never be able to decide in fifteen minutes. Fifteen days would not be long enough.

Just then, a painful jolt of vibration, energy and noise shot through the young man's head down to his feet, and with a yelp he sprung up in the bed. As he sank back onto the bed, exhausted, the jolt repeated. On the third ring, he had worked out what was happening and didn't need to hear the words of the doctor, who had run shouting back into the room.

"The alarm. The smartphone's alarm setting is still on. The woman told us she set the alarm on the smartphone every ten minutes between 9 am and 10 am. It's 9 am now, so you'll have to bear with it another six times. I'm terribly sorry to have forgotten to tell you. It must have been a great shock."

The young man nodded. The doctor turned away towards the door.

The young man couldn't believe his bad fortune. Not only was a functioning smartphone lodged in his brain, but its alarm was set and in vibration mode too. And yet, if he could somehow put up with it six more times, surely its battery would run flat and he would never hear the alarm again. Maybe then, he could live with the smartphone in his brain.

The doctor glanced back.

"Ah, I almost forgot to mention that the smartphone, while not only being the world's slimmest, is also the world's first fully self-charging one. Technology is amazing, isn't it? Of course, this means its battery will never run down and its alarm will ring at the same time, every day, in perpetuity."

The young man shook his head from side to side, gently at first, then stronger until a pulse of pain burst across his forehead forcing him to stop.

"Are you okay?" asked the doctor. "Do you wish to say something?"

The doctor drew closer, close enough to feel the warmth of the exhausted young man's breath swirl in his inner ear.

"Get it out of me!" the young man screamed. "Get it out of me, now!"

Swirl

The call came on a Saturday morning, around nine-thirty.

Mrs Hideko Berlin, known as Hide-chan to her friends, was on the balcony, transferring the morning's washing, piece by damp piece, from an oversized laundry basket to the washing line. Through the window glass she heard the phone ring in the living room.

Hide-chan thought about rushing inside to pick up the phone, but thought again. The phone was on answer-machine mode and if it was important, the caller would leave a message. After the third ring, the answer machine greeting began to peal out.

Hide-chan slid the balcony's sliding window open so she could clearly hear any message the caller may leave.

"This is Amano from the *Asobi* Newspaper Group," the caller started by saying.

Hide-chan was sure she'd paid for the monthly delivery of the *Asobi* Newspaper just the other day, and told them she was cancelling her subscription. Maybe the newspaper was calling to beg her to change her mind.

"I'm calling to speak with Mr Donald Berlin about his entry to this year's *Asobi* Newspaper haiku competition."

Hide-chan caught her breath. Why on earth had Donald entered a haiku competition?

"We are pleased to inform you that you have won first prize."

Hide-chan dropped the sock she was holding. It fell like a wet fish onto her foot. She shook it off, opened the sliding window further and slipped her feet into her indoor slippers. She shuffled closer to the phone, which was still taking Mr Amano's message.

"We'd like to tell you more about your prize and ask for your—"

Hide-chan snatched at the phone.

"Hello. Hello. This is Mrs Berlin speaking."

"Hello. I, err…Mr Donald Berlin's wife?"

"Yes, that's right."

"It's nice to speak with you. I'm Amano from the *Asobi* Newspaper Group's Marketing Department. I'd like to speak with Mr Berlin if possible. Is he available?"

"I'm sorry, he's not."

"Oh."

"You're calling about a haiku competition, aren't you? I heard your message."

"That's right. Your husband's entry into our haiku competition was appraised by our judges and awarded first place."

"I can't believe it."

"Yes. I called to congratulate him, and tell him we will send him details in the post. If possible, we'd like to interview him about what inspired him to write the haiku, so we can run an article alongside it. He'll have his photo published in the newspaper too, if he wants to."

"I see."

"When will your husband be available? I can call back then."

"I'm terribly sorry to tell you this but, he passed away last month."

"What?"

"He passed away last month. It was an aggressive cancer and, unfortunately, he didn't have the strength to overcome it."

Hide-chan heard the creak of Mr Amano's chair over the phone and imagined him shifting his weight, moving the phone from one hand to another and struggling to come to terms with the situation. Hide-chan had spoken with many people in the weeks since Donald's death and knew how difficult this situation was for everyone.

After a few seconds, Mr Amano spoke again.

"I'm awfully sorry to hear that. Terribly sorry. Please accept my apology for calling and disturbing you."

"That's alright. A month has passed and we don't feel the loss quite as intensely now. There is no way you could have known."

"Nevertheless, it is rude of me to have called you at such a time. What shall we do? I think, yes, I think I need to confirm with our team how best to handle this. It's the first time this has happened and, well, to be frank, I don't know…well…we can't interview your husband and as for the photo and sending him the prize… I'm sorry, really sorry, but I'm going to have to check and call you back."

"That's okay."

"Please accept my apologies."

"That's fine."

"Goodbye."

Mr Amano hung up.

Hide-chan set the phone back on its stand and then shuffled to the balcony. As she hung out the remaining items she thought of all the years she had walked past Donald's writing room, lingered by the door, wondering if he'd ever come out, wondering if she could knock and go in. She never for one moment imagined he had been writing in Japanese, and certainly not something as delicate and nuanced as haiku. Donald was one for putting down his thoughts on business in unequivocal terms for magazines and blogs, as well as in the books he wrote. The sensitivity, sensibility and understanding of Japanese culture required to write excellent haiku in Japanese is something only those in the highest echelons of Japanese haiku writing could aspire to, or so Hide-chan had thought. Who would have believed it?

After lunch, Mr Amano rang again, just as Hide-chan's body was nagging her for an early-afternoon nap.

"We've discussed the situation and have decided we'd like to award your late husband the first prize, as planned," Mr Amano said brightly.

"That really is most kind of you."

"We'd also like to send you the prize money."

"Ah. Well, I don't think you need to do that. I don't actually need the money, and…"

"We thought you may say that, but you would be doing us a great favour if you accepted it on behalf of your late husband. You see, if you don't, we'd have to account for it in our accounting system, which would be quite troublesome. You'd really be doing us a favour."

Hide-chan nodded to herself. She knew how things worked in such companies and how something unexpected like a death could throw a heavy spanner in the works.

"Well, okay then, I'll accept the prize money. Thank you."

"That's most appreciated. And, as for the interview, would it be possible for you to supply a few words about your husband, I mean your late husband?"

"I, well, I suppose I could. What exactly are you wanting?"

"Just a sentence or two about his writing. Where he got his inspiration for the haiku, if it was based on an actual event, that kind of thing."

"To be honest, I didn't even know he had written the haiku."

"You didn't know?"

"No."

"You mean to say, you haven't read it?"

"I haven't."

"That's most surprising. Most surprising."

"I'm surprised too. He wrote quite extensively in English about business and had a couple of books published, but I didn't know he was doing any, how can I say, creative writing."

"Allow me to tell you the haiku he submitted was about looking at plum blossoms on a cold morning and the white air he exhaled swirling, like brushstrokes in a Van Gogh painting. Let me find it and I'll read it to you…"

"No, no, that's fine, you needn't."

"It will only take a few seconds."

"No, I think I'd rather see it in print, in the newspaper."

"Very well. His phrasing is highly original. As Japanese wasn't his native language, maybe he used words which were not what a typical Japanese writer of haiku would choose."

"That would make sense."

"So you don't know anything about the subject matter?"

"Well, now you ask, I do remember him asking me how many syllables 'Van Gogh' has in Japanese. I was watching television at the time, so I told him to use 'Gogh' instead of 'Van Gogh', as that's what most Japanese do. He must have worked out the number of syllables for 'Gogh' himself."

"That's a nice memory. We will send the letter, as I mentioned earlier, and it will include a form on which we'd like to ask you to write about your late husband's haiku. If you could write about helping him with 'Van Gogh' we'd be really grateful. And if you could send us a photo of your husband too, we'd appreciate it. But of course, only if you feel up to it."

"I guess I can do that. I will take a look on his computer too, as he may have left some notes there about the haiku."

"Oh, thank you very much, that's really helpful. Once again, please accept my apology for disturbing you."

"Not at all."

After the call, Hide-chan didn't feel like having a nap at all. Her mind was still spinning at the thought of Donald writing haiku in Japanese, and not just that, writing one that was good enough to win a prize. What else had he been up to? she wondered.

Unable to settle in her apartment, she took a stroll along the river and allowed the rustle of the wind through the leafy trees lining the riverbank to calm her.

A day or two passed and Hide-chan forgot about the call. In fact, she barely had time to think about anything but her own work, making meals for herself, chatting online with her daughter, keeping the apartment tidy and watching variety shows on television.

And then the *Asobi* Newspaper's letter arrived.

Hide-chan opened it and found a handwritten note from Mr Amano, again thanking her for her cooperation and apologizing for the inconvenience caused. In addition, there was a typed page about winning the award. The prize money was enclosed in another envelope. And finally, there was the form asking for the words to be published alongside the haiku, and a space to which to attach a photograph.

Later that the evening, after she had finished watching the television and had nothing else pressing to do, Hide-chan read the letter again, then strode down the corridor and entered Donald's writing room. She hadn't been in it since the funeral. It was just as he had left it, spotlessly clean and tidy. Pride of place was a bookshelf crammed with books like *Ten Team Leading Techniques That Work*, *How to Run a Successful Japanese Company* as well as several copies of his own books.

On the wall were his framed certificates; a qualification in Project Management, an MBA from Thunderbird University, and Japanese Language Proficiency Level 1. A cork board hung on one wall, to which he'd pinned photos of his suited self, beaming alongside other suited persons she assumed leaders of various companies, none of whom she knew or had even the faintest interest in knowing.

This was the room in which Donald had spent most of his hours when at home. He'd typically come home from work late in the evening, eat the meal she'd prepared, then retire to the room. She assumed he was sat at his desk writing as there was no other chair in the room and nowhere to lie down. Often he wouldn't come out again until she had gone to sleep. She knew he networked, spouting off here and there his thoughts about Japan and how to do business, even going as far as referring to himself as a "thought leader", which embarrassed Hide-chan, especially when teased by her friends about it.

She prised open the lid of Donald's laptop and pressed the power button.

The computer whined softly and within a few seconds the prompt for a log-in name and password appeared. Hide-chan flicked through her spiral notebook to the page on which Donald had scribbled various IDs and passwords in his last days, found the combination for his computer and tapped it in.

The computer's screen was a monotone shade of blue, with only three icons, one of which was "Writing". Hide-chan tapped it and found a "Haiku" folder. In that folder, were other folders, each titled with a year, going back to 2012. Had he really been writing haiku for almost ten years? And he had never shared his writing with her?

She found a folder labelled "*Asobi* Newspaper" and opened the most recent file, which had a date of a few weeks before his death.

Hide-chan knew immediately that this was what she was looking for.

The document began with free-flowing, stream-of-conscious rambling in English about Dazaifu shrine near Fukuoka and a visit in early spring 1983. Donald wrote of his disappointment at it being too cold for cherry blossom to bloom, but there were plum blossoms. And while there, he had supped a cup of hot, bitter green tea to warm himself up.

Further down the document, was a reference to Van Gogh, and a link.

"Van Gogh. Copied Utagawa's ukiyo-e masterpiece of plum gardens in Kameido."

Hide-chan clicked a link and a page opened that displayed Utagawa's and Van Gogh's masterpieces side by side, with a detailed explanation of the differences, such as the colour pallets used, some minor items omitted in Van Gogh's version, and the Japanese writing Van Gogh had painted around the border to give the painting an unmistakably oriental feeling.

Hide-chan knew that Van Gogh had been influenced by Japanese art but she hadn't known this much detail. So, this is what inspired my husband to write the haiku, she thought.

There weren't any swirls in Van Gogh's painting, but Donald must have invented the swirl of white air, perhaps inspired by Van Gogh's other paintings like *The Starry Night*. Donald had been creative, an attribute Hide-chan had never thought him capable of.

Hide-chan read on, intrigued by how Donald had tried various combinations of haiku phrases about Dazaifu, plum blossoms, cold morning, white breath, and Van Gogh, before settling on the composition at the very bottom of the page, which she assumed was the haiku that Donald had sent to *Asobi* Newspaper as its beauty and precision took her breath away.

As Hide-chan sat there, stunned by what she had found, she saw a photo album sitting on a shelf above the desk. It had "Japan 1983" written on its spine. 1983. The year he had visited Dazaifu shrine, and the year before she had met him.

Hide-chan flicked through page after page of photos from various locations in Japan, each labelled meticulously with the date and place name.

One photograph, from the entrance to Dazaifu Tenmangu shrine, was of the bronze statue of a bull, its head shiny, no doubt from being rubbed countless times by students craving more intelligence before sitting their exams.

Under that were photos of swirls of white breath flowing from a woman's red lipstick-lined mouth. The woman had made the white swirls for Donald, and she had clearly had fun doing so. And there was a photo of Donald too, standing under the blossoms, arms folded, grinning. It was clear to Hide-chan that the woman must have taken that one of him, in return.

Donald had met and married Hide-chan a year later, in 1984. She knew he had spent 1983 in Japan as an English teacher, travelling and playing the field. Dazaifu and the woman had clearly been checked off his list. She couldn't blame him for that. But why, after all these years, had it inspired his haiku? Why had he not been inspired by the years he had been her husband?

Hide-chan slapped the album closed, rose and left the writing room, tramping down the corridor to the living room. She dropped the album on the table next to the letter from the newspaper company, and sat down.

Hide-chan gathered herself, then used a ballpoint pen to complete the form, before sliding it into the self-addressed envelope.

Although late in the evening, Hide-chan slipped a jacket on, grabbed her shoulder bag, stuffed the letter in it and left the apartment. Some five minutes of determined striding later she reached the post office. She pushed the letter through the gap in the postbox, turned and began the journey home, but changed her mind and headed for the river. She needed to calm down. A stroll along the river, its charcoal waters reflecting the mazy star-spotted sky, would do the trick. Hide-chan chuckled. Perhaps there was still time for her to make a late entry into the world of haiku writing.

As Hide-chan strolled along the river she wondered if she had been too impetuous.

"Sorry, unable to find any source material" is what she had written on the form in the space for a comment. She had also drawn a large cross through the box to which a photo was to be attached. *Asobi* Newspaper would be disappointed, but they'd survive, unlike the photo album, which had hit the bottom of the kitchen's waste bin with a resounding thump.

Hide-chan felt a light breeze on her back and picked up her pace.

Impetuous? No. She had done the right thing. She had always done the right thing. Donald had been blowing his own trumpet long and hard for all these years, but now that he was gone, the only trumpet blowing would be her own.

Crimes for Dummies

The Criminal

Jiro Higa.
September 17th, 1965.
Kichijoji, Suginami ward.

I've lived there all my life. My folks, God bless them, bought the land.

Just my wife. No children.

Why do you want to talk with me?

I fell down the stairs at home and my wife drove me here. It was bad luck, but I've done nothing wrong.

Of course I'll answer your questions, but can you keep them short? I'm in pain, you know. Kuniko says I've broken a few ribs. I'm getting x-rayed any minute now.

Yes, Kuniko, my wife.

I'm vice president of Higa International Consulting. It's Kuniko's company. It works out nicely for the tax breaks we get. Maybe I shouldn't have said that. Could you delete that last part? About the tax?

I don't specialize. I'm a master of all trades. "Never say no" is my motto. Just the other day I delivered a package across town for a client. Sometimes I get asked to collect unpaid rent.

Most of the day I'm on the phone doing business, negotiating, investing, that sort of thing.

I was at home, upstairs. I'd got my pyjamas on and was heading downstairs to the bathroom when Midgy, our cat, came out of nowhere and got under my feet. I tripped over him and fell head first down the stairs. I thought I was a goner, I really did. I landed on my belly first, which is why my ribs are hurting so much, and my face also clattered into the wall at the bottom of the stairs, that's how it's all bruised.

A fight? Me? No, no, I don't fight, not at my age.

They may look like fist marks, but that's just from rolling down the stairs and hitting the wall, like I said.

Look, Kuniko's in the waiting area, why don't you ask her? She was there, she'll tell you. I guess you'll want to interview Midgy too?

You're right, I shouldn't have said that. Of course you can't interview a cat. I have a strange sense of humour and I'm in a lot of pain.

No, no, you go and talk to Kuniko.

The Wife

Kuniko Higa. (Former name was Takebayashi. You can call me Kuni.)
January 6th, 1970.
Kichijoji, Suginami ward.

I live with Jiro, and our two cats, Bruce and Lee.

Yeah, I'm a Kung Fu fan. Are you?

I own Higa Consulting, but I don't do any of the grunt work. Jiro does all that. I just handle the paperwork, balance the books, file tax returns. Jiro's sweet but he couldn't add one and one if he had all day to do it.

Hasn't he told you everything? Why would my story be different?

If you insist. We were at home. I'd just got out of the bath, got dried and was in the living room watching TV. Jiro was upstairs getting his pyjamas on and tripped over our cat, Midgy, at the top of the stairs. I didn't see him fall, but I certainly heard him. Thump, thump, thump, like an eighty-kilo bag of rice rolling down the stairs, followed by screaming. I ran to help him. I used to be a nurse, you know. I could tell he was hurt but not bad enough to call an ambulance, so I drove him here. That's it. You think I pushed him down the stairs or something?

Last four digits of the licence plate? The plate is personalized and there is only one number, the number 1. If you saw the car in the car park, why bother asking me the number?

So that's your game. Why didn't you just say you've got the car on camera in Ikebukuro?

Don't look so pleased with yourself. You're not that smart. I've done more with my life than you ever will.

Okay, he didn't fall down the stairs. I got a call from a bar in Ikebukuro about ten this evening. They said Jiro had been beaten up. I drove there as fast as I could. Like I said, I used to be a nurse and could tell he'd broken a couple of ribs. His face was red and swollen too. The guys who did it had fled. Some argument about money, it was. The owner of the bar didn't want to make a fuss by calling an ambulance, so he helped me get Jiro into the car.

The name of the bar? Sorry, it's slipped my mind.

Okay, keep your hair on. It was the Broadway Bar.

Jiro was crying with the pain. I drove him here as it's our local hospital. We only live a couple of minutes away.

I drove fast because I wanted to get him here as quickly as possible. In an emergency you don't worry about sticking to the rules of the road, do you?

I told the doctors he'd fallen down the stairs at home. They didn't believe me and called you guys, right?

You've got to hand it to them, they know how to do their jobs.

So, are you happy now? I've told you everything.

What robbery? I don't know anything about a robbery.

Jiro was playing tennis this morning, like he does every Sunday morning. It's like a religion to him.

A local court, I think. He always plays at local parks, with the usual bunch of guys. Just harmless fun, that's all it is.

He came back home about ten. I went straight into the kitchen and made him breakfast. He's hungry after his tennis.

He wore his blue tracksuit and carried his tennis bag. All his rackets and stuff are in it.

Tennis? Me? No way. It's a silly game, chasing fluffy yellow balls. I go to a fitness club every day. I look damned good, don't I? Not bad for a fifty-year-old.

He dumped the tennis bag in his study, then had a bath. He sings in the bath when he's in a good mood, and today he was singing before he got in and after he got out.

He had a nap after breakfast. I drove to the fitness club for my hot yoga class, had coffee with friends, then drove back home. He wasn't at home. I thought he'd be at the festival in Kugayama as he'd talked about it over breakfast.

A video of him at Shin Urayasu station this morning? It wasn't him. It can't have been. Why would he go to the other side of town for a game of tennis? It doesn't make sense. You guys are making this stuff up.

Of course I know about his past, but that was a long time ago. He's been clean for years now.

He used his rail pass at Shin Urayasu! The idiot! The stupid, stupid idiot! I should have kicked him out a long time ago, the good for nothing…

Well, look, now I think of it, maybe he did tell me about playing tennis at Shin Urayasu this morning. There's nothing wrong with that, is there? It isn't a crime, is it? So what? There's nothing to link him with a robbery there this morning. Nothing at all. You're just barking up trees. And you know it.

Where are you going? You just leave my Jiro alone. Stop harassing him. I'll report you. You won't work again. You'll spend your days sleeping in a cardboard box in some park somewhere.

The Criminal

You again?

I can talk a little, but it still hurts, hurts a hell of a lot actually.

I've had the x-ray and it was just as I said, three broken ribs. I'm going to take a couple of weeks off work, but that's okay, I've been working hard. I deserve a break.

You spoke with Kuniko? Good.

She said what?

Broadway Bar in Ikebukuro? She said that? Really?

But, that's not what she told me to…I mean, we agreed to, I mean. Shit!

Speeding? She always drives too fast. I'm always telling her about it. But, look, maybe it was somebody else?

It's a white Lexus, yes, but there are lots of them on the road. How can you be sure?

If you got the plates on camera then I can't argue with that.

Robbery in Shin Urayasu? I was nowhere near the place. I was playing tennis this morning.

She told you that?

If she's told you that I was in Shin Urayasu then I have no choice, do I. She told you, right?

Yes, yes. You're right. I won't waste your time any more. I didn't fall down the stairs.

I got a call about a job a couple of weeks ago. Like I told you before, I never say no.

Who from? Suzuki. He told me nothing when he called. He said to meet him in West Ikebukuro.

It's called Broadway Bar. Being Sunday afternoon the place was closed. I had to knock on the door and give a password to get in.

"Cats". Suzuki always uses weird passwords. Last time it was "sound of music", the time before "phantom of the something". You'd think it was a high security bank, not a bar.

Suzuki was there, and two others. I'd never met either of them before.

Their names? Ohshima and Matsumoto. I don't know their first names.

Suzuki gave me an earful for being fifteen minutes late. He's always like that. After he calmed down he told us about the job.

I didn't want to be the one looking after the cash, but Suzuki said he'd find somebody else to do it if I complained.

I don't know exactly where Suzuki lives, but he did mention his daughters going to school in Fukasawa. High-class area, right. The bastard is always tight with the information he gives us. I don't even know his phone number. Just the other day I asked him what car he drives and do you know what he said? "A better car than you do." That's what he said.

For sure I could identify him in a lineup. I could identify them all. The bastards. Beating me up over something like this. Look at the state of my face. Anyone can make a mistake, right?

My memory is excellent, don't you worry about that. I was up this morning at about three-thirty. I wanted to run through the plan in my head a few times to make sure it would work like clockwork.

Why are you laughing? I'm a professional. You don't expect me to turn up for a job without preparing for it, do you?

That wasn't my fault, it could have happened to anyone. Just one of those things.

Look, my ribs are still really sore. Can't we do this another time? Tomorrow?

Well, if you really must.

I left the house at five, on the dot. Kuniko was asleep. I walked to Kichijoji station and took the Chuo line to Tokyo station. I changed to the Keiyo line for Shin Urayasu. The target was about twenty minutes from Shin Urayasu station. Suzuki had a bike ready for me at the station. He didn't tell me I had to pay to get it unlocked. I thought the bike would have a bit of speed in case I needed to get away quickly, but it was a rusty granny bike with no gears. It looked like he'd picked it out of a ditch somewhere. I was exhausted when I got to the store. Dripping in sweat. I kept my distance so I couldn't be picked up by the store's security camera.

It's an upmarket area. Nearby are a couple of hotels used by families visiting the Disney parks. Nobody uses the store that early in the morning as they are asleep or having breakfast in their hotels, but we weren't taking any chances.

Matsumoto was standing outside, his back to the shop window, having a smoke. He had his cap pulled down so the camera couldn't catch his face. Ohshima trundled up on his bike and leaned it against the side of the store, and waited there. I turned my bike to face away from the store so I could make a quick getaway.

At six the night shift ended and the morning shift started. The replacement staff were a young woman and a middle-aged one. Two women made it even easier for us. At ten past six Ohshima and Matsumoto pounced on them while they were both in the storeroom at the back and tied the older one up. They walked the young one to the till and got her to open it and hand over the cash. Kids these days, they don't put up a fight. Matsumoto shoved the cash in a cloth bag. They locked the women in the storeroom and left the store, really casual, not attracting attention. Matsumoto split off on his bike. Ohshima ran to his bike, rode over to me, threw me the bag, then sped off.

Yeah, he said, "Don't lose it."

I stuffed the bag into my tennis bag and pedalled back to the station. I had the toughest job, no question about it. Suzuki told me to ride slowly, as if I was going to casually meet friends for a game of tennis. He didn't want me drawing attention by riding too fast. All the while I thought I could hear the sound of police car sirens, wanted to pedal fast, but had Suzuki's words eating away at me. I left the bike in the exact same spot

I had picked it up from, wiped my fingerprints off the handles, walked into the station and got the train back to Tokyo station.

It was the perfect crime, like clockwork it was.

Well, yes, perfect up to that point, but like I said, what happened later could have happened to anyone.

When I got home, Kuniko was up and asked if I'd won the game. Of course, I told her I had.

Just a minute. I never told Kuniko about the robbery. How did she know?

You told her! You bastards! You tricked me. You can't do that! That's not fair. Not fair at all.

There was a camera at Shin Urayasu station? Just my luck. There are cameras everywhere these days.

Artificial intelligence? What's that?

Well, like I said, I got home, had a shower, breakfast, then I had a nap. I was worn out.

The plan was for me to take the money to the bar in West Ikebukuro that evening, nine-thirty. I still had half the day to kill. I watched TV for a while. Kuniko was out and I started to feel hungry again. Kugayama Park summer festival was on. I knew I could get something to eat there. I've been to it every year since I was a kid, and I didn't want to miss it. I transferred the bag of cash from the tennis bag to my tote bag then left.

The tote bag? Black with a grey logo on the side, you know, the one with three or four bars. I don't like flash, colourful bags.

I took the train to Kugayama station. The festival was busy, it always is. I was starving so I bought some fried chicken and a beer, then found a space to sit in front of the stage. The beer tasted great.

The bag was with me all the time. Well, a couple of times I felt hungry, so left it as a place marker and got a sausage on a stick and another beer. This is Japan, you know. Have you ever had something stolen? Well, you wouldn't I guess, being policemen.

I had another nap after the second beer. It must have been all the cycling this morning. It was dark when I woke up, about nine. The music had stopped and some guy from the city hall was making a closing speech.

There were plenty of folks around at the time, sitting next to me, in front and behind me. I can't remember their faces. Like I said, I spent most of the time with my eyes closed.

Well, I panicked, having to be in Ikebukuro by nine-thirty.

You're right, I had plenty of time to get to there but I was sure Suzuki would bawl me out for being late. I picked up the bag and ran to the station. Once on the train I felt excited, like the winner of a marathon about to step onto the podium. I thought they'd all greet me with open arms. I thought we'd have a drink to celebrate, count the money, split it and be on our way. Instead, I opened the bag and, well, look at what they did to me.

Could you do me a favour and call a nurse? My ribs are hurting like hell. Must be all this talking. I need more painkillers.

The English Teacher

Troy Vaughan-Jones.
September 12th, 1991.
Kichijoji, Suginami ward.
English teacher.

I walked to the festival. The park is pretty close by. Toby, my partner, was teaching English until late evening, so yeah, it was a little lonely by myself but still a lot of fun. I love Japanese festivals, even the local ones.

I took a mat to sit on, and my phone, my wallet, my notebook and a pen.

I sat in front of the stage. Sometimes I got up to get a beer and something to eat.

I really enjoyed the performances and the atmosphere. Everyone was real friendly. I love the way women still wear Yukata when they get a chance, some men too.

The final performance was the Obon dance, which I love. It's so exotic and yet so simple. I left my bag on the mat. This is Japan, real safe, right, but I still slipped my wallet and phone into the back pockets of my jeans just to be sure, and joined the dance. We danced for about twenty minutes, round and round the stage. I could have danced all night, but you know what it's like here, the show has to end on time. The music stopped, somebody, from the town hall I think, made a speech and then everyone clapped and started to drift away. I helped pick up litter but most folks took their own trash home, so there was hardly anything to do. I just love it here.

When I got back to my mat I noticed the bag was on it, but to the side. I thought somebody must have moved it while tidying up.

I walked home, had a shower and waited for Toby. He walked in about ten. We ate sushi he'd bought at a convenience store, and that was when Toby asked whose bag it was. I was shocked. I hadn't noticed in the park, it must have been too dark, but it wasn't my bag. It was almost the identical shade of black, but had a different logo.

I panicked, thinking somebody had my bag and my notebook. All those ideas in the notebook are priceless. Well, to me anyhow. To anyone else they would be completely useless, they'd never be able to read my scrawly handwriting. Hah!

We opened the bag and there was a cloth bag there. I wasn't going to open it but Toby grabbed it from me. Just from its shape it looked like it had a stack of cash inside, and it did. I freaked out, knowing it wasn't ours and it looked like a lot of money.

We walked over to the police station right there and then, rather than wait until morning. We wanted to do the right thing. We thought that maybe the person with my bag would do the right thing too. What goes around comes around, as they say.

The guys at the station were really cool. They must deal with this stuff all the time. They didn't even blink an eye when they opened the bag and saw the cash inside. They took our names, address and my phone number, and said they'd be in touch if anything turned up.

We walked home. Toby was in the shower and I was watching a movie on my tablet when there was a knock at the door. It was almost midnight. I assumed it was you guys with my bag, but I opened the door to three rough-looking guys. The smallest guy was holding my bag. Even their dress sense made me feel uneasy.

I said, "Oh, you've found my bag, thank you," and reached out, thinking he'd pass it to me, but he didn't. That was when I knew for sure something was wrong.

He said, "We found bag. We give you bag. First, give bag to us."

I said I'd taken their bag to the police station. My voice was shaking.

The older guy exploded. "Where is money?" he shouted. "Where?"

I told him again, as calm as I could, that I'd taken the money to the police.

They argued among themselves, pushing each other about until the small guy said, "You have money. We go inside."

They pushed past me and went inside. It was scary. They did take their shoes off, which was nice, but they were invading my privacy and were rough about it, poking about here and there.

I asked them to stop but of course they just ignored me. Then Toby came out of the shower, and in a flash he was in the living room all naked and dripping wet, shouting, "Who the hell are you?" and, "What the hell are you doing in my apartment?" That shut them up.

Yeah, he's almost two metres tall, and almost a metre across the shoulders. He played American Football at college.

What happened next? Well, that's when you guys burst into the apartment. The men in blue saved the day. Actually, if you hadn't I think Toby would have ripped them apart, so it was just as well.

Toby and I didn't realize that one of your officers is a woman. Sorry about that. She had her hair up, under her cap. Toby was walking around drying himself off, thinking nothing of it. He's really big, all over.

I'm really impressed with you guys. You must have traced the cash we handed in to a robbery and figured out those guys would be paying me a visit to get it back. It's hard to believe a hardened criminal would leave his bag filled with all that loot unattended just to get a beer and a sausage on a stick. I know it's Japan, but still…

No, no problem at all. I'm thrilled I got my bag back, my notebook especially. What happened tonight is great material. All grist to the mill. Maybe I'll write a novel about it when I return to the UK.

The Leader

Satoshi Suzuki.
October 18th, 1961.
Fukasawa, Setagaya ward.

I like the changes you've made to this place since the last time I was here. Back then it was cold, grungy and poorly lit. Now, it's like being at home, brightly lit, white paint slapped everywhere, open plan. Clever stuff. You want to make it easier for the public to come in and talk, but not too comfortable or they'll want to spend more time here than in their own homes.

What? Sure, I know why you brought me here.

Yes, yes, I'll keep answering your questions. What's the next one?

My wife and three girls. Yeah, three. Would you believe my luck?

Wife's name? What do you need to know that for?

What?

Okay, keep your hair on. It's Fumi. Fumiko if you want to be exact.

I do this and that. I get by. I look for opportunities, use my connections, that sort of thing. If there's a job I'll plan for it, put a team together, train them to succeed.

I was one hundred per cent sure we'd nail this job. I planned it to perfection. I gave them each their alibis and their props. But I overestimated Higa. All that stuff he spouts about having studied at Waseda. It can't have been Waseda university, must have been Waseda primary school. And even then, I don't know how they would have let him in, unless his folks made a donation.

You caught us in the act, and you've already talked to Higa, am I right? So what more can you want?

And he's squealed, right? So why waste time with your questions if you already know the answers?

Yes, it was the Broadway. The owner talked too, right? Not as much as Higa, though. Nobody talks as much as Higa.

Higa told you all our names? All of them? The bastard. We should have killed him, we really should. I thought he was faking while we were beating him up, all that screaming and shouting. With all that fat on him, we should have kicked him even harder.

After we got tired of kicking him, we turned the bag inside out. A notebook fell out, and it had an address written on the inside cover, in English. Everything was written in English. That guy sure has the messiest handwriting.

Oxford? Really? Would you believe it. Education standards must be slipping in England too.

Ohshima knows English from working in my bar in Roppongi and chatting with the foreigners that come in. He worked out the postal address was in Kugayama, near the park where Higa had lost the bag.

I thought of paying the police station near the park a visit to see if you had the bag. Maybe somebody had found it and handed it in. But that would have been too risky. I'd have had to show an ID card. Anyway, I was sure that foreigner had just kept the cash and not reported it. With that sort of cash they'd spend it on a new car or something, right? So I decided to pay the foreigner a visit and get our money back. Why waste time? I took Ohshima to speak English, and Nakamura to scare the crap out of the foreigner. Of course we didn't realize the foreigner had a friend even bigger than Nakamura.

198 cm? To be honest, close up he looked even bigger. Nakamura said he wanted to run the moment he set eyes on him, but couldn't as his legs were shaking. We really had some bad luck. What does that guy eat?

Yes, yes, it was my mistake for getting that idiot Higa involved. I can't fix that now.

If I ever get my hands on him again, well, I'll just, I'll…

Bodies

I came to Japan in 1990, deployed by my company for a month-long business trip. My flight touched down at Narita airport on a morning in mid-July and trundled down the runway towards the terminal buildings. The pilot nonchalantly told us over the intercom that it was a fine, sunny day and the current temperature was thirty-nine degrees. Being from Thurso, a town near the northern tip of Scotland, I had never experienced such heat. Neither had my leather jacket, which gave up any pretence of structure and strength and transformed into a sloppy piece of chamois leather as soon as I left the terminal building. I could have cleaned a car with it.

I was met at the airport by Mr Ariga, who was to be my boss. I had mastered some basic Japanese greetings before leaving for Japan, but with my brain barely functioning due to jet lag and the heat, I slipped into English from the off. Luckily Mr Ariga was a fluent English speaker, and being a member of the Japan Rolling Stones Fan Club, or "the club" as he called it, he never missed an opportunity to quote a lyric. "I'm a man of wealth and taste" he told me as he drove us into Tokyo in his tired Toyota Corolla.

I hadn't wanted to go to Japan. Two years earlier I had graduated from Aberdeen University and had fortunately landed a job with an oil company with an office near Aberdeen airport. After all the years of studying, all I wanted from life was to do my job, return to my flat on the edge of town and listen to my LP collection, play a little air guitar and watch the occasional movie. So when the company asked me to go to Japan, I was compromised. And yet, I figured I couldn't say no – the company had after all just put its faith in me by employing me and I was being paid for working for the first time in my life. A little more discomfort, and I would soon be back in Aberdeen.

After only one week in Tokyo, I regretted my choice. I sorely missed Aberdeen's grey granite and sea breeze. In Tokyo, the streets, pavements and buildings soaked up the scorching sun and, when the sun went down, the heat oozed back out into the evening sky. I fought a running battle with my apartment's air conditioner over the ideal setting for sleep. With disrupted sleep disrupting my brain, I felt useless in the office. I was shocked that Mr Ariga asked my company to let me stay longer, and dismayed at having my return date put back to December.

Tokyo's metropolis was filled with more people than I had seen before. Everyone was polite and thoughtful, going out of their way to help if I looked lost. But there were so many of them, and their bodies were improbably close together. On the pavement, crossing the road, on the subway, in elevators, in restaurants, I seemed to act as a living magnet to bodies. I'd leave a gap between myself and the platform edge, and somebody would stand in front of me. If I left a gap between myself and the person in front when queuing for anything, the person behind me would start coughing or grunting or draw close enough for me to feel their breath on my back.

And then there were the trains. I'd read about passengers being pushed onto morning trains but thought it was an exaggeration, until it happened to me. I could feel my ribs bending with the pressure and one time was squeezed so hard by the passengers around me that my feet lost contact with the floor of the train and I hung, suspended like a rag doll, unable to find my feet again until the doors opened at the next station and passengers burst out.

The heat and the congealing bodies began to take their toll. I wasn't a city slicker. The scene from my childhood bedroom window had been Thurso beach, the sea and, on a clear day, the Orkney Islands in the distance. From my apartment in Tokyo, I looked out over the road to the apartment opposite. It was occupied by a middle-aged Japanese couple who left their windows open in the summer, for ventilation, I assumed. They would sometimes walk around in their underwear, even when hanging out their washing on the balcony.

I had to get out into nature.

I found the answer in the English book section of a bookshop in Shinjuku. The book was titled *Hiking In and Near Tokyo*, and every other page showed a hand-drawn hiking route from a station at least one hour out of Tokyo, the routes varying in length from two hours to eight hours.

I studied the book, read the explanation of each hike and the sights to be seen, imagined myself walking in the footsteps of the writer. I made a list, narrowed it down to two, and finally to one. I was ready for my hike up Mount Kumotori on the coming Sunday.

What I hadn't factored into my planning was my reluctance to get out of bed on Sunday morning. I should have been up at 5 am, standing on the platform at Shinjuku station at

6 am with the other walkers heading out of Tokyo for a hike up a mountain. It wasn't until 9 am that I convinced myself I'd rested enough, rolled out of bed and stumbled into the shower.

I boarded a train just after 10 am. I wore my usual weekend jeans and trainers, a plain white T-shirt and in my bag, as backup, a Rolling Stones T-shirt my boss had given me that I had been too shy to wear in the city. The train creaked out of Shinjuku station and picked up speed, passing tower after tower. It was only an hour later, after changing trains at Ikusabata station, that the city fell away to bushes and trees, thick and lusciously green on both sides of the train.

At almost 12 pm exactly, the train reached its final destination, Okutama station. I stepped onto its platform. Over the station roof I saw green mountains all around. I held my ticket out to the station clerk, got it clipped, and strode out into a side street. To my left was a public toilet. I debated whether to join the queue but concluded there was no time to waste and I would do my business on the way up, behind some bushes. I pulled the hiking book out of my backpack, found my position on the map, and took my first steps forwards. Two minutes later I'd reached the edge of the village and was walking up an earthen track with rice paddies below me to the left and deep forest to the right. Ahead and behind I could hear the chatter of fellow hikers but consoled myself that on a three-hour hike up a large mountain, the bodies would eventually thin out and I would have the solitude I was seeking.

On the way up, I drank my water bottle dry in the first hour. Fortunately I came across a small shrine, lovely and immaculately clean, with equally clean vending machines at either side. I bought a bottle of water and drank it straight

away, so bought another two and stuffed them into the side
pockets of my rucksack.

I tramped on. The incline got steeper, the footing looser,
and the view of the valley below even more stunning. The
sun's heat scorched through my baseball cap and sweat rolled
down my neck and back. The back of my trousers got damp
with the sweat and my T-shirt was almost thoroughly wet
through. Eventually I gave up attempting to push the growing
discomfort to the back of my mind, stopped and with no
hikers coming up the path bent over, let the T-shirt fall off, and
changed into the spare.

All the way up to the top, I was greeted with a cheery
"*konnichiwa*" by those on their way down. "*Konnichiwa*," I
replied, a little disheartened by the thought they had reached
the peak well before I did. I pushed on, as tiredness crept into
my legs and back. I thought of my morning train to work and
the complete absence of happiness on my face and those of
my fellow passengers; of how we stood and swayed in silence,
despite our faces being only inches apart. We were now outside
the big city and smiling at each other. Nature had brought out
the best in us.

The peak came into sight. Rocks littered the area like a
crown of misaligned teeth, on which some folks sat, sipping
from their bottles of tea and munching on rice balls. I
manoeuvred between the rocks and dangling legs and reached
the pole at the very top, turned and looked for a rock of my
own. A couple were just leaving and I took their spot. I had
unhindered sight of the scenery that stretched magnificently
out in front of me. The sun smouldered in whispers of clouds
just above the mountainous horizon. The voices around me
dwindled and weakened. Silence. Utter silence. I had the peak

to myself. The sun glinted on the roofs of cars far below in the valley, winding their way along the country road that would take them to one of the main highways back to Tokyo. And yet, I hadn't had enough. I was surrounded by nature, alone and out of sight and earshot of any other human being.

It had been more than twenty minutes since the last body had left the peak and headed down. They were right to go and I should have followed but my darker, obstinate side told me no, I would wait until the sun had gone before making my way down the mountain path – even if I would have to rely on the moon to do so. It would be worth it, for the view, and for these precious minutes alone.

I watched entranced as the sun leaked into the horizon and the copper-coloured landscape turned a burnt blue. The sky above the mountain tops still blazed.

I stood, slung the rucksack on my back and took my first steps down the path that would take me back to the station. The darkness had permeated the hillside more quickly than I expected. The path was gloomy, even with the full moon above. From memory there was little in the way of rough terrain on the path down, just a few twists and turns and a short section of man-made steps. I convinced myself that as long as I kept my eyes down and concentrated, I would be alright.

I soon lost sight of my feet in the gloom, panicking when I had to step into the gaping darkness between rocks. I slowed and trod on, whistling the Rolling Stone's "Satisfaction" badly, and yet it gave me confidence.

About an hour after starting down the path I came to an intersection. I couldn't remember it being there on the way up. It was only a slight split in the path, it was possible I had been so lost in my thoughts and footing going up that I hadn't noticed it. Whatever the reason, the question was which path should I choose.

I walked a few steps down the right-hand path and then turned around and walked back to the split, just to get a sense for what it may have felt like to walk up from that path. It didn't feel familiar at all. But then neither did the same test on the left-hand path. In a way I was glad for the darkness. If I was doing this in the light it would look hilarious to any other hiker. I chose the left-hand path, chiefly as it seemed to be more exposed to the moonlight than the other, and comforted myself that as there was only one town and one station in the area, both paths should lead there.

Five minutes later I was not so sure. On the way up, the path had run parallel with a mountain stream for a short distance. There was as yet no sound of running water. I stopped and calmed myself. I must have chosen the wrong path. I turned around and headed up the path from where I had come. The increase in effort to walk uphill soon brought warmth to my chest and thighs. Reaching the split, I turned sharply down the other path without a pause.

This path did not look familiar to me either, from what I could see of it. It was even gloomier than the other, the moon's light filtering down through the tall tree trunks had withered by the time it reached the floor. I held out my arms and gripped any tree trunk that came into reach. It was slow progress, but it was progress. I approached a moonlit clearing. I had passed no such clearing on the way up and knew with a moan of anguish that this was not the path. But in the centre of the clearing stood a signpost and walking up to it I saw how arrow-shaped planks had been nailed into the hard wooden post. Each plank pointed to one of the paths that led from the clearing, with a name written in kanji painted in white paint. I couldn't read kanji, certainly not when it had been handwritten, but thought I recognized what was written on one of the planks to be similar in shape and complexity as the three characters for Okutama, the station I had got off the train at.

I had started to tread cautiously down it when I heard something. There it was again. A shout. I shouted "help" back, and thinking I may be understating it followed it quickly with a louder, "Hey, over here." A rod of light cut through the trees and I knew that somebody had a torch. I walked back to the clearing in time for the silhouette of the man carrying the torch to enter it too.

"Ah, there you are," the man said, walking up to me and switching off the torch. "Are you all right?"

"Yes, I'm fine," I said. "I got a little lost, it's so dark."

"Yes, we thought you had. My girlfriend and I were waiting at the bottom for you to come down, but when you didn't, we figured that maybe you had left it too late and got lost in the dark. I'm sorry. It's my fault. I should have told you it was time to go down before we left you at the top."

"Oh. You were on the summit?"

"Sure. Didn't you see us?"

"Er, well, I saw you but I didn't look at your faces closely."

"I see. Well, let's go down before it gets any darker. My girlfriend is waiting for us."

"Okay. Thank you so much."

The man switched his torch back on, casting a powerful beam ahead, and then set off down the path from where he had come. Following behind, I wondered where I would have got to if I had kept on the path I had chosen.

Some twenty minutes later we entered a soba restaurant on the street behind the station. Sitting at a corner table was a young woman with long hair who watched us enter the restaurant with a beaming smile.

"Oh good, you found him," she said to the man.

We took a seat and she poured us glasses of steaming tea. Cold and hungry, we ordered bowls of steaming ramen.

"I'm Ryu," the man said, "and this is Emi."

In the light I leaned back and took a good look at them both. Ryu was a little older than myself but still young. We hadn't spoken on the way down, save for a few words of caution from the man such as "Watch your step here" or "Look out for that branch".

"Thank you for rescuing me, it really was very kind of you," I said.

"Not at all. I should have spoken to you when we were sitting on the rock up there. But you seemed to be concentrating very hard on something and I didn't want to disturb you. Emi urged me to but I was too scared."

I looked over at Emi. I had never seen a woman as beautiful in my life.

"That's okay," I said. "It really was my fault. I thought I would be able to get down in the dark. Obviously, I was wrong." I raised my palms in self-mockery. They both laughed.

As we hurriedly slurped down our noodles, I learned they worked at the same company and had been together just over a year. And they, like me, had come out of Tokyo for the day to get some fresh air.

"I'm really from the countryside," Ryu told me. "My parents live in southern Chiba and that's where I was born. If I don't get out of Tokyo every few weeks, I go crazy."

107

"He really does," Emi said, nodding.

"So do I," I said. I told them of where I had come from.

"You must find it tough in Tokyo," Ryu said. "Maybe it's tougher for you than for me."

On the last train out of Okutama station, we sat next to each other and talked about what we did in Tokyo. I found it strange that this couple were so interested in me. Crammed together on the train, they asked me about Scotland and what I did there and I was eager to tell them. The journey to Shinjuku station seemed to take half the time of the one from Shinjuku to Okutama. It was just past midnight when we got off the train and said our goodbyes. Before we separated Emi pressed a slip of paper she had torn from her Filofax into my hand. It had their names, a telephone number and email address.

"Keep in touch," Ryu said, shaking hands. He meant it. "Let's go for a hike together next time."

*

Over thirty years later, I've found my feet in Japan. In fact, I never did leave.

I live near Okutama and do my work at home on my computer. If the weather is in my favour I enjoy stunning views from my office window and can sometimes see Mount Fuji's peak. Once a week Emi and I take the train into Tokyo, where I do the face-to-face stuff in the company's headquarters while Emi goes shopping or takes in a movie. Later we have a beer with Ryu and his wife. It's nice to catch up and talk about the old times. I like to feel the buzz of Tokyo and hear the roar of the traffic, but when we head back and finally get off the train at Okutama station approaching midnight, we exit the station into darkness. My heart thumps at the silent force of nature thinly cloaked in black, and at the slumbering mountains in the distance. At the taxi rank, our taxi's headlights turn on, the car glides forwards and stops in front of us, its door opens and the driver beckons us inside for the short ride to our home in the hills.

Magpie Man

I'm a tall man and walk with a bit of a stoop. Although still in my thirties, I have developed a slightly rounded back and, by extension, my neck tilts downwards. I peer at the floor so often I see things that others who walk with a straight posture wouldn't notice. I have been hiking through a forest and found the freshly discarded black tail of a lizard. I have found somebody's house key while strolling in Greenwich Park. And a SIM card on the pavement of the local high street. What I'm trying to say is, I am a "spotter".

After I graduated, I worked in London for a major Japanese bank. I applied myself and moved up the corporate ladder without difficulty. A couple of years ago, out of the blue, the bank asked me to relocate to Tokyo. At first I told them I didn't want to go. I had never travelled outside the UK and Japan was too far away. Colleagues who had lived in Tokyo, however, enthused about the great time they had there. They said I would regret not taking the chance. I softened and told the bank I would go.

I soon found myself caged by the office culture of the bank's head office in Murunouchi, not far from Tokyo station. I worked long hours during the week and had the weekends to recover. My daily commute to the office started with a five-minute walk from my apartment in Takadanobaba, known locally as "Baba", to the train station. I endured a painful twenty-minute ride on a cramped train to Ohtemachi station, followed by a five-minute walk to the office. I often arrived exhausted and had to fight the urge to slump at my desk.

Given the hordes of commuters in Tokyo and their close proximity when on the move, things inevitably get dropped from time to time. Smartphones slip out of hands and slam into the floor with a bang that shocks the owner and all those around. Smaller items when dropped don't make enough noise to rise above the din, their owners locked into the commute sometimes not noticing until it is too late.

There isn't much you can do when you get to the office and find that your company badge, for example, is no longer on your jacket lapel. There are meetings to attend and work to be done. You could at best report the loss to a train station's office at lunchtime, and ask them to call you if the badge is found. Or, if still bothered by the loss, pop your head into a station's office at the end of the day. But then again, the badge will surely have been swept up by an enthusiastic cleaner or sucked up by a powerful vacuum cleaner and thrown into the bin.

One morning in an underground passageway at Takadanobaba station, as I walked head-down towards the ticket gate, my briefcase slung over a shoulder, a metallic glint from the granite floor caught my eye. I slowed, turned and took a stride closer. It was a pin badge.

Cut in the shape of a Snoopy character, the front of the badge was painted in bright colour enamel. The character's name didn't come to mind, so I popped the badge into my jacket pocket and told myself I'd search for the name on the internet later. It didn't occur to me to visit the lost and found office. I was excited by the find, even though the badge had no clutch plate and couldn't be used. When I got to the office, I opened a web browser and began typing. The character was Linus, true to form holding his security blanket.

Within a few days I found a pink plastic holder for mechanical pencil leads, with only one length of lead left inside. I didn't even have a mechanical pencil, but I took the holder home and stood it on end next to the badge, like a trophy, on the top shelf of my bookcase.

Over the months that followed, my collection of odds and ends grew. I kept them in a cookie tin. Almost anything would find its way into the tin, from a snapped and irreparably broken necklace chain to a one cent Euro coin. There were tiepins, company badges, hairpins, pin badges, earrings, a guitar pick, a cufflink, a ring, and a few things I had no idea about.

One morning I picked a smartphone strap off the steps of an escalator. The strap, sea green in colour, had the words "Seattle Mariners" printed on it in white. When I arrived at work I showed it to a colleague, a baseball fan, thinking he'd be interested.

"That's official Mariners' gear," he said. "Whoever dropped it is sure to be looking for it, so you should take it to the station."

"Yeah, I think you're right. I'll do so this lunchtime," I said.

"You must. Besides, I heard that anything found has to be reported. It's the law."

I hadn't even thought about the law. If I had found something of obvious value or importance, a wallet, passport, pearl necklace or such, I would have reported the find. I stopped at the station during my lunch break and passed the strap over the counter to an employee. "*Otoshimono*," (dropped object) I said, and walked away before he had time to question me.

My work life got busier and I found myself managing a small team of multinational staff. Every day I struggled to handle their varied personalities and demands while making sure the team and company objectives were achieved. Although I was fulfilling the bank's vision for my role in Tokyo I couldn't wait to leave the office in the evening and get back to the peace and quiet of my apartment. I earned more money than I needed, but had no interest in dining in Michelin-starred restaurants or buying a luxury car. I was content to keep myself to myself, but one day, to my surprise, a woman in the accounting department asked me out for lunch. During lunch, Tomoko's quirky imitation of our fellow employees' mannerisms had me holding my sides with laughter. I hadn't laughed so hard for a long time. We had lunch a few more times over the following weeks and stepped our relationship up to dating on evenings and weekends, spending time in each other's apartments. And then Tomoko found the cookie tin.

"Why are you keeping this junk?"

I explained. As my words left my mouth, I wished I had been smart enough to hide the tin away.

"You shouldn't do that. It's not yours, it's stealing."

"No, it's not. All this stuff was on the floor, the owners clueless or not even bothered to look for it."

"That's not the point. It's wrong to take it and not even give the owners the chance to find it."

Tomoko was clearly angry, however I could think of nothing to say.

"You're like that bird," she continued, "you know the one, big, black and white."

"Penguin?"

"No! You're making fun of me. I mean the one that gathers shiny things and puts them in its nest."

"Ah, magpie?"

"Yes, magpie. They find things like coins and jewellery and fly up high into their nests and drop them inside, out of sight from everyone. The people who own those things have no chance of ever finding them again."

I laughed at being compared to a magpie. My laugh made her angrier.

"You know what, you are a magpie. You are a magpie man."

"Now you are making fun of me!"

"No, no, it's real, it's the truth. I'm not making fun of you."

She uttered those final words with a broad sweep of her arm, as if pushing me away. Those are the last words I remember Tomoko saying to me. After we broke up, I asked myself if Tomoko was correct? Had I been denying the owners of the objects in my tin their right to finding them?

*

I changed my walking style. With my shoulders pinned back and chin raised, the ground became a blur. It took a surprising amount of effort and persistence. My chest and upper-back muscles ached for a while. My reward though, was a new and fascinating world opening up to me. The world of fashion. I gazed at people's clothes, their jackets, their skirts and their bags, peered at their shoes and admired their hairstyles. I made a mental list of the obscure English phrases on their t-shirts and came to the conclusion I had been missing out on a lot of fun.

It was a glint of metal on a walkway at Ohtemachi station that brought the fun to an end.

I had already bent at the waist to pick the object up when my brain sent me a message asking why I was doing this yet again. I ignored the message. It was a delicate earring, gold-plated I sensed from the weight, with a garnet stud. How could that drop off an ear and the owner not know, I wondered. I stood up straight and unthinkingly slipped the earring inside my jacket pocket, intending to study it when I got home. I stepped forwards, slapped my pass against the ticket gate reader, passed through the gate, avoided the glare from the station office window to the right and veered left towards the escalator that would take me down to the platform.

"Stop," a woman shouted from close behind, almost at the same time as her hand pulled on my shoulder. "Stop, I said."

I turned. A young woman with excited eyes peered up at me. Her cheeks were pink and she was a little out of breath.

"You've got my earring, haven't you? I'm sure I just saw you pick it up."

"Sorry?"

I scanned her face, desperate for a clue as to how to respond.

"Well, you have my earring don't you? Please give it back to me. It's mine. Look, here's the other one," she said, flicking the earring dangling from her left ear.

"Oh, yes, here it is," I said. I reached into my jacket pocket, took the earring out and dropped it into her cupped hand. "I was going to hand it in to lost and found."

The woman shook her head. "No you weren't. You could have dropped it off here, at this station office," she said, emphatically nodding at the open window to the office, "but you didn't. You're just a thief."

"I'm not a thief," I said. "There's a lost and found office at the station I get off at. I thought I'd go there."

"That doesn't make sense. What were you going to do with my earring? Sell it?"

"Oh, come on…"

The woman moved a step closer and stood almost under my chin.

"It's not fair. I always hand in things I find, even though it takes a few minutes of my time. What goes around comes around, you know. But people like you, well you just don't care about anyone else but yourself."

Her proximity and the force of her argument had my legs trembling, but one thing I had learned in my professional life was not to show weakness, even when in the wrong.

"Hey, like I said, I was going to take it to lost and found. You're making a mountain out of a molehill."

The woman's expression did not change. She opened her mouth, about to cut me down to size I was sure, and, yet, the station master who had appeared by our side, spoke first.

"Would you kindly both move to the side? You're blocking the path to the ticket gates."

The station master had a point. We had attracted a small group of passers-by, which had in turn slowed the stream of commuters through the ticket gate, causing a tailback. The station master, a thin grey-haired man wearing rectangular silver-framed spectacles over his close-set eyes, spread his arms wide and herded us like sheep towards the window of his office. The throng of bystanders dispersed.

The woman thrust the details of the incident on the station master, opened her palm to reveal the earring and lifted it up to his eye level. She tried to lay the "thief" label on me again, but to my surprise the station master was having none of it.

"Don't be silly," he told her. "Look, the earring is there, in your palm. If it was in this man's palm, it would be a serious matter. Besides, what use would this ugly guy have for such a beautiful earring?"

I didn't agree with the "ugly" tag, but preferred it to "thief" and the possibility of the police being called.

"I had to stop him and force him to give it back to me," the woman persisted. "If I hadn't, he would have disappeared and I'd never have got it back. He lied and said he was going to hand it to lost and found where he lives, but he's a liar, and a thief."

"Hey," I interjected. "I already told you I'm not a thief."

"Where do you live?" the station master asked.

"Takadanobaba."

"Well, there you have it." The station master turned to face the woman square on. "There is a lost and found office at Baba station."

The woman stared glumly at the station master, shook her head, wheeled around and stormed away.

I thanked the station master, turned towards the escalator and ran down the steps to the platform.

On the train home, I decided I had to kill this habit once and for all. The woman's anger had shaken me. My behaviour towards her had been appalling. Even the station master had treated her roughly. I couldn't let this happen again.

I knew I had to do something about the items in the cookie tin. However, I couldn't simply take it to the police, or to a train station's lost and found office. I wouldn't be able to explain in Japanese what I had done. The risk was too high. And so, on the morning of a rubbish pick-up at the building I lived in, I placed a handwritten note in the cookie tin stating "All items found at Tokyo train stations between 2016 and 2018. Please return to their owners". I sealed the edges of the tin with cellotape and took it to the rubbish pick-up area. There, I pushed the tin deep into the metallic bin, so it was concealed under empty cans of tomatoes, olives and beer.

A few weeks later, I was back in England.

I had for a while been seeking a way back home. On a recruitment site I found a role with a British bank in their Reading office. It gave me what I yearned for, a relaxed and yet professional work style with much less responsibility. The new job wasn't as well paid, but I didn't mind. To compensate, the lush green Hampshire Downs were only a few minutes' drive away. I joined a local metal-detecting group and spent many a weekend detecting in fields and on public paths. The other day I dug up an old RAF lapel badge with its elegant blue enamel still intact. The badge had an engraving. After a little searching on the internet, I found the owner's family and sent the badge on its way to them.

Apartment 601

On Saturday afternoon, I stood on the roof of my apartment building for the very first time. It seemed a good idea at the time. My son, Jake, wanted to fly his kite. A mere ten minutes' walk away is a park with a wide stretch of grass, perfect for kite flying. Just about every member of the neighbourhood wants to be there, flying their own kites, kicking their balls, throwing their frisbees and playing catch. I couldn't face the turmoil and tussle for space, so, when Jake and I left our apartment on the third floor and got in the elevator to go down, I pressed the button to go up, all the way to the eighth floor, the top floor.

"Why are we going up?" Jake asked.

"To see if we can fly the kite from the roof," I said.

"The roof! I want to go to the park. I want to fly my kite in the park."

"You will. We'll just have a look at the roof first," I said, as the elevator doors parted on the eighth floor.

I held Jake's hand and stepped out. I peered left and right, scanning the passageway for any difference to the third floor. It was just the same. However, in front of us was a steel door. Through its frame I could see stairs leading upwards, to the roof I assumed.

"Can we go to the park now?" Jake asked.

"This isn't the roof, we have to go up those stairs," I said, pointing ahead.

I turned the handle of the door. There was no resistance. I leaned into the door, half expecting it to be locked. It swung open. A few steps later, Jake and I were standing on the roof.

"Oh, look at the view," I found myself blurting as I saw Tokyo Skytree in the distance, head and shoulders above the throng of downtown Tokyo's high-rise buildings.

The only thing of note on the roof was a lightning rod, which stood a good six metres high in one corner. I steered away from the rod towards the opposite corner as I didn't want to wrap the kite around it.

"Let's fly the kite here," I said.

"Why?"

"There's lots of room here," I said, waving an arm in the air and smiling in an attempt to paint a picture of the fun we were going to have.

"But I want to go to the park."

"We'll go," I said, "I promise. But we're here now. It'll only be for a minute or two."

I unravelled the line before Jake had a chance to reply, held the kite at arm's length and felt it rustle in the breeze. I let go. The kite shot up into the sky. I let the line course through my fingers. The kite was immediately buffeted from side to side by the bustling breeze, making controlling difficult, but fun.

"Let me try," Jake said.

I handed Jake the handle, but didn't release my hold on it. His face turned sour.

"We'll fly it together," I said, "just until you get used to the wind."

The kite must have sensed our discord for it fluttered, hesitated, and dived. I yanked the handle down to force the kite's nose up, but it was too late and the kite ploughed over the edge of the wall. The line sagged and lay limp on the floor.

"My kite," Jake shouted.

"It's alright," I said, running to the edge. "We'll get it back."

Bending from the waist over the wall, I saw the tail of the kite streaming from the railings of a balcony two floors down. I groaned, wound in the line till taut, then tugged in an attempt to dislodge the kite. The kite didn't budge.

Jake peered over the edge.

"Stand back," I told him, holding my arm out.

I walked a few metres to one side and jerked the line again, hoping a different angle would free the kite. No luck. I tried the other side, again without success.

"Let me," Jake begged.

I handed him the handle, knowing he wouldn't be happy until he had tried.

"There you go, but keep away from the wall."

Jake mimicked what I had done, with the same result.

"What are we going to do?" Jake cried.

"It's stuck in the railings of an apartment two flights down. Let's go and ask them to free it for us."

There was no railing to which I could tie the kite's handle, so I resorted to unravelling just about all the line and wrapping the handle around the base of the lightning rod.

Dejected, Jake and I trod down the stairs to the eighth floor and took the elevator to the sixth floor. There, I took a few seconds to check my bearings as I wanted to be sure I would knock on the door of the correct apartment. It turned out to be apartment 601, three floors above my own.

Outside the apartment a lilac-coloured sun umbrella stood in a simple stand. There were no other personal effects, other than the name "Yamada" in Japanese script in the name slot above the number "601".

I pressed the door bell and waited, mentally rehearsing what I would say and straightening my hair. There was no response. I rang the bell again, and again there was no response.

"Must be out." I sighed. "Let's go home."

"But, what about my kite?" Jake said.

"I'll come back later and get it. There's nobody here right now."

My wife, Ami, was surprised by our premature return to the apartment.

"Did the kite break?"

Jake explained what we'd been up to. Ami wasn't pleased.

"You shouldn't have gone up there. We're not allowed on the roof."

"I didn't know."

"The strong wind is dangerous. Don't go up there again, especially not with Jake."

"You're right, it was windy up there, surprisingly windy."

"That's what I mean. You shouldn't have been able to get on the roof so easily."

Ami didn't know the Yamadas on the sixth floor, but suggested I call them on the building's intercom system. I'd forgotten all about the intercom. A few months back, Ami had used it to call the mother of one of Jake's school friends living in the same building. I punched 601 on the intercom, listened to it ring a few times, and gave up.

By now, Jake was in his room, listening to music. I decided to give up on apartment 601 for the day.

On Sunday morning I went to the gym, as I always did. Returning home, just before midday, I tramped around the side of the building. Craning my neck, I saw the kite's tail dangling from the railing of apartment 601. The railing ran around a small balcony at the side of the apartment, on which air conditioners are sometimes placed. It was more a ledge than a balcony, too dangerous to stand on. My apartment also had one. I decided to visit, explain what had happened, and convince the Yamadas to let me be the one to free the kite. I entered the building and rode the elevator to the sixth floor.

Standing once again in front of the door to apartment 601, I took a calming breath, prodded the door bell and waited.

I was about to give up and walk away when the door edged open and the face of a middle-aged woman appeared. With the chain on, the gap was narrow and I couldn't see all of her face, but she was in her late forties I guessed, pleasant-looking with her hair tied up in a bun.

"Yes," she said, offering no trace of warmth.

I tensed, sensing difficulties ahead.

"Ah, hello, I'm Smith and I live in apartment 301."

"Yes," she repeated.

I found myself talking faster.

"I'm sorry to bother you but the other day my son and I were flying a kite on the roof and, well, it got wrapped around your balcony rails."

Whether it was my poor Japanese or the torrent of words I didn't know, but she didn't appear to absorb what I had said, until, as I was about to repeat my words, she spoke.

"You must have the wrong apartment. I haven't seen a kite."

"Oh."

"I was just on the balcony, hanging out the washing. There was no kite."

"Ah, sorry, I didn't mean the balcony at the back of the apartment, I meant the small one at the side. There is a little balcony on which you have an air conditioner, maybe outside a bedroom?"

The woman nodded. "I see. However, I can't check it now. I'll check it later."

"Later?"

"Yes."

"What time will that be? I'll come back then and collect the kite."

"I don't know. I'm busy. If there is a kite I'll leave it outside your apartment. What apartment do you live in?"

"301. Are you sure it won't be too much trouble for you? The balcony is small and dangerous to climb out onto. I'd rather get it myself."

A door creaked open behind the woman who, startled, turned her head. The shuffling steps of slippers on a wooden floor drew near. I prepared for a Mr Yamada to give me a piece of his mind for disturbing his Sunday.

"Akihiro," the woman gasped.

"I'll take care of it," a man's voice said. I had the urge to leave.

The woman shut the door. There was a rattle of a chain, the door opened again, wider than before.

A man, young, tall and thin, stood in front of me. He wore loose-fitting, heavily creased pyjamas. He flicked his shoulder-length hair away from the side of his face with a forefinger, the nail of which was white and long. A straggly beard hung from his chin, in need of a brush, or a trim.

126

The woman, now hidden behind him, spoke. "Akihiro," she said, "shall I make a pot of tea?"

"Later."

The woman sidled down the corridor towards a half-opened door and was met by the sharp tweet of a bird, a canary I guessed.

"My name is Akihiro. How may I help you?" the young man said, with a lilting British accent that sounded all too familiar.

"You speak English?"

"Ah, yes, I spent a year in England, doing an MBA. Have you heard of Warwick Business School?"

"I went to Coventry University, just down the road from Warwick," I said.

"You don't say."

"Yes. I studied international marketing as an undergraduate."

"What a coincidence. When was that?"

"2009 to 2011."

"I was at Warwick in 2009. We must have been in the UK at the same time."

Akihiro smiled.

I laughed. "Yes, you're right. I've been to Warwick a few times as well, so we may have even passed each other in a street."

"Small world."

We looked at each other for the few seconds it took our smiles to cool.

"So, you're here about a kite?" Akihiro said.

I explained the turn of events that had brought me to his doorstep.

"I thought I heard something," he said, "but figured it was a crow. They like to sit on the railing and take in the view. I'll have a look. Why don't you come inside?"

He stood back and held the door open for me to enter. As my hand took the weight of the door he stepped away and padded into his room, pyjamas flapping around his thin frame. Had he lost a lot of weight, perhaps due to illness, or was he simply wearing pyjamas a couple of sizes too large?

Down at the other end of the corridor his mother was watching proceedings. We exchange a glance. The bird twittered again.

I heard curtains being parted in the room Akihiro had entered. A rectangular beam of sunlight burst out of the room and lit up the corridor wall. His mother drew closer, from curiosity or concern, I couldn't tell. From the room came the sound of a window being unlatched and slid open.

"Akihiro, what are you doing?" his mother said, projecting her voice towards the open door.

"Getting the Englishman's kite."

She sniffed. I realized she was crying, ever so softly.

"Take care, it's dangerous," she said, wiping away tears with the end of her apron.

She moved over to the entrance of the room and looked inside, peering here and there as if it were the first time she'd seen inside.

There was a clattering sound, which I imagined to be the kite's frame fighting with the railings.

A few seconds later, Akihiro emerged from the room clasping the kite, an embarrassed smile on his face.

"I'm awfully sorry," he said. "I had to cut the line. You must have tied it to something on the roof."

"The lightning rod. Don't worry, I'll sort it out later. Look, I really appreciate you getting the kite. My son will be over the moon."

"Not at all. It was my pleasure. It was good to speak English with you."

"Likewise."

"You know, I've been thinking to study English again. I haven't spoken it for a few years now and I've forgotten so many words."

"I think you speak perfect English."

"No, no, I'm very rusty. Do you teach English?"

"I don't."

"Ah. That's a shame."

The woman retreated to the living room. A second later there was the sound of a kettle being filled.

"Look," I said, "if you like, we could have a chat over a cup of coffee. There's a cafe just opened near the station."

"A cafe?"

"Yes. I'd like to hear about your time in England. And I'll pay, to thank you for your help."

"That's really kind of you. I'd like that."

"Great. How about next Saturday, 10 am?"

"Should be fine."

"I'll knock on your door."

"I'm already looking forward to it."

I let myself out. I skipped down the three flights of stairs to my apartment and entered the living room, protectively clasping the kite to my chest, as if it were the *Mona Lisa*.

Jake was delighted to have his kite back. I told him we'd go fly it in the park, after lunch.

Ami was also relieved to see the kite.

"Were the Yamadas put out by your visit?"

"Not at all. I think they were happy to see me."

"Happy?"

"I'll tell you later, after we've got Jake to bed."

That evening, sitting on the sofa sharing a bottle of wine, I told Ami what had happened.

"Poor woman," she said. "It may have been the first time she's spoken to him in months. You did her a favour, enticing him out of his room to speak English to you."

"He's a nice bloke," I said. "I wonder why he's been cooped up in his room."

"Maybe he'll tell you on Saturday."

"Maybe he will."

The Tree

One evening in early autumn I returned home from my job at Kyoto University, put an unlit cigarette in my mouth and stepped out into the garden. I lowered my cap to shield my eyes from the shimmering evening sun, pulled out my lighter from a trouser pocket and lit the cigarette.

Over the garden fence I saw the peak of Mr Hamada's sun hat. I walked over to the fence to say hello. He stood with his back to me, gloved hands on hips, taking in the spread of his tree. Its branches graced the garden like the outspread wings of an eagle, their ochre-tinged leaves rippling in the breeze.

The cigarette fumes must have reached Mr Hamada, for he swung around to face me.

"Hi, David, what's up?" he said.

Mr Hamada's company had sent him to Redmond, Washington to get their North America operation started. He was there for three years, during which he had got fluent in English, and he didn't miss a chance to use it.

"I'm fine thanks, Ken. Just taking a smoke, hope you don't mind."

"Not at all." He pointed with unrestrained joy at the tree. "Isn't it magnificent?"

"It certainly is."

133

I couldn't tell if it was an elm or a maple, but it wouldn't have looked out of place in the garden of a Kyoto temple.

"Aren't you taking photographs today?" I said.

"No, the light is a little strong right now."

I'd seen him spend hours in the garden, macro-lens camera in his hands, taking close-up shots of his plants. During one visit to his home he had shown me some of his photographs. Despite my ignorance of both flora and film I was impressed by their crystal clarity and beauty.

"This is the best time of year to appreciate Acer japonicum," he said. "It really is a tree of rare presence."

We talked until the cool breeze got the better of my thin t-shirt and, not wanting to catch a cold, I said goodbye and went back inside.

It was only a couple of weeks later that Susan returned out of breath from a visit to the local supermarket, kicked off her shoes in the entrance hall, hurried into the living room and dropped the shopping bags onto the table.

"Anything wrong?"

"Mrs Hamada, she was in the store."

"That's nice."

"No, no, she was there, at the checkout."

"She forgot her purse?"

"No, silly, she was working, working at the checkout."

"What?"

"Yes. Can you believe it?"

I couldn't. Mrs Hamada's work had always been in her home, raising her family, keeping the house impressively clean and tidy.

"What did she say?"

"She said she liked my new coat."

"That's all?"

"Yes, she was busy. I wonder why she's working there."

"Maybe she got bored, wanted something to do," I said. "It must be quiet for her now that the children have left home. And you can't work any closer to home than the store."

It was true; the store was only a few minutes' walk away.

"Or maybe she wants some extra pocket money?" I continued. "You know those things she collects, natsu, netsu…"

"Netsuke?"

"Yes. They're not cheap."

"You know, that could be it," she said. "Extra pocket money."

As it turned out, there was another reason. By chance I met Mr Hamada on the train coming home one evening during the week. He seemed unwilling to be drawn into conversation in the crowded carriage, and didn't make an effort to stay close to me when people squeezed themselves between us in their quest to get into the train. But after we got off at our station and passed through the wicket, we walked together and Mr Hamada was the first to talk.

"I lost my job," he said.

"Oh my God. How? Why?"

"Restructuring. Our director hired a consulting company to make an independent analysis of the company's strengths and weaknesses, and then without question he accepted the consulting company's recommendations. Two hundred jobs will go this year. Forty went last month, including my job."

"Oh, I'm sorry to hear that."

"Me too," he said, his smile exposing the sharpness of his white teeth. "I took redundancy pay, but it was not as much as I expected. It's been quite a shock, especially for Kumiko."

"Yes, it must have been. So you've been out looking for work today?"

Mr Hamada was dressed in a pinstripe navy blue suit, his company badge present on its lapel.

"No," he said. "Today those that lost their jobs met to discuss what we can do. We may make a claim against the company. We don't want to, the company has supported us for many years, but we don't think it's fair to be dismissed in such a way. Some of us will find it difficult to find other work."

We walked by the supermarket, and through the ever-present "Sale" notices on the window and the shoppers thronging the entrance I could see the back of Mrs Hamada. She wore the same turquoise jacket that all store employees wore and was passing a customer's goods over a barcode reader and placing them in a basket. I saw Mr Hamada look too, and waited for him to say something. But from the supermarket to our homes the only word he uttered was a final goodnight.

At home I found Susan had yet to return from work. From the assorted vegetables that rattled around inside the refrigerator and a couple of sausages, I came up with an inspired stew and had it bubbling away awaiting her return.

My thoughts turned to Mr Hamada. I couldn't imagine him being in sudden financial difficulty, given the managerial position he had held in the telecommunications company. But he had put both daughters through university and then seen them marry within the past year. Having three daughters marry was once considered enough to bankrupt a family, and even two would have made a dent in most people's savings.

"So she must have taken that job because she had to," Susan said later that evening. "It must be tough for them."

"It looks that way. But he's sure to find work soon; he has so much experience and talent."

"Is there anything you can do?"

"You mean finding work for him? I thought about that, but the only people we need now are in our IT department, to manage our open-source learning management system, you know, geeks with Java experience. Not his area at all."

"That's a shame."

It was. After our meal I put on a jacket and spent a couple of minutes outside with a cigarette, the moon looking as if it were stuck in the upper branches of Mr Hamada's maple tree.

Heading into late October, the weather turned ugly. Successive storms trampled down the length of Japan, pummelling it and us into a state of exhaustion. In the early hours of one morning we lay in bed listening to the wind and the cacophonous rattle of windows in their wooden frames. Incessant rainwater streamed off the roof and gurgled down the guttering.

Suddenly there was a crash, followed by the wrenching sound of splitting wood. I found myself standing by the bedroom window without knowing how I had got there. In Mr Hamada's garden a stay that had supported his tree lay flat on the grass. One branch had ruptured at the trunk and now rolled around on the grass, held to the tree only by leather-like slivers of wet bark.

"What was the noise?" Susan said.

"His tree. A branch has broken."

"Oh my." Susan came to the window.

A light came on in the Hamadas' house. Soon Mr Hamada appeared in a dressing gown under the expanse of a golf umbrella, which he fought to keep above him. He made his way over to the tree and we saw him look back and forth, from the white of the fractured wood to the branch that lay near his feet. He crouched down and placed a hand upon the branch, and stayed that way for a few seconds. He then stood, turned and ran back inside.

I woke to the alarm clock. My head throbbed from lack of sleep and I thought of staying in bed and making a late appearance at the office.

"I'll make coffee," Susan said.

Downstairs in the kitchen my curiosity got the better of me. Instead of sitting down for the coffee Susan had made, I unlocked the door, wedged my feet into Susan's slippers, and braved the damp, chilly morning air. Had what I'd seen in the night actually happened?

As I drew closer to the fence the sound of a saw grew louder. Dressed in a business suit, Mr Hamada raked the hacksaw he held with both hands back and forth across the trunk of the tree. Yellow chips spat out onto the lawn and over his shoes. The tone of the saw peaked as the blade finished its job, and with hardly a sound the tree flopped onto the grass.

He shook the dust from his trousers.

"Good morning, Mr Hamada."

He turned his head sharply.

"Oh, good morning, David, you surprised me. Have you seen what the storm did to Acer japonicum?"

He lifted the end of the branch that had sheared and held it towards me.

"That's a real shame, Mr Hamada," I said, struggling to find the right words. "I heard the branch break in the storm last night. But why did you cut the tree down?"

Mr Hamada pursed his lips. "I didn't make the supports strong enough, you see. When the branch snapped the tree became lopsided and put pressure on a stake which then broke, which made the balance even worse and tore some of its roots right out of the ground. It's my fault. I was thinking so much about the leaves, when all along it was the roots that were most important."

"I don't think you could have done anything to protect it from last night's storm," I said. "It was pretty wild."

"You know, perhaps you're right. This morning's television news was full of reports of damage the storm caused. I saw pictures of much bigger trees that had fallen during the night."

He rested a foot on top of the stump.

"When I get time I'll dig this out," he said. "How would you like to take a drive with us to a garden centre this weekend, to look at some saplings?"

"You're getting another tree?"

"Why, of course. The best time to plant it is fall, before winter comes along and the ground turns hard. We were thinking Sunday morning. It would be nice to spend some time out of the city. If you and Susan would like to come, let us know."

"I will, thank you."

From the Hamadas' house Mrs Hamada approached at pace holding a long-handled broom.

"Come on, come on, I'll tidy up," she said. "It's already eight o'clock. You shouldn't be late for your interview."

"Eight? I didn't realize I had spent so much time out here."

He turned to me. "Sorry, I must be going."

"No problem. Good luck with your interview."

"Thanks, but I've already been lucky. It's a second interview with a company that used to be a competitor. They know my work. Today is just a formality; we'll tie up some loose ends, that sort of thing."

"That's great news," I said. "Congratulations."

"The salary isn't so good, but it's enough to get by, especially with Kumiko's help."

"Yes, yes, I know, I know," Mrs Hamada said, reaching for the broom. "Just get going, won't you? You can talk all you like at the weekend."

"Okay," he said, raising his eyebrows in mock irritation. He waved to me and strode off towards his house.

I watched him go and was about to say goodbye to Mrs Hamada when I found she had come so close to the garden fence that our faces were almost touching.

"He's making a big mistake if he thinks I'm going to keep working in that supermarket," she said. "A big mistake."

Her eyes sparkled and the corners of her smile pushed her cheeks into shiny balls. She turned around and set to work on sweeping up the chippings. As I walked back to the kitchen I heard the peal of her laughter spill over the fence.

Misdirection

Ash was on his commute home. He worked as a manager for a stock broker in Tokyo's Hibiya area. His apartment was in the Makuhari area of Chiba. Door to door, one hour five minutes, with one change of train at Hachobori station. The company had looked after him all these years and he wore the company badge with pride on his jacket lapel, pleased to think of himself as a small cog in the company's success.

As the train pulled into Hachobori station, Ash felt for his train pass. There it was, right-hand trouser pocket. The train slowed and he inched closer to the door, careful not to nudge the man in front of him. The door opened. Ash lowered his head to avoid bumping it on the door frame. He stepped out of the train and found himself sucked into the surge of passengers heading for the stairs at the end of the platform.

"Excuse me," somebody said in a voice too low for Ash to hear over the platform announcement for the train arriving at the opposite platform.

"Excuse me," the woman shouted. This plea didn't pierce Ash's bubble of consciousness as he focused on reaching the stairs. Somebody wanting help would scream, or reach out to…

A hand grasped Ash's forearm. Ash glanced up and saw behind a mess of hair, the green eyes of a small, slim woman, her cheeks pink, with thin red lips and a t-shirt that needed a wash. She had a huge backpack strapped over her shoulders and behind her stood a hunk of a man, with matching hair, t-shirt and backpack.

"Ebisu," she rasped, her hand clamped on his arm. "Is this the right train?" she said, with an exaggerated nod at the train Ash had alighted from.

"Err, yes, yes it is."

"This one, Ed," she bellowed. She fought through the commuters and into the carriage, Ed in tow. A "thanks, mate" hung in the air, the doors shut, the train slid away.

Later that evening, after Ash had finished gleaning all the meat from the bones of his grilled salmon and licked the points of his chopsticks clean, he told his wife Sayuri what had happened.

"You mean to say, you gave that poor woman the wrong directions?"

"Well…"

"On purpose. You put her on the wrong train on purpose, didn't you?"

"Not on purpose. It was a misunderstanding."

"No, no, it was on purpose."

"What do you mean?"

"Don't you remember? That time a car stopped in the high street in Ainthorpe and the driver asked us for directions to Rosedale Abbey. You sent that family in completely the opposite direction, on the road to the coast."

"Oh come on, that wasn't deliberate. I just got confused."

"How come? From their dress it was clear they were on their way to a wedding reception at the abbey. You can't stand the idea of other people having fun. Going to a wedding, going

144

on holiday, you envy them because you've chosen a no-risk lifestyle stripped of all its fun."

"Hey, that's going too far."

"They must have been fuming when they realized they were on the wrong train."

"You're making a mountain out of a molehill. They will have found their way to Ebisu. The subway is easy to navigate these days. Every station has a number now. You don't even have to read Japanese."

"Yes, but they were in a hurry and you slowed them down. What if you meet them again? What if they are waiting for you on the platform tomorrow night at the same time? Have you thought of that?"

He hadn't.

"They won't be, they were on holiday and won't waste time looking for me. They could even be in Kyoto or some other part of Japan by now. Or maybe at Haneda airport just about to board a flight home."

Although he spoke with conviction, he hadn't managed to convince himself.

The next day Ash struggled to concentrate. In the morning he cleared his inbox but it took much longer than usual. In the afternoon he couldn't get going on any of the tasks he had planned. Deciding it was just "one of those days" he left the office early and headed for home. At Hibiya station he boarded a carriage in the middle of the train and, as it pulled into Hachobori station, he peered at the platform ahead, looking for signs of the couple he had bumped into the night before. There were plenty of baggage-lugging folks, but none with the same bad hair. The train stopped. He stepped out halfway and stared up the platform towards the steps. The going was safe. He hurried along the platform and made his way home.

The following day was one of his company's "no overtime" days. Ash left the office at five-thirty and, as usual, turned down the offer to go drinking with his colleagues. He waved goodbye to them when the elevator doors opened on the ground floor. He soon found himself on the train to Hachobori station, forefinger tapping away on his smartphone screen.

The train doors opened and Ash was the first person out. He made a right turn and headed for the stairs, only to find a man in his way. Ash leaned to his right to take himself around the man, but the man leaned to his left at the same time and continued to be in his way. Ash took an instinctive step to his left, the man in front mirrored the move. Irritated, Ash looked up at the face of the man.

Ed. That Ed. The man wore a sharp navy blue suit, was clean-shaven and had his hair bound in a neat ponytail, and yet he was, without doubt, the same Ed.

"Do you remember me, sir," Ed said.

"Err, I'm not sure I do. Would you mind, I'm in a hurry to get home."

Commuters shoved their way around them as they took a position in the middle of the platform.

"Two nights ago, my wife asked you for directions. Right here, right on this spot."

"Really? I don't recall that. She must have spoken to somebody else."

"No, that man was you. I was there too. Most certainly you. I don't forget faces. And you were wearing the same company badge on your lapel."

Ash shuffled his briefcase from his left hand to his right, aware of how sticky they had become. From the start he had decided to show his ignorance and there was no way back now. With a blank expression on his face he looked Ed in the eyes and shook his head.

"I'm sorry, I have no idea what you're talking about. I'm in hurry, you know."

"Is that so," said Ed. "We were in a hurry too. We had to get to Ebisu to pick up our daughter from the childcare centre before it closed."

"Oh."

"Because you told us the train was going to Ebisu, we jumped straight on board. Two stations down the line we realized the train was heading the wrong way. Of course, we had to get off, then onto the train going the other way, which didn't arrive for a few minutes. We got to the childcare centre twenty minutes late. My daughter was very upset. She thought we'd forgotten about her. The owners of the centre were waiting for us to lock up and weren't happy either."

"I'm sorry to hear that."

"Sure you are."

Ed took a step forwards. Ash leaned back, fearing what was to come. Ed reached out an arm, which he slung around Ash's shoulders. The arm lay heavy and warm like the trunk of an elephant. Ash's heart thumped.

"Look, mate, you don't seem to be the kind to deliberately mislead my wife and me," Ed said. "You work for a brand-name company, in a responsible job it seems. The only reason for your misdirection must have been you were confused by my wife's question."

"Well…"

"I know, I know, you're embarrassed to talk, especially here on a station platform with your fellow commuters all around you."

Ash sensed hope.

"I tell you what, let's just drop this and let bygones be bygones."

Ash wasn't sure what a bygone was, but he wasn't going to argue. He just wanted to be gone. He nodded, careful to show no trace of relief on his face.

The arm around Ash's shoulders slipped down and he felt an enormous hand pat him slow and firm on the back, once, twice and then a third and final time.

Ed looked down at Ash. "No hard feelings, mate. I'll let you get on your way."

Ash hesitated for all but a second, then light on his feet he padded towards the stairs. Up he sped, two steps at a time, through the ticket gate and on towards the Keiyo line, gathering pace all the time as if there were a tailwind.

Standing in line on the platform at Hachobori, Ash had a couple of minutes to wait for the train to arrive. Sweat cooled on his brow and under his armpits. Ash had time to reflect on what had happened. He had extracted himself with more ease than he could have hoped when Ed first accosted him. Some people are just too good-natured even when they have the right to be angry, he thought. A smile stretched across Ash's face and from the depth of his chest a laugh leaped from his mouth.

"Hah."

He had a tale to tell Sayuri.

His mood was good as the train for Makuhari arrived. The doors opened and he followed those in front into the carriage. From behind there was laughter, which lifted his spirits. He couldn't wait to get home. The carriage doors closed and the train glided forwards. He pulled his smartphone from his jacket pocket and sent a quick text message to Sayuri to say he'd be home in about forty minutes' time.

The passengers who boarded the train with him also were in a good mood. Perhaps they had had a little too much to drink. At Shin-Kiba station a throng of passengers pressed their way into the train. Goodwill seemed to be all around. A family of four dressed in matching Disney t-shirts boarded at Maihama station. One of them tried to swing on the straps.

Ash replayed the incident in his mind, all the while imagining himself explaining to Sayuri what happened, editing the story to show himself in the best possible light. After a while, the edited version became the reality.

He got off at Makuhari station and stayed in a good mood all the way home, at the bus stop, in the bus, at the convenience store where he stopped to get some peanuts to nibble on with the beer that he would drink later in the evening.

He opened the door to his apartment. He heard Sayuri's footsteps get closer and she appeared in front of him, smiling and taking his bag from his hands. The evening ritual. Ash removed his shoes and stepped inside. He slid his feet into a pair of slippers. He turned his back to let Sayuri pull off his jacket. Sayuri's scream jolted him forwards, and he bumped his head against the wall.

"What are you doing?" he shouted.

With trembling hands Sayuri held up his jacket by the shoulders and turned it around. Stuck on its back, a large white square of cloth, on which written in two thick black Japanese characters was the word "aho".

The meaning was clear.

Arsehole.

Plastic Irises

On a Tuesday morning in May, after my workout at the gym, I entered the cafe La Baguette. I was hooked on La Baguette's paninis, sandwiches and pastries and dropped in as often as I could. Those opportunities had increased since my retirement in March at the young age of sixty-five.

La Baguette is decorated in the colours of the French flag, and pinned to its walls are tasteful shots of the Arc de Triomphe, Eiffel Tower and Mont-Saint-Michel. In the bathroom there are flower pots of plastic irises. My wife Setsuko, a flower fanatic, hates the plastic form of all flowers.

Famished, I took a tray and picked up a ham and brie sandwich, salad Niçoise and apple tart, then stood in line. I ordered a large iced coffee to help me cool down. The cafe has two jugs of chilled water available for customers, one jug of which has thin slices of lemon in it. I drank two cups of the lemon water while I waited for my iced coffee.

I carried my tray into the seating area. There was a choice of tables; one next to a woman sitting alone, and one trapped between two young women chatting and a middle-aged couple sat staring vacantly at their phones. I chose the seat next to the woman sitting on her own. Having once been a single person myself, I know how lonely it can feel to eat alone. Even having somebody sit next to you is better than a vacant seat.

I always say something to the person sitting beside me, just a few words like "Is this seat free?" I have, of course, been ignored but that is the price you pay in these days of smartphones and social media. People have lost the ability to communicate on a personal level.

Setsuko says I talk to strangers too much.

"Excuse me, is this seat taken?" I said.

The woman glanced up from her book. "No, go ahead."

Before she had finished speaking, she was locked back into her book.

I slid the tray onto the table, released my rucksack from my shoulders and lumped it onto the opposite chair. Relieved of the weight, I sat down. I gulped down half of my iced coffee and devoured the sandwich and salad.

The woman next to me was engrossed in one of the Harry Potter stories. I hadn't read them but had seen a Potter film or two, perhaps on a business flight, and made a mental note to ask her about the book after I had eaten the apple tart. I always look for something to talk about with the people I sit next to in cafes. The topic of the conversation could be what they are reading, the type of phone they are using, or even the clothes they are wearing. In a French-style cafe like this, for example, I can always ask if they have been to France and share some of my own experiences.

After eating the apple tart I felt content.

I rose to get a couple of cups of iced water, one lemon flavour and one plain. The cups are made of paper, and on the small side. Holding a cup in each hand, both cups lightly squeezed together for stability, I made my way back to my seat. I was at the point of sitting down when for no reason at all, the wall of one of the cups collapsed. A spurt of iced water shot upwards, then descended on the head of the young woman.

The woman leaped up, shrieking as she did, knocking her table backwards and sending its cup, saucer and her phone crashing to the floor. She shrieked, loud and long.

The water dripped off her hair down her cheeks and the ice slipped off her clothes onto the floor.

The cafe froze.

The woman's chest heaved as she struggled to catch her breath. She held her palm out to me. I thought she was going to ask for my help but the palm transformed into a single forefinger pointed straight at my face.

"You idiot," she screamed, her face flushed with rage. I didn't think the accident warranted such anger, but I had been responsible, without a doubt.

"I'm terribly sorry, really awfully sorry," I said, and reached out to pick a lump of ice off her sleeve.

She knocked my hand away.

"What are you doing?" she cried.

"The ice, it's melting on you."

"I know that, you fool. I'll take care of it. Stay out of my way."

She clattered around in her handbag, found a packet of paper tissues and patted her hair to soak up the water.

A member of staff appeared with a cloth and mop. I stood to the side and watched as he righted the table and wiped it down before picking up the fallen objects, thankfully unbroken, and placing them back on the table. He apologized all the while, as if it had been his fault. The word "Manager" was on the badge pinned to his jacket and he was taking full responsibility, as any good manager should.

I had no tissues or cloth of my own, but seeing the mop I thought I would make myself useful and help him clear up the remaining drops of water.

"Sir, please don't do that. The mop is the cafe's property," the manager said.

The woman glared at me. "I told you, stay out of the way," she growled.

The other customers remained silent, watching things unfold. I was embarrassed and wished they would get back to what they were doing, but one of the two young women sitting together at the nearby table stood up and strode over to me.

"You should leave," she said.

"What?" I had never been spoken to like this before.

"Leave."

"But, why?"

"Because, you're a creep."

"What? That's not nice. It was an accident."

"It wasn't. You were in here a few weeks back and pestered me too."

"Pestered? What are you talking about?"

"I was having a coffee and a few minutes to myself and you kept talking to me, asking me if I had been to France, and other boring stuff. You should be ashamed of yourself, harassing young women in coffee shops."

"I don't remember that," I said. And to be honest, I couldn't recall her face. "I wasn't harassing you, or this lady. It was just an accident. The cups I was holding collapsed."

"You were carrying two cups, right? Why? Why were you carrying two cups?"

"Because I was thirsty."

"No."

"No? What do you mean, no?"

"You were going to offer this woman one of the cups, weren't you?"

That had been a possibility, I suppose, but I wasn't going to own up to it.

"Not at all. The cups are small and so I always drink two at a time."

The manager interjected. "Sir, I think I have to ask you to leave."

"Why? I haven't done anything."

"Sir, I'm afraid I don't agree. You aren't abiding by our rules to make this cafe an enjoyable place for all customers."

"Look, I'm just being friendly. It's tough sitting by yourself, feeling lonely."

"Sir, you may be lonely, but our other guests have a right to use this cafe free from interruption and disturbance."

"Me, lonely? Me? No, you don't understand."

"It's you that doesn't understand," the woman shouted. "I'm not lonely. I have a husband. He's working today. I don't need your pity."

There was nothing I could say to that.

"Sir, really, if you don't mind," said the manager, stretching an arm in the direction of the door.

I wasn't about to give in to him. There were many other cafes, but I wanted to come back to this one.

"I'm not going."

I sat down.

The manager turned his back on me and, mop in hand, walked away. The woman beside me dropped a heavy sigh followed by a string of tuts as she rearranged the objects on her table. Avoiding eye contact I reached into my bag and pulled out a copy of *President* magazine, determined to show I would not move until I wanted to move.

I was near the end of an article on improving workplace motivation when a male voice interrupted me. I looked up into the worn, weary face of a police officer.

"I'm Officer Sudo. Sir, would you mind joining me for a discussion in the Police Box?"

The officer's question left no room for refusal.

The Police Box is near the entrance to the station. It has at its front a large curtain-less window. Anyone passing by can see its bright and modern interior. There was a single counter at waist level—no chairs. The female officer standing behind the counter nodded at Officer Sudo and he nodded back. I didn't want to be standing in full view of passers-by as I accounted for my actions in the cafe. A neighbour or one of my wife's friends may see me. Or Setsuko herself if she was in the area. Officer Sudo must have read my mind for, with a key attached to his trousers, he opened a door I hadn't noticed set flush into a wall. He flicked on the light and ushered me inside.

"Take a seat," he said.

I did so. There were only two chairs, separated by a low, rectangular table.

There was something about Officer Sudo. I felt a deep connection I hadn't felt with another person for such a long time. There, in the cramped yet private space in the Police Box, I talked and talked. The story of my business success is important to me, but here it was irrelevant. I told him instead about my life in retirement, clinging to a thin, fragile routine, living with a wife who I believed had lost all respect and feeling for me. I was tolerated at home and ignored, if not invisible outside. I used to have control over my work, my family and myself, and now, I wasn't even sure I had control of my own actions and thoughts. I couldn't even start a conversation in a cafe without raising barriers. I could feel tears brimming in my eyes. Tears of frustration and tears of self-loathing.

"I'm very much like you," Officer Sudo said. He nodded a few times as if confirming with himself that this statement was true. "I will retire next month, after almost forty years in the force. I have no financial worries, thank God. A while back I got to thinking of the future, what I will do when I retire and, more importantly, who I will do it with. The kids have left home and it is just me and the wife. If my wife and I both remain healthy we could be together for at least another twenty years. As you said, I wasn't sure if things could be put right. Bringing up the subject of our future together wasn't easy but in the end I begged her to sit down with me at the living-room table, and then asked her to give me one more chance."

Officer Sudo stared at the bare wall behind me.

"My work had become everything and I'd lost myself in it. My home had become a hotel, my wife, a servant. I never, ever thought of her like that, or even said anything like that to her, but my actions must have made her feel that way."

A bitter smile. Officer Sudo blinked a few times, cleared his throat and spoke again.

"We took one small step every day. At first it was a few minutes together, eating breakfast or an evening meal. We started to watch television together or do some shopping for groceries. Recently we've been visiting the places where we used to date. We walk around, sharing our memories, perhaps visiting an old coffee shop or bookshop. By doing that, I recalled what attracted her to me all those years ago. And maybe, just maybe, she remembered why she married me in the first place."

Officer Sudo chuckled and so did I.

"I think you will also find the answer is close at hand," he said, "closer than you think. You look like you're trying too hard to find it, but trust me, you don't need to."

A few minutes later I said goodbye to Officer Sudo and left the Koban. I was welcomed by a searing blue sky that looked as if it had been ripped out of a Van Gogh painting of French wheat fields. I strode in the direction of the bus stop. A passing couple smiled at me. I thought it odd, until I realized I was smiling, and they had simply smiled back. The mere idea of myself smiling amused me so much I started to laugh.

As I passed the entrance to the train station I saw a flower shop. I stepped inside. It would be my first small step.

The Jogger

Satoshi thrust out an arm from under the cover of his summer futon and silenced the alarm clock with a single jab of a finger. Seven o'clock, Sunday morning. He slowly turned over and looked at his wife Miwa who, undisturbed, continued to sleep with a warm smile across her face. Satoshi marvelled her ability to enjoy everything, even the act of sleep.

Satoshi felt that sleeping in on a weekend made it harder for him to get up for work on Monday morning, and so he woke at the same time, seven o'clock, every day. This was an idiosyncrasy that his son had remarked upon as being a sign of increasing age, and to which Satoshi had retorted as being nothing but a sign of increasing common sense. Either way, seven o'clock on a Sunday morning meant only one thing to Satoshi, a jog in Mizumoto Park.

Rising a little stiffly he slid back the door to the tatami room and padded along the dim passageway to the toilet. After relieving himself he entered the bathroom and changed into the jogging clothes Miwa had set aside for him the night before.

Satoshi recalled the advice his doctor had given him at this year's medical check-up. "Exercise", he had urged, in a way that conveyed his doctor's growing impatience with Satoshi's softening physique. But working until late every night at the construction firm he was employed by in Shinjuku, combined with an hour-long commute home, left only the weekend open for exercise.

Saturday passed by with Satoshi dozing on the living-room sofa, television for company, recovering the energy he had expended during the week. Sunday was different. Refreshed and for once in a good mood, he chose to start the day with a jog. Mizumoto Park was long and beautifully landscaped, with a tidy cinder path winding through gushing greenery. The pleasantness of jogging there was the reason he gave Miwa for choosing it over parks closer by. But the real reason was that it was far enough away for him to have to drive there, and he loved to drive.

In fact, going for a jog in Mizumoto Park was the only reason Satoshi had to drive the family car, and he treasured the opportunity. The car was mostly used by Miwa for her part-time job as a cosmetics distributor. Bought some ten years ago, it fitted easily into the basement garage and left space for the children's bicycles. The bicycles were still there but the children had grown and in the last two years moved out to university accommodation. The car's box-like shape made it stand out from the rounded contours of modern cars, but Satoshi was still strongly attached to it.

After pulling on his jogging shoes in the hallway, Satoshi let himself out and locked the door. He skipped down the stairs and opened the garage door, the early morning sun slicing into the darkness and bouncing off the car's white paint. He tapped the bonnet and got inside. The engine responded reluctantly, it had started to show its age of late, but after a few seconds it was turning smoothly enough for Satoshi to release the hand-brake and guide it out onto the narrow street.

As always, Satoshi chose an obscure route to the park, roads with fewer traffic lights and longer stretches where he could put his foot down and enjoy the speed. This morning he wound down his window slightly and felt the cool air rapidly fill the car.

Cars had been his passion since his junior school years. At that time he had stuck pictures of red Italian sports cars in his locker and pinned them to his bedroom wall. He had also started a collection of miniature cars, which was now, to Miwa's irritation, fully occupying a glass cabinet in the living room. His tastes had remained with European cars, and these days the refined elegance of German sports cars captivated his interest the most, and he pored over every page of the foreign motor magazine that he subscribed to. Still, owning such a car would remain a dream until he had finished paying for his children's education.

When he arrived at Mizumoto Park Satoshi pulled into the cramped parking area near the main gate. Even though it was early, a car was already parked there and Satoshi recognized it as the same metallic blue German sports car he had seen the previous Sunday. At that time he had also seen a confident-looking man, mid-thirties and dressed in smart white jogging clothes get into it and drive away. Satoshi had recently read an ecstatic review of the car's road-handling ability and powerful but silky engine, and knew the feeling in the pit of his stomach to be envy. He tried to ignore it.

Keeping to his Sunday morning routine he strode into the park and headed for a nearby group of trees under which he would do some gentle stretching. As always he looked around for somewhere to hide his car keys; he didn't like to have them in his pocket rubbing against his leg as he ran. Spotting a length of log cutting he rolled it over with his foot. A bunch of keys was already there. Squatting down he looked closely and confirmed what he had already guessed; the key ring bore the distinctive bold logo of the car in the car park. Following with his eyes the cinder path that ran around the park, Satoshi picked out in the distance the white figure of the owner and estimated that he must have got to the park only a couple of minutes ago.

Turning the log back over he looked to hide his keys elsewhere, but soon found himself standing in front of the same log. He rolled it over again, this time plucking up the keys. The quality of the sports car had been deliberately encapsulated into the key ring, which pressed into the palm of his hand. He compared it with his own key ring. One of the first family outings after buying his car had been to a theme park, where his son had won and presented Satoshi with the key ring. The plastic cartoon character's colouring had long since worn away, and its tail had fallen off. He pushed it back into his pocket.

Looking to where he had just seen the figure of the owner jogging, Satoshi now saw only a white speck. Keys in hand, the urge to experience sitting in the sports car grew more powerful by the second. He felt himself striding back towards the car park. Without as much as a glance towards his own car, in a few steps he stood by the sports car. Pressing his thumb on the central-locking button the door locks popped open, but just as quickly popped closed again. He had kept his thumb down too long. It was the first time he had ever used such a device and his hand was shaking. He pressed the button once more, heard the door locks pop, and eased open the driver's door. The pungent smell of newly fitted leather hung in the morning air and drew Satoshi closer. He looked once more for the owner, and not seeing him, slid into the driver's seat.

Satoshi had entered another world, a world that made him feel impoverished at the thought of his own car. The leather seat wrapped around his back and thighs; it was without doubt the most comfortable seat he had sat in. The leather-clad steering wheel, although smaller than expected, felt like a part of him on touch. He found the accelerator pedal to be directly under his foot. Teams of designers and engineers had spent their lives in the creation of what he felt and saw, and Satoshi revelled in it. A panel of buttons to his right allowed adjustment to the car's computer system, but as for how you would use it, he had no idea.

To his left Satoshi heard footsteps. A leashed poodle entered the car park, followed by a middle-aged woman dressed in a scruffy, shocking-pink jogging suit. Cigarette hanging from her lower lip she looked up and returned his stare. Satoshi flinched, grabbed the door handle and pulled it shut with a slam, causing the dog to yelp in fright. Feeling secure behind the car's tinted windows, Satoshi watched as the woman bent down to unleash the poodle. The dog made a beeline for Satoshi's own car where it spent rather a long time relieving itself against one of the wheels. The woman leaned back heavily against the fence surrounding the car park and inhaled slowly from her cigarette, all the while switching her gaze between the dog and the car.

One minute passed, then two. Satoshi's enjoyment of the car had been curtailed by the arrival of the woman and her dog and he sat tensely waiting for them to go so that he could get out. He was trapped. What was he going to do? Simply getting out of the car, putting the keys back under the log and then going for his jog was fine, but what if the woman was still leaning against the fence when the owner came back and got into the car? Wouldn't she think it strange that two men had got into the same car at different times, and wouldn't she tap on the car window and tell the owner what she had seen? Satoshi would come back from his jog to find the owner, the woman and the police waiting for him.

Another minute passed. In desperation he decided to start the car. Maybe that would break the deadlock. He inserted the longest key into the ignition and turned it. The engine was so smooth that he only realized it was running when he clumsily stood on the accelerator. The engine roared and the dog yelped again. Clearly irritated the woman scowled in Satoshi's direction, let the remains of her cigarette fall from her mouth and stubbed it out with her foot. She then leaned back against the fence and lit up another cigarette.

Satoshi's heart sank. The situation had become worse. He would appear stupid to now switch off the engine after just starting it, but he couldn't just sit there indefinitely with it running while waiting for the woman to go. The owner would be coming back sometime. With every second the need to flee grew stronger and stronger, until he could contain it no longer.

Satoshi knocked the automatic gear into reverse, released the hand-brake and the car edged backwards past the woman and out of the parking space. Legs trembling with nervous tension he found it difficult to keep his foot on the pedal and the car lurched awkwardly out onto the road. Putting the gear into drive, head above the wheel in concentration, Satoshi nosed the car forwards. He glanced in the rear-view mirror and caught sight of the woman's stare, following him.

He drove slowly, searching for a side road to park in, where he would wait for the woman to leave the car park before returning the car. But no side road appeared and he found himself driving more quickly, conscious that time was running out. The road ran around the park's perimeter, and he estimated that it would take about ten minutes to drive all the way round, back to the car park. But that was too long. Surely by then the owner would have jogged back to find his car missing, and he would call the police and Satoshi would be arrested for car theft. He would lose his job, his driving licence, and what would Miwa say? But, if he drove quickly and got back in five minutes, then he may just make it, and the woman may just have gone by then. Satoshi pressed his foot down on the accelerator, and the car effortlessly gathered speed. "Please," he pleaded to the empty road ahead.

Three quarters of the way around Satoshi saw the white figure of a jogger appear inside the park, and his stomach twisted in terror. It was the owner of the sports car, who if seeing his own car would surely think it was being stolen. Satoshi slammed a foot onto the brake pedal, the new brake pads gripped viciously, and the car screeched to a halt. The ensuing squeal was no echo, but the tyres of the car behind struggling to grip to the tarmac. With a sullen thud it struck the back of the car, shoved Satoshi forwards in his seat, and his head bounced off the windscreen.

Satoshi slumped back into the seat. He felt a throbbing pain spread across his forehead and down his neck, and a tear of frustration ran down the side of his nose into the corner of his lips. He couldn't fix this mess now, it was time to accept it and face the consequences. Or so he thought, until he saw the door of the car behind open and a man get out. He was big, and Satoshi had no desire to argue with him.

He pushed the accelerator to the floor and the car shot away. Satoshi hoped that the registration plate had been sufficiently damaged for the driver not to have been able to read it. He had just added "escape from the scene of an accident" to his list of crimes and, even worse, he was now thinking like a criminal.

The sports car swept along the still empty road. The only other car that Satoshi had seen was the one that ran into the back of him. "Why?" Satoshi cried out to himself, pushing the car on to an even higher speed.

The car park appeared and Satoshi turned into it, wheels churning gravel, and pulled into the same space the car had occupied before. The woman and her dog had gone.

After turning the engine off, he scrambled out of the car, slammed the door behind him and ran towards the trees. On the way he saw the owner some way off, head down in exertion, coming back. Satoshi reached the log and fell to his knees, shoving the keys underneath. Everything seemed to be spinning as he stood back up again. A jog was out of the question. He turned and ran back to the car park, opened his car door and slumped into its worn seat. It felt heavenly. He watched through oily windows as the owner approached the trees and slowed to a walk, before stopping to rest against one of the trees. Satoshi felt truly sorry for what he had done.

After a couple of minutes the man looked around, walked over to the log and crouching down, rolled it over with his hand. From the way the man stood up sharply Satoshi knew that something was wrong. The keys weren't there. He must have put them under the wrong log. Frantically the man looked around for another log and spotting one ran to it and kicked it over. Bending down he picked up the keys. Satoshi felt relief flush through his body; he could now leave.

It was a terrible shame about the damage and he hoped the man had insurance to cover its repair. Somehow Satoshi had extracted himself from the mess he had stupidly put himself into, but now he was so tired that he just wanted to get back home and lie down. Turning the ignition key, he heard the engine's familiar complaint, but realized how much he appreciated his own car. He selected reverse, put his foot on the accelerator, and pulled back.

Maybe he was tired, or maybe he had failed to readjust to his own car, he didn't know, but he ploughed straight into the parked sports car.

Stories of Other
Places and Times

Venus

On a crisp, early spring morning, Lotto Parodi paused in front of the doors leading out to the courtyard of the Villa di Castello and leaned on his sturdy walking stick. His heart thumped with the effort taken for him to walk this far, and with excitement.

On opening the door, the courtyard's fine lawn was revealed in all its glory. A gathering of sparrows, disturbed by Lotto's presence, billowed into the air and fell back to the lawn in almost the same place it had left.

Lotto stepped cautiously out onto the gravel path that surrounded the four sides of the courtyard and which was lined with flower beds of white jasmine. As he laboured along the path, his nostrils twitched at the citrus fragrance hanging in the air, a product of the lemon trees prospering in the villa's vast gardens. On reaching the other side of the courtyard, Lotto stopped in front of his destination, a simple yet elegant wooden bench, one he had often shared with his recently passed wife.

Lotto sat, the busy sparrows and the distant Florence hills keeping him company. Behind him stood the villa's annex, home to a gallery of fine art, inside which joiners were hard at work. Lotto's left ear no longer functioned but his right caught the distinct metallic tapping of a hammer on a wall bracket and the shriek of a wooden crate's frame being parted with a hammer's claw. He was impatient for the work to be done, yet had promised Signor Medici, the master of the villa, that he wouldn't slow the workers down with his questions. Instead he made do with the pictures his imagination painted from the sounds inside and the faded images of his memory.

From his right came a rapid crunch of shoes on gravel. Fiora, his master's youngest daughter and Lotto's favourite, stood before him, blocking out the hills and the gardens.

"Good morning, Lotto."

"Good morning, Fiora. It's a glorious morning, isn't it?" Lotto said, glancing up at the cloudless blue sky.

"It is. Did you sleep?"

"A little. I woke in darkness, but was unable to fall asleep again."

"I thought you'd have trouble. It's so exciting, is it not?"

"Indeed it is."

"When the crate came yesterday I couldn't believe how enormous it was," Fiora said, stretching her arms as wide as she could in an attempt to imitate the size of the crate.

"Ah, yes, your late grandfather wanted the painting to take the breath away, not only with its beauty but with its presence. Of all the works I helped him with, it is the most imposing."

"You must be proud."

"Yes, I am. Proud, and relieved."

"Relieved? Why?"

"Because after these interminable sixty years, Teacher's masterpiece has a home at last."

Fiora raised a forefinger to an eye, stemming a tear.

"Tell me, Lotto, what happened? Why has it taken so long?"

Lotto looked at his hands resting on each of his knees, the translucent skin stretched across the veins and knuckles, the dark spots that had enlarged with each passing year.

"I'll tell you what I know."

Lotto shuffled to his left and Fiora sat to his right, her long tresses disappearing behind the back of the bench. She closed her eyes and listened intently as Lotto spoke, as if she were a priest about to take his confession.

"I was just eighteen when I started working in Teacher's workshop," Lotto began, "and terribly nervous. I spent the first month watching Teacher and learning, forbidden to even put charcoal to paper. Then the workshop got busier and busier, and of course, so did I. Teacher's work was in great demand. Everyone loved him. People would drop by and leave gifts of food and drink in appreciation for the fame he brought the region."

"Food? What kind of food, Lotto?"

Lotto chuckled. "I thought you would ask. Let me see, there was wild boar ham, pecorino cheese and wine of course, lots of it."

"It doesn't sound much of a gift to me," Fiora said with unrestrained disappointment.

"When you are older, you'll understand that there is no better gift, believe me. Now, where was I? Ah, yes. One year, your grandfather, then master of the Medici house, commissioned a painting to commemorate the marriage of his cousin. Teacher asked me to help. He told me his vision for the painting and the themes he would meld into it. I watched as Teacher sketched the painting on paper, over and over in fluid lines of pen and ink. And when, at last, he began to apply paint to canvas, his brush flowed as if guided by a higher power. He would work long, long hours then suddenly tire and say, 'Lotto, finish this part for me,' and pass me his palette. In silence, slumped in his chair, he would watch me add to his work. In this way, stroke by stroke, day by day, we came closer to completing the painting. But Venus, the painting's focal point, remained unpainted, just an empty space on the canvas."

"Why? Was she difficult to paint?"

"In a way…"

"In a way?"

"The difficulty wasn't so much with the act of painting, it was with personal relationships."

"Between you and Teacher?"

"No, no, there was never any problem between Teacher and myself."

"You can't possibly mean between Teacher and my grandfather?"

"It isn't easy to say it, but yes, that relationship."

"Nonno? Surely not. He was so terribly sweet!"

"Perhaps he sweetened with age, but in those days, he would often visit the workshop to, how shall I say, inspect the progress of the painting. At first we didn't mind, but as the date of his cousin's wedding drew closer, he began to voice his frustration. 'It must be special,' he would say, over and over again, 'a painting to look at every day and never tire of.'"

"Now you mention it, Nonno did have his foibles."

"Foibles? That could be one word for it, I suppose. Tensions really came to a head with the painting of Venus. Teacher had imagined Venus rising from the water, on the back of a giant sea turtle, but your grandfather argued against it, saying he didn't want a beast of slowness in the painting. Teacher then

176

suggested a dolphin, but your grandfather thought it frivolous. Only when Teacher suggested Venus ride a huge scallop shell did your grandfather finally concur."

"A scallop shell? The dolphin sounds a much better idea to me."

"I agree, but your grandfather wished his cousin a large and joyous family. And apparently there is nothing better to symbolize fertility than a scallop shell."

"If you say so."

"I didn't, Teacher did, and there was nobody more knowledgeable about symbolism than Teacher."

"I see. Then, after deciding on the shell, Teacher must have found painting it straightforward."

"No, no, not at all. Teacher couldn't expunge your grandfather's words from his head. I was in the workshop the very day the model came to pose as Venus. Teacher spent the morning sketching ideas for the pose he wanted the model to take. 'Must be special,' he kept muttering to himself, imitating your grandfather. But each attempted sketch ended up as a ball of paper on the floor. Finally he leaped off his chair. 'What am I going to do?' he raged. 'Nothing I draw will be special enough for that man!' And that is when I opened my mouth. I regret it to this day."

"Why, what did you say?"

"'Why not pose in contrapposto?' is what I said. 'Contrapposto? What's that?' Teacher replied."

Fiora snorted. "I was thinking exactly the same thing."

Lotto laughed at her humble honesty.

"'It's a pose first used by the Greeks centuries ago,' I told him. 'But it's come back into fashion. Our young sculptors are smitten with it.'

"'Show me,' Teacher urged. 'Show me what this contrapposto looks like.'

"So I posed in contrapposto, as well as I could.

"'No, no, you fool,' he shouted, 'I don't want you to POSE in contrapposto, I want you to DRAW it!'

"Feeling foolish, I sketched it for him. And he liked it, very much.

"'This is what I have been looking for!' he shouted. 'Venus's grace enhanced while at the same time emphasizing her beauty.'

"Overjoyed, Teacher got to work, quickly drawing several sketches of the contrapposto before the model arrived."

"Who was the model?" Fiora asked. "You must tell me. I heard she became Teacher's lover, despite being so young."

"You did, did you? Well, that is a story in itself. When I tell you that story, you will understand the real secret of the painting which is, as I speak, being hung inside the annexe behind us."

"Tell me now! You must!"

Lotto chortled, then ran his fingers through his thinning hair.

"Well, well, if you insist. But do try and be patient."

Fiora briefly looked chastened, then her smile returned. "I'm sorry. Please continue."

"Well, you may recall, your grandfather thought of himself as a leader of fashion, and believed his sense of taste was more refined than anyone else, even Teacher. From the start your grandfather had a particular lady in mind for Venus and nothing, and I mean nothing, would deflect him from it. None of Teacher's suggestions were good enough for him."

"Who was she?"

"She was the daughter of the manager of his most profitable wool factory, and a promising artist herself. She frequented the Accademia of Leonardo da Vinci, and was desperate to gain, how can I say, first-hand experience of Teacher's work. One day your grandfather visited the manager's home and the man pleaded for his daughter to be painted by Teacher. Your grandfather was reluctant, but on meeting the girl he was swayed by her beauty and promised the manager that Teacher would paint her."

"And Teacher agreed?"

"Not on your life. They had many arguments about it, terrible arguments. Your grandfather even threatened to never commission another painting to Teacher's studio. Teacher had no choice but to agree."

"Oh, how awful," Fiora said with genuine feeling.

"It was."

"Poor Teacher."

"Yes. Well, actually no. You see, I also had my doubts about the model, but I kept myself busy at the workshop until she arrived and, on my mother's grave, she was stunning. I couldn't tear my eyes away from her."

Fiora giggled. "Lotto!"

"I know, I know, these words sound appalling coming from the mouth of an old man, but you must remember I was younger then, unmarried, and not that bad looking, if I do say so myself."

"I can believe it," Fiora said.

"See!"

"And then what happened?"

"I had to leave, that's what. Teacher wouldn't let me stay."

"No, no, something happened, didn't it?"

"Yes, of course it did. Why else do you think it has taken sixty years for the painting to arrive at the Villa di Castello?"

"I thought it was lack of space. There just wasn't a wall large enough on which to hang it."

"No, no, no. This isn't a painting you keep waiting for a space on a wall. This is a painting you build a wall for. This is a painting you build a house for. This is a painting…"

"Lotto, Lotto…"

"A painting…"

"Lotto, I understand… really, I do."

Lotto's cheeks flushed.

"You will see," he said. "Trust me, you will see."

"I'm sure I will, but please tell me what happened, please," Fiora said, leaning over and tugging softly on Lotto's jacket sleeve.

"I haven't told you?"

"No!"

"Ah! Let me see. Well, Teacher told me the model disrobed and was at first terribly shy about it, but they quickly began to work and she, being an artist herself, knew exactly what Teacher wanted, almost before he had said it. They were making tremendous progress, until the accident."

"Accident?"

"Yes."

Lotto shifted his gaze to the pure white blossoms of jasmine flooding the flower beds at his feet. He spoke slowly and softly as he described what had happened.

"I feel shame telling you this as it was I who gave Teacher the idea of the contrapposto. Teacher showed the model the sketches he had drawn earlier and she made the pose for him. But Teacher couldn't get the angle and depth he wanted. Remember, Teacher had to find a way for the model to imitate Venus standing on a huge scallop shell floating on water. He scoured the workshop but found nothing. And then he remembered that above the workshop was his apartment, and in his bathroom was a large copper tub he used for bathing."

Lotto nodded to himself as he recalled what had taken place.

"They climbed the steps to the apartment and made their way to the bathroom, where Teacher made her stand in his empty copper tub. But that wasn't quite right either, as he couldn't see her feet. So they rolled the heavy tub over and he helped her climb up onto its upturned base. Now he had everything exactly as he wanted. The afternoon sun flooding in through a skylight and illuminating her skin, a gentle breeze buffeting her hair. Teacher said it was as if God were watching."

"Amazing."

"Yes. Until…"

"Until?"

"She fell."

Fiora pressed the palms of her hands against her temples and squealed.

"Oh, no!"

"Oh yes, she fell. You see, your grandfather's words were still haunting Teacher, reminding him of how the painting had to be special, how you should never tire of looking at it. And so, in his quest for perfection, Teacher asked her to lift her chin a touch, raise her right knee a fraction, and lower her left shoulder just a little more, and with that, she unravelled, like spaghetti twisting off a fork, lost her balance and crashed onto the marble floor."

"Gosh!"

"It was a disaster. The poor girl had broken her arm and was screaming with pain. Her screams carried outside and people came running in off the street to help her. Of course, they didn't expect to find a beautiful woman lying naked on Teacher's bathroom floor. And worse still, some of them knew the girl, for she sometimes sold her father's wool at the market. The physician was called for and the girl taken care of and eventually she was transported to her parents' home. Fortunately, although shocked, Teacher was able to work from memory and paint Venus, standing in contrapposto."

Fiora puffed out her cheeks and let the air burst out of her mouth.

"Oh, thank goodness it all ended well! Nonno had Venus modelled by his manager's daughter, and Teacher finished the painting and could look forward to many more commissions."

"Not quite. You forgot about the sixty years."

"So I did! So what haven't you told me yet?"

"I haven't told you of the embarrassment."

"Embarrassment? Who was embarrassed?" Fiora asked with a shrug.

"Your grandfather."

"Nonno? Why?"

"Because the painting became a laughing stock. With the painting complete, people dropped by the workshop to see it. But they didn't visit to see its beauty, grace and finesse, they came to see why a model had fallen off an upturned bath-tub and broken her arm. They stood in front of the painting, snickering, so much so that your grandfather could never give it as a wedding gift to his cousin. He didn't want the painting put on display here at the villa either, and risk the embarrassment of visitors seeing it. So your grandfather and Teacher came to an agreement."

Fiora looked confused. "Agreement?"

"Yes. The painting would be kept at the workshop, in a back room, under cover of cloth, until the time was right for it to see the light of day."

"And today, sixty years later, it will see the light of day?"

"Yes. Today is that day. The risk of embarrassment has faded with time. As you know, your grandfather, I'm sad to say, passed away many years ago. Teacher too. The girl, who became a woman, a married woman, and mother of six children, grandmother of many more, she has recently left this world too. So your father, Signor Medici, was able to give the instruction, at long last, for the painting to be collected and brought here."

"Of course! I hadn't thought! The girl must have been embarrassed by the incident as well."

"Yes, the most embarrassed. Which is why the painting has been unseen for all these years."

"Now I fully understand."

Relieved, and with a wide grin, Fiora threw her hands up high in celebration.

Lotto leaned his head back and laughed.

"I'm pleased to hear it. Today, the final chapter of this story will play out in front of our very eyes. Is it time? My hearing isn't what it used to be. Have the workers finished?"

Fiora sat forward and listened intently. Not a sound came from the annex.

"I'll take a look."

Fiora jumped up, tiptoed to the side entrance, and eased open the door wide enough to peer inside.

"They are sweeping up," she hissed back to Lotto. "The painting has been hung, but it's draped in a cloth, the colour of Tuscan wine."

By the time Lotto had reached the door and stepped into the cool interior, the workers had finished their sweeping and disappeared. Lotto's eyes grew accustomed to the dimly lit gallery and he focused on the frame hung on the wall, draped as Fiora had said, in a red cloth.

Behind them, a clatter of footsteps. Fiora's father, Signor Medici, was approaching fast, arm in arm with Signora Medici, and behind them two servants, each holding a stepladder.

"Mother, father, look at this! Isn't it exciting?" Fiora shouted.

"Incredibly exciting," her father agreed. "Good morning, Lotto."

"Good morning, master."

"I think you must be the most excited of us all, Lotto. Am I wrong?"

"You are not wrong, master," Lotto said. "When will we get to see her?"

"Now is as good a time as any," Signor Medici said. "If you are in agreement?"

"I am. The sooner I see her, the sooner I can be at peace."

Signor Medici nodded at his servants who strode to the painting and placed their stepladders at each side. The servants climbed the stepladders and in unison unhooked the cloth from the top of the frame, lowering it to the marble floor.

"Let's get some light into the room," Signor Medici shouted, heading for one of the windows. His wife, Fiora and the servants joined him in pulling open all the curtains in the room, flooding it with light.

Lotto stood silently gazing at the painting, filled with emotion. The figures of Zephyrus and Aura, afloat on a panorama of sky and sea. A Hora of Spring holding open a blanket to welcome Venus, who was floating naked and gracefully towards the shore on a huge scallop shell.

"Oh my," gasped Fiora.

"Magnificent," Signor Medici acclaimed. "A painting of beauty that transcends words."

For a while, all in the room stood and stared in silence, their eyes flitting from character to character, their minds playing out the story being told.

A servant coughed.

"Ah," Signor Medici gasped. "Excuse us, we must leave, we are expected for lunch."

Signor Medici rested a hand on Lotto's shoulder. "Take your time, Lotto."

With that, Signor Medici, his wife and servants departed the room.

"It is as Nonno had wished," Fiora said in a hushed voice. "A painting you can never tire of."

"Yes," Lotto said. "Teacher and I gave your grandfather just what he asked for."

"However," Fiora continued, "I also feel a little hungry. Shall we go and have lunch?"

"You go ahead, Fiora. I'd like to spend a little more time here, with my wife."

"Did you say 'wife'?"

"I did, my dear Fiora, I did. For it was I, not Teacher, who fell in love with the girl. She became my wife and mother of our children. Gazing on this picture again, I give thanks for the precious times we had together."

"Oh Lotto! What a surprise! And what a fabulous end to your story! The model was your wife. I can't wait to tell my father. You will let me tell him, won't you?"

"I will. Although I should warn you, he already knows."

Henry Sparkles

Eyes half-closed, Henry Sparkles swung his bat at the ball and missed. The ball smacked into the stumps behind him, the bails scuttling across the grass.

Henry's head dropped to his chest as his schoolmates let out a collective groan.

"Henry! Out first ball again!"

Out first ball. It was often so. He loved cricket and yet he didn't like to bat. The ball was hard and if he was hit by a fast one it hurt, the bruises taking days to heal.

"Who's for another game?" someone shouted.

"I'm done," Henry said, laying the bat on the grass. "See you tomorrow."

He pulled his school bag onto his back, raised an apologetic hand, then ran off towards the school gate. At the gate he kept on running, down the lane to the main road. He crossed the road, jumped the fence and cut across a field of thick grass, the blades tugging at the hems of his trouser legs. Along an earthen path he jogged, tiring a little, then through the cemetery, keeping his eyes on the gravel path and away from the gravestones. Out of the cemetery, out of breath, he walked downhill to his house.

"I'm home, Mum," he shouted on opening the front door. In the kitchen he let his school bag slip off his shoulder onto the grey granite floor.

His mother, chopping vegetables at the kitchen table, raised her head and smiled.

"Hello, Hen."

"I'm going to the woods."

"Thought you might. I made a bacon butty."

The butty sat on the table, wrapped in white paper.

"Thanks."

Henry grabbed the butty and took the stairs two at a time to his room. He changed into his outdoor clothes. He found a sketchbook with blank pages and stuffed it along with a few sharp pencils and the butty into his sketch bag. With the bag slung over a shoulder Henry flew down the stairs and out of the house. He wheeled his father's bike out of the shed, sat on the slate-hard seat, freewheeled down the driveway to the road, steered left and pedalled off for Deepdale Wood.

From a hideaway Henry had made in the wood, he would watch red squirrels chase each other around the higher branches of the oak trees. When the squirrels scuttled head first down the trees to dig for buried acorns, Henry would draw them, from their russet red tails to their tufted ears. A pair of tawny owls were also a favourite, yet, of all the wood's inhabitants, the sparrowhawk made Henry's heart beat the fastest. The bird would flit effortlessly through the wood, stalking a meal. If Henry was lucky, it would perch on a nearby branch in front of his eyes and feast on its catch. Henry adored the bird's orange-barred chest and ruthless eyes.

Throughout his school years he drew what he saw in Deepdale Wood and the surrounding countryside. He drew trees, wild flowers, wild animals, birds, farm animals, their proud owners and whatever else took his fancy. Sketchbooks crammed with drawings lay scattered on his bedroom floor. His skill in demand, Henry was asked to display his work at agricultural shows and in the town halls of Teesdale valley.

After studying in Leeds, Henry returned to Barnard Castle with a degree in fine art and a reputation for being one of the finest wildlife artists in the land. The idea of painting for a living thrilled Henry. He dreamed of travelling the country to paint its wildlife, with a base in London where he would meet and learn from the best artists.

And yet, it was 1915. The Great War raged and bombing raids by Zeppelins pummelled London and other cities across England. A move down south to the capital was out of the question. Day after day, Henry, his mother and father sat around the kitchen table, reading the newspapers and wondering if the war would ever end. The days passed into weeks, the weeks into months. One December morning an envelope addressed to Henry dropped through the letterbox. Inside, was a letter requesting Henry attend military training in the Yorkshire Dales.

"You should object, Hen," his father urged. "The Western Front is no place for the likes of you. You couldn't hurt a fly if you tried."

"I know, Dad, I know," Henry answered, "but I've got to go. I'll do what I can."

Henry reported to the windy, frost-covered fields of the Yorkshire Dales camp for three months training. The brutal bugle call of the first morning tore Henry from his dreams. A cup of steaming tea helped calm his nerves and shaking limbs, but there was no breakfast for Henry or any man until they had spent a solid two hours in the fields doing drills. After breakfast the men returned to the fields and were drilled all the way through to lunch. Lunch was followed by rifle training until dinner, after which the men scrubbed their boots and returned to their tents. Exhausted, Henry flopped down on his straw mattress and was asleep before lights out.

As the weeks passed Henry gained strength and confidence. His unit mastered the art of trench digging and the laying of barbed wire. Henry grew skilled in handling a rifle and fixing its bayonet. After days of target practice, the men were taught first aid and learned how to don a gas mask and survive a gas attack.

At the end of their training the men had no time to rest or return to their families. They were urgently needed at the front. Henry's unit boarded a train to London. On the way, Henry received startling news. His unit was to join a battalion of the West Yorkshire Regiment, and he would become the battalion's adjutant and resident artist. Henry was ordered to report to the battalion's colonel, Colonel Turner, as soon as he arrived at the front. Somehow, those in power had found out he was an artist.

From London the unit took another train to Dover. They crossed the Channel in a steamer, fearful of a U-boat attack, and docked in Calais. From there they travelled inland by train, making the final leg of the journey by foot to meet up with their battalion at the front.

A few miles short of the front, Henry detached from the unit and marched on alone to the farmhouse where Colonel Turner was staying.

Colonel Turner was in his early thirties, taller and more angular than Henry, and wore a beaming smile. He shook

Henry's hand with a grip as firm as any farmer in Teesdale, yet spoke as if he were stood on stage imparting lines from Hamlet.

"Good to have you with us, Sparkles. Your room is at the top of the stairs, first on the right. Have half an hour rest, freshen up and I'll see you down here at six."

"Yes, sir."

Henry's room was clean and dry. When he opened a window and looked out, he saw a distant copse that reminded him of Deepdale Wood.

Over dinner, the colonel told Henry about the situation at the front. He tasked Henry with the battalion's paperwork and the writing of its War Diary. That first evening, Henry had plenty to write about. The artillery on both sides exchanged fire, followed by infantry charges and countercharges. Henry found himself in the farmhouse's living room, or "war room" as it had been renamed. There he watched Colonel Turner and two colonels from other battalions pore over a sea of maps scored with lines and arrows simulating the movement of the troops on the front line. Henry worried about the friends he had made in the battalion and prayed they had returned safely to their trenches.

A few days later, at the breakfast table, Colonel Turner finished his pancakes, washed them down with French coffee, and spoke.

"Sparkles, it's time you paid a visit to the front line."

Henry acknowledged the colonel's uncompromising gaze.

"Yes, sir. I'll get ready."

They left the farmhouse mid-morning, riding in the colonel's army car. Henry, sketch bag clasped to his knees, sat up front alongside the young driver, Jacques. In the back of the car, Colonel Turner and the two other colonels sat shoulder to shoulder, exchanging soft-spoken words only meant for their ears.

The front lay only twelve miles away but they stopped first at a Casualty Clearing Station. The hospital, a collection of huge tents, was where the most recently wounded soldiers were treated. The colonel hastened inside, shared a joke with the doctors, praised the nurses, and had warm words for everyone he met. Behind him, Henry had come to a stop. He explored the room with his eyes, its row upon row of beds, limbs protruding from them, some swathed in white bandages stained red and brown. The acrid smell clogged his nostrils. He turned and stumbled outside, breathing heavily. Several minutes passed and with a clear head, Henry entered the tent again. He opened his sketchbook and drew. Henry recalled how Degas's hero, the painter Ingres, had told Degas to "Draw lines, young man, many lines". Henry did the same, filling his page with line after line, nervous ones at first, truer ones later as the act of drawing calmed him and gave him confidence.

The colonels and Henry returned to the car. As Jacques drove closer to the front line, horse-drawn carts laden with bodies passed the other way, as well as huddles of men, injured but able to walk.

Jacques brought the car to a stop and the passengers piled out. An officer greeted them, gave them each a helmet and then led them towards the line.

Henry surveyed the lifeless landscape of brown and grey mud before him. Here and there the skeletons of blackened trees protruded from the earth.

They entered a trench. Every fifty yards soldiers stood guard, their stomachs pressed against the bank of the trench, their eyes peering through the sights of their rifles into no man's land. The colonel and Henry tramped ahead to where the men of their battalion were stationed. Henry stood and sketched what he saw; the cornflower blue sky flecked with strips of cloud, and the men, asleep in hollows they had carved into the bank of the trench, which snaked into the distance.

"Henry," a voice cried out. "Henry, is that you?"

A soldier rose to his feet. It was Tom, a friend from his training camp days.

"Tom? I can't believe it. It's so good to see you."

They shook hands.

"What you doing here?" Tom asked.

"I'm with Colonel Turner, making sketches and writing the War Diary."

"Good for you, Henry. Do your best."

"I will, Tom, I will. How are things?"

Tom's chin sagged.

"There was a gas attack the other day. Sudden. Chlorine, they said. Me hands shook so hard I thought I'd never get the mask on. I was sure I'd die. Some did. It was horrible, watching, not able to do a thing. Just horrible."

With the sleeve of his jacket, Tom wiped away the tears that had streaked his cheeks.

"I'll be okay."

Henry didn't know what to say, but Tom did.

"Will you draw me?"

"Of course, of course I will, Tom. I'd love to."

Henry sketched Tom, standing proud and to attention, in that very trench on the Western Front.

From that day, Henry joined the colonel on his visit to the trenches. On quiet days Henry talked to the men in the battalion, wrote down what they said and took their photographs. On days following offensives, he watched the stretcher-bearers return exhausted from deep within the battlefield, carrying the wounded. He followed them behind the lines to dressing stations where the wounded were lowered onto blankets to be treated by medics.

In the farmhouse Henry would work on the War Diary and the battalion's paperwork. The colonel would ask him to draft letters of consolation for the families of the men who had fallen. At night, Henry sat with the colonels as Allied forces raided German positions, shuffling nervously in their seats as they waited to hear how many men had made it back.

With so little sleep, a tiredness weighed on Henry like a heavy cloak, a tiredness not even French coffee could shake off. No end was in sight to the conflict. There was nobody Henry could share his thoughts with. He longed to return home, to sit at the kitchen table and talk to his parents.

From the window of his room Henry gazed at the distant copse and felt it pull at his heart. The black dots he saw flitting above the trees were birds, he assumed, but what kind of birds? And what animals could be living there?

As dawn broke one gusty late April morning, Henry slipped out of the farmhouse, rifle on his shoulder and sketch bag strapped tight across his chest. He strode along a path, headed in the general direction of the copse. After several minutes, the copse rose to his left like a leafy cathedral. Henry found a weakness in the hedgerow that lined the path and forced his way through. He traversed a field of knee-high grass and came to a beech tree, majestic, its glossy green leaves rustling in the breeze. He had arrived.

A nervous frog croaked. A bird sang, another chuckled in reply.

Henry crept around the copse until he found a gap in the trees, then stepped inside. The air was cool, the ground soft underfoot. At the centre of the copse was a clearing where the sunlight danced and sparkled. A mesh of twigs lay on the ground. A nest, he thought, and crouched to examine it. Two shattered eggs lay close by. His heart sank. Looking up he saw the remains of the nest sitting in the branches of a swaying tree. Had a pine martin ravaged the nest? Or a cruel gust of wind? Henry turned the twigs over. Another egg, this one miraculously intact and warm to his touch.

It was too dangerous to climb the tree and return the egg to the broken nest. Henry teased a handkerchief from his jacket pocket, lay it flat and nudged the egg onto it. He tied the ends of the handkerchief snug around the egg and eased the bundle into his bag. Out of copse he crept and headed back to the farmhouse.

As a child, Henry had tried and failed to hatch a chicken's egg. He had learned the reason too late. The egg had to be kept warm, yet not too warm. There had to be humidity, but not too much. Back in the farmhouse, Henry foraged in the kitchen and found a baker's bowl and an egg cup. He lined the base of the bowl with a folded towel and lay the egg on top. On one side of the towel he set the egg cup, and filled it with water. He put his bedside lamp beside the bowl to provide the light and warmth to evaporate the water and keep the air humid.

Caring for the egg was the distraction Henry needed. When returning from the front he would rush up to his room to make sure the lamp was still glowing and the water hadn't evaporated. He would pick the egg up, turn it, and settle it back down on the towel. The thought of the egg hatching excited him and it was also a major talking point in the farmhouse.

"Has it hatched yet?" Colonel Turner asked whenever they sat for a meal.

"What kind of bird is it?" was another often-asked question.

One early May morning, a tapping noise broke Henry's sleep. In the bowl, the egg was rocking on every stab the bird inside made with its egg tooth against the eggshell.

Before his eyes, a fine crack appeared. The crack widened and the shell parted to reveal the bird, its pink skin covered in fluffy feathers. A twitch, and there was the bird's head, shaky, with two sparkling black eyes.

At the breakfast table, before Colonel Turner could ask, Henry told all present that the egg had hatched. In an instant everyone stood, left their meals and followed Henry up the stairs. The bird was wobbling in the bowl. The men slapped Henry on the back.

"What is it, an owl?" asked the colonel.

"It's a sparrowhawk, sir."

The bird opened its mouth and shrieked.

"Sparkles, you must feed it," said Colonel Turner.

"Yes, sir," replied Henry.

Henry went hunting for food in the kitchen. In the waste bin were scraps of meat the cook had discarded. Henry chopped the scraps with a short chef's knife and took them up to the bird on a saucer. He clinched a piece of meat between the points of a pair of nail scissors, held the meat above the bird's gaping mouth and dropped the morsel in, repeating this time and time again until the saucer was empty.

In the days that followed, Henry made visits to the kitchen whenever he could. The cook helped by keeping back odds and ends of meat, sometimes chopping it. The bird ate voraciously and grew fast, its feathers thickening, its neck and legs strengthening with every day. Henry moved the bird to a crate, layered with paper. The bird devoured its food and grew larger and louder before Henry's eyes. Henry tidied the garden shed, sweeping out the dust and grime, throwing out old newspapers, bottles and a rotten, broken wheelbarrow. Henry carried the crate in which the bird sat, down the stairs, out the back door and across the garden into the shed, setting it on an oak bench.

"Here's your new home, Barney."

Barnard Castle's nickname had become the bird's name.

As the days dragged into weeks the battle at the front line ground on. Gains and losses of territory were small. Shelling was heaviest during the night. Dawn revealed the withdrawal of the wounded. Some struggled past the farmhouse on foot, others lay in creaking horse-drawn carts, destined for distant hospitals.

After a few weeks, Barney's feathers had grown strong and brown. He flapped his wings often, a sign he was ready to take to the air. Henry shoved open the grimy windows of the garden shed. The young sparrowhawk hopped and bounced up onto the windowsill. The sun was low and bright. Barney's eyes took time to adjust to this new world. Mustering courage, he pattered the window frame with his wings and was gone, plunging down and then up, and up, soaring to one of the posts from which the washing line hung. Henry whooped with joy. Barney could fly.

Henry ran into the farmhouse to find Colonel Turner and give him the good news. Everyone stood in the garden, admiring the bird perched on the washing line pole.

Henry left the windows of the garden shed open from then on. Barney would take wing and fly out to the fields to catch his own food. When Barney did return to the garden, he was often tired. Henry would sit on a stool, sketchbook on his knee, and draw Barney at rest.

At the front the battle intensified. For several days the Allied powers' artillery battered German positions. Day and night the onslaught continued, a rhythmic boom, boom, boom as shell after shell blasted from gun barrels, followed by thuds as the shells impacted and exploded.

Henry could sense the heightened tension at the front and in the farmhouse. Maps lay worn, tattered and torn, across the tables of the war room. The drinks cabinet was stripped of its bottles and filled with a wireless telegraph set, in front of which a soldier sat, relaying the conditions at the front to the colonels. The colonels stood around the table, backs arched, peering at the maps, running their fingers over the blue lines of the Allied trenches and the red lines of the German forces.

At seven on the morning of 1st July the shelling ceased. Silence engulfed the trenches. The men lit up cigarettes and nervously awaited instructions. In the farmhouse, the colonels sat at the breakfast table and talked in hushed voices of the imminent attack on German lines deemed to have been weakened by the severity of the Allied forces' shelling. After breakfast they returned to the war room and the Allied forces launched their attack.

The soldiers forged ahead across no man's land, expecting little resistance, unaware of the machine guns lying in wait for them. The loss of life was overwhelming. A counter-attack drove the men back to where they had come and the conflict raged on into the night. At the farmhouse, the colonels were grim and silent. Heads shook, steadied, and shook again. They could do nothing but endure the few hours to dawn and head for the trenches to assess the damage.

At about seven o'clock, Jacques turned the colonel's car off the road close to the Allied trenches. Henry and the colonels clambered out and surveyed the scene through their field binoculars. Under a rising sun a thick, angry fog rolled across the battlefield. All was not quiet. Stray shells fired by the Germans exploded in the vicinity. The cries of the wounded and the dying floated on the air. Injured men emerged from the fog like ghosts, some alone, some clinging to others, seeking help, unsure of which way to turn.

Henry hauled the army camera and tripod out from the boot of the car and followed Colonel Turner's footprints through the mud towards the trenches. Henry slowed to a stop, determined to capture what he could on film. The shutter snapped just as the colonel forged ahead, undeterred, into the fog.

A few seconds later Henry was also enveloped in the fog. It flowed like milk, thickly over his boots. He decided to wait for the fog to thin. A minute or more passed. Henry grew impatient. He imagined Colonel Turner looking back, wondering where he was. He decided to move forwards, one cautious step at a time. As he did so, the blast of an exploding shell blew him off his feet and into the air. He landed on his back, a crumpled mess.

When he came to, Henry gazed up on a clutter of faces peering down at him. The explosion had brought Colonel Turner and others running to Henry's side. Henry was carried to the colonel's car, placed on its back seat and the car driven at speed by Jacques along the undulating country roads to a hospital in Étaples. There, the surgeons who assessed the damage decided on emergency surgery.

Not expected to survive, Henry was squeezed into a ward crammed with other men who, like him, were fighting for their life.

During the night Henry regained consciousness. His eyes struggled for focus. He believed himself to be in a church, gloomy yet candlelit, white-cassocked priests in motion and in prayer. The cassocks mutated into the white uniforms of nurses, pacing in and out of a hospital ward. When a nurse came close enough Henry raised a hand and waved to catch her attention. She nodded, solved the maze of beds and crouched at his bedside. Henry tried to turn his head towards her but failed, his neck stiff as a plank of wood.

"Don't move," the nurse said.

"Where am I?" Henry asked.

"A clearing hospital."

"How long have I been here?"

"About eighteen hours."

"Eighteen hours!"

The nurse removed Henry's records from the foot of the bed and peered at them.

"Yes, eighteen."

"Can I have some water, nurse? I'm awfully thirsty."

"You can have a little. I'll fetch a glass."

"That's okay, I'll get it myself."

The nurse pressed the palm of a hand gently into Henry's chest to pin him to the bed. "You're not going anywhere," she said, "you've been badly injured. You need rest."

"Injured?"

"Yes. I'm sorry to have to tell you this, pet. Your right leg was badly damaged in an explosion. It had to be removed."

"Removed?"

Henry attempted to move his right foot but got no response. He moved his left foot with ease. He shifted his left foot over to where he was sure his right foot was. Nothing.

For days Henry drifted in and out of consciousness, shielded from his injuries by painkillers. His dreams were filled with scenes from his childhood, his school friends, games of cricket and visits to Deepdale Wood. The wood revealed itself in stunning detail; tree roots exposed and twisted on the floor, the bark on each and every tree, bird's nests, his hideout, the birds and the chuckling squirrels.

Henry was relocated by train to a Red Cross hospital. As the days passed Henry's body responded to the intensive care and kindness of the nurses. He gained the strength to sit up and saw the extent of his injuries with his own eyes. Over the days and weeks, the doctors and nurses worked hard to fashion a stump on which an artificial limb would be attached.

Henry's days were filled with uncertainty and swings in emotion. The nurses helped keep him calm but what got him through each and every day were the men lying in adjacent beds. They listened to Henry and shared their own stories, fears and plans for the future. Revived by their camaraderie, Henry regained his desire to draw. He convinced the nurses that drawing would speed his recovery and urged them to track down some pencils and paper. Over the next few days, an assortment of pencils and paper of all shapes and sizes soon arrived at his bedside.

From memory, Henry drew the battlefield, the farmhouse and Barney. His love of drawing confirmed, Henry decided that after the war, he would act on his plan to move to London and make a living as an artist.

And yet, he had unfinished business in France. He had to return to the farmhouse to collect his sketchbooks, paintings and photographs. He was determined his work would be delivered to the army and be put on display. Henry wrote all this in a letter to Colonel Turner and passed it to one of the nurses, asking her to find a way to get it delivered to the battalion.

Several days later, when Henry had just about given up hope, an army envelope arrived at his bedside. Inside was a handwritten letter from Colonel Turner.

"Dear Adjutant Sparkles," it started, "It was wonderful to get your letter. I hear you are making a speedy recovery from your injuries. I understand your wish to return to the farmhouse and collect your artwork. However, I have bad news. The farmhouse was destroyed by a stray bomb less than a week after you yourself were injured by one. There was fortunately no loss of life, however we had no time to attempt to recover any of our belongings and had to move on as quickly as possible. As a result, I am now based in army quarters in Ypres. The situation is not ideal but we must make the best of it that we can. You have my permission to visit the farmhouse to attempt to recover your artwork, although I fear it will have been badly damaged, possibly destroyed, by the blast of the bomb and the fire that raged thereafter."

The destruction of the farmhouse was an unexpected blow. And yet, Henry resolved to visit and find what he could. The retrieval of even one picture from the ruins would mean his time in France had not been wasted.

Near the end of his third month of care, Henry was allowed to leave the hospital. His wounds had healed well and he had regained the strength to walk a few steps, albeit with the aid of crutches. He would travel back to England and continue his recovery there.

On the morning of his discharge, the colonel's car rolled to a stop on the cobbled street outside the hospital. News of the car's arrival reached Henry who was sat on his bed, waiting. Henry bade farewell to the friends he had made, promising to meet them again after the war. He hugged the nurses who had worked to help him through his recovery. Henry grasped his crutches over firmly and made a slow and nervous exit from the hospital.

Jacques appeared from the driver's side of the car and opened the rear door as Henry approached.

"Good to see you again, Henry," Jacques said, squeezing Henry's arm.

"It's good to see you too, Jacques."

Clasping the top of the car door, Henry threw his crutches onto the back seat, lowered himself to a sitting position and slid inside. Jacques slammed the door closed, ran around the car and jumped into the driver's seat.

The car's engine churned into life. Henry waved to the nurses as the car trickled forwards and out of the gates of the hospital.

Jacques pressed down on the throttle, the car growled and surged on up the road towards the countryside.

On the way to the farmhouse Jacques told Henry about the stray bomb and how, miraculously, not a soul was in the farmhouse when the bomb had hit.

"Everyone but the cook was out at the front, and the cook herself had stepped into the garden for some fresh air," he said. "She got the shock of her life when the shell hit and the farmhouse collapsed around her."

Some thirty minutes later they came to the British Sector of the Western Front. Sodden, brown earth covered the distant landscape. It was as if all the greenery had been rolled up like carpet and taken away. The car forged ahead and a few miles later they came towards a ruined building, which from its location Henry knew had to be the farmhouse. Jacques stopped the car in front of its iron gates that had somehow survived the blast intact. From his seat, Henry gazed at the rubble. The roof and middle of the house had crumbled, leaving the two ends of the building standing in a rough M shape.

"You wait here, Henry, I'll look for your things," Jacques said. "I wouldn't get your hopes up."

Jacques left the engine running and clambered out of the car. Henry watched Jacques slip through a gap in the collapsed wall and pick his way through the rubble towards the crumbled remains of the building.

Henry eased open the rear door and wriggled sideways until the foot of his good leg made contact with the ground. He jabbed the ends of his crutches into the soft earth and leaned forwards, using his arm strength to push himself into a standing position.

It took a few seconds for Henry's head to settle. Then he set off, with determined steps, towards the garden. The fence that had once surrounded the garden had been flattened by the force of the bomb blast. The garden shed had also collapsed into a heap of fractured, splintered wooden panels. Had Barney been inside at the time of the blast? Had Barney survived? Henry had come for answers but in front of him lay a mound of bricks and mortar he couldn't navigate on foot, and shattered wooden panels he didn't have the strength to lift. It was plain to see he would never know what had become of Barney.

Despondent, Henry turned his back on the garden, paused to get his sights on the car and pushed off on his crutches.

Halfway to the car, a shadow flitted across the ground.

Henry flinched, fearing a shell and an explosion. There was only silence. With relief he lifted his head in time to see the flap of broad wings and a bird alight on the iron gate. It was Barney.

Barney's talons clasped the topmost bar of the gate. In the months that had passed since Henry had last set eyes on him, Barney had grown into the handsomest of birds. His wings were cobalt blue, his chest lined with bars of orange down to his belly. Those commanding, yellow eyes peered down at Henry, as if asking "Where have you been?"

"Barney, it's me, Henry. Do you remember me?"

Henry eased closer to the gate.

"I remember you, Barney. Every day I wondered what you were doing. I had to see you again. It's what got me through."

Barney's head twitched.

Henry shuffled closer, close enough to see Barney's yellow, twig-like legs.

"You have a nice pair of pins, Barney. I envy you."

Henry extended his right arm as far as he could and beckoned to Barney.

"Come on, boy."

Barney puffed his chest feathers out, padded his feet on the iron bar as if to take flight, then settled to gaze at Henry again.

Henry nodded.

"It's okay, Barney, it's okay. You're right to keep your distance."

Henry lowered his arm and grasped the handle of the crutch. For a while they gazed at each other, then Barney's claws opened, and with a beat of his wings he was in the air.

"Take care, old boy," Henry shouted as Barney flew away, in the direction of the wood. "Take care."

Henry watched until Barney disappeared from sight. Snow began to fall. Henry struggled back to the car to find Jacques leaning against it, a cloud of smoke rising from the stub of a rolled cigarette gripped between his fingers.

"Find anything, Jacques?"

"Not a thing. Sorry. Your artwork must have been destroyed in the explosion, or been blown away in the wind."

Henry sighed and shook his head.

"What a waste."

He surveyed the bludgeoned, bloodied earth that stretched out to the horizon and knew he would never understand what had happened here, and would never forget. All he had to take back to Barnard Castle were his memories, but they would be enough. From those memories he would paint the Western Front, just as it was.

Henry pulled open the car door and thrust his crutches inside.

"To the station please, Jacques, to the station. I've seen enough."

The Pool

"I'm going out to play," Andy shouted down the hall, shuffling into his red, lace-less shoes at the doorstep and pulling on a floppy hat over his ginger hair.

"Don't go far," his mother replied sternly from the back bedroom. That was where she often was those days, bent over the cot or sat in the rocking chair, cradling the baby in her arms.

At the top of the porch stairs, Andy stood and peeked over the fence at the neighbour's garden, a world he yearned to enter. A glint of sunlight bounced off the surface of a swimming pool, the lawn lay green and trim, and a tall gardener sporting a broad white hat sprayed water onto the lawn from a hosepipe.

Hard plastic wheels rumbled across a paved path and into sight came his friend John, perched on his toy tractor, propelling it forwards with frog-like pushes of his legs towards the gate.

Andy frantically tackled each step down to the bottom one, ran past his father's car in the driveway and onto the backstreet he lived on in a suburb of Grootvlei.

"John!" he shouted on seeing the tractor rolling away. "Where are you going?"

John slapped his shoes into the tarmac, stopped the tractor and looked back.

"To the pool, Red."

"Pool? But your pool is over there," Andy yelled, pointing in the direction of the garden pool.

"Not that one, Red, the big pool. I'm going to sail my boat. Do you want to see my boat, Red?"

Andy did.

John faced forward and kicked off, spraying loose gravel over Andy's approaching ankles.

For a second Andy watched John go, then scurried after him.

John forged on to the end of the road and turned the tractor left. Andy pumped his stocky legs and a few seconds later turned the same corner.

John's tractor was moving faster now, and Andy began to run out of puff. Just as Andy was afraid he would lose sight of the tractor, it stopped at the edge of a park. John hopped off and ran across the grass. A few seconds later Andy caught up to the tractor, peered into the park and saw John, poolside. Out of breath, Andy shoved his hands in his pockets and shuffled across the grass to the russet brick paving that bordered the pool.

Tied to the handrailing at the side of the pool were three wooden boats, each as long as Andy himself and as wide. They were grand models of ships, two of which had sails that stretched high, the other a steam ship with red-tipped chimneys. Other than the boats and the two boys, not a soul was present.

John untied one of the sailing ships and with the string wrapped around a hand walked along the length of the pool, the boat in tow. Andy followed John's steps, wishing he was the one holding the boat. Together they navigated the four sides of the pool, back to where they had started. John tied the boat to the railing. Andy looked on, speechless. He didn't even know how to tie shoelaces.

"Why don't you sail on one, Red," John urged.

"Sail?"

"Yes. The steamer, look, it has a place for you to sit." John pointed at the flat middle of the boat.

John pulled the steam ship closer to the poolside and held it steady.

"On you go," he said.

Andy placed a foot hesitantly on the boat and watched it bob.

"Take your shoes off and crawl on," John said.

Andy did what he was told and managed to get both hands onto the boat, followed by one knee and then the other, finally dropping his bottom onto the boat. The pool's water lapped up over the sides of the boat and filled his shorts with warm water. It was just like wetting the bed, Andy thought, but it didn't smell, and his mother wouldn't shout at him later.

John untied the boat. "Kick, with your feet, Red. Kick to go forwards."

Andy kicked, splashing water in John's direction. The boat swayed, tilted and floated away from the pool's edge to the centre, the end of the string slipping free of John's hand. The boat turned in the water, like the hands of a clock, and when the full circle had been completed, John had disappeared.

From the centre of the pool, Andy peered into every corner of the park for John, but there was no sight of him or his red tractor. He had to find out where John had gone. He kicked with his feet, the boat lurched, wobbled, and Andy tumbled into the water.

Andy thought he would float, like the boat, and wondered why he didn't as he drifted down, watching the pool's surface and the blue sky recede above. Eventually Andy's back made contact with the bottom of the pool. The warm arms of the water embraced and comforted him. At peace, he couldn't help but smile.

It's nice here.

A blanket of blue encroached and smothered him in soft sleep.

Wrenched upwards like a gaffed tuna, Andy's eyes opened as he broke the pool's surface and the air smacked his face. He gulped the air, gasped again, and screamed.

Andy had been hooked by the metal end of a long rake, ensnared in his shirt. On the other end of the rake, waist-deep in the shallow end of the pool, stood John's gardener, his long and sinuous arms grappling with the weight at the end of the rake.

Thrust up onto the poolside by those same arms, Andy stood shaking, his legs weak and trembling. Tears streamed down his cheeks and into the corners of his open, howling mouth. He cried, not in fear or in shock, but in despair.

The gardener stood in the pool, tall and dripping, head shaking with a fiery scowl.

Andy ran. He didn't know why he was running or where he was running to, all he knew was he had to run. He kept running until a car screeched to a stop before him. His father's car.

From inside, his father pushed open the passenger door and Andy climbed in. His father stretched over and pulled the door shut, turned the car around and headed back home.

His mother made him strip off all his clothes just inside the door and dried him with a towel. Upstairs in his bedroom

Andy was helped into his pyjamas and ushered into bed. A little later, his mother came in with a bowl of steaming chicken soup that warmed him from the inside out, after which, he slept.

*

A couple of years later, the family returned to the UK. Andy went to primary school. The years passed, he grew tall and skinny. In secondary school he joined the swimming team. He wasn't any good, he just wanted a reason to spend more time in the school's pool. Whenever he could, he would be the first in, diving to the bottom, or the last out, lurking in the depths until the teacher came looking for him. The water was never warm, the chlorine stung his eyes, and he could never feel as he had at the bottom of the pool in South Africa.

At home, at bath time, he would try lowering himself into the water until his whole body was covered. It wasn't quite as good as the pool, the water shallow and without the same pressure. And when he looked up, all he could see was the glare of the naked light bulb.

After graduating and finding a job, Andy moved into an apartment of his own. Working life was stressful, he was not successful, and the only release at the end of the day was at home, in a bathtub filled to overflowing. Living alone and without the danger of anyone barging into the bathroom, he could spend longer and longer underwater, at first three minutes, then as much as ten minutes at a time.

In his early thirties, Andy met someone. They moved in together. They shared everything, and when Andy felt the time was right, Andy told that someone about the water.

There was understanding at first, then silence and doubt. His partner used to lie in bed, waiting for Andy to emerge from the bathroom after his evening bath. Andy took an age to come up for air, and his partner realized they would always come second best to a bath full of water. Andy was alone again.

It was not until Andy had worked for a few more years and had money saved that he thought he had the answer. There was nothing to stop him from travelling to warmer parts, sun-bleached beaches and the blue depths of warm water. He took a trip, alone, to Greece. At Kokkini beach he swam, buffeted by the waves and the excited screams of those around him, unable to find a place of calm. He tried the hotel pool, but no matter how early he went, people were already there, laying their blankets on the couches, and life guards ever on patrol. Andy knew it wouldn't work, and at the same time it was clear what he had to do next.

*

One mid-winter morning, Andy boarded a South Africa Airways flight. The following morning, he disembarked at O. R. Tambo International Airport. He picked up a hire car, punched in the phone number for the lodge he would stay at into the car's navigation system and set off. He headed south, down the R21 and then the R23, passing Springs, joining the N3 near Heidelberg and arriving at the lodge a few kilometres to the east of the town of Grootvlei. Andy recognized none of it. Much had been built since he was last there as a boy. Besides, what he recalled from his childhood wasn't the mundane like roads or houses, it was the sudden and unexpected, like bush fires, falling off his bed, his pet dog biting him, and lying at the bottom of the pool.

He had expected to relax at the lodge, enjoy the evening meal and get a good sleep, then drive into Grootvlei the following morning. But with a large map of Grootvlei spread across his hotel room's floor and a blue circle his father had drawn identifying the location of the old house, Andy couldn't relax.

With a couple of hours still left until sunset, Andy stuffed the map into his rucksack, lathered his arms and face with sun cream and locked the door on the way out.

He drove a kilometre or so up the road to Springfield Avenue. A couple of minutes later a residential area appeared to the left. Andy stopped the car and checked the map for the location of the blue circle. Andy drove on. He rounded the inner road of the housing estate twice before something in the shape of the houses and their roofs took him down a road to the front of a house that sent tingling sensations down his fingers. He studied the front of the house that stood before him. The steps. The blue roof. It was the one. Now he had to find the pool.

Andy climbed out of the car and slung his rucksack on his back. He would look for the pool on foot, retrace the footsteps he had taken all those years ago, imagining John riding ahead on his tractor, his stubby shoes flaying at the tarmac. He strode to the end of the road, turned left and a few seconds later he found a large area of bleached grass. In one corner a group of boys were kicking a scruffy ball between them. In its middle were two huts, at ninety degrees to each other, and in front of them a bricked area with a rectangular hole in it. It had to be the pool. It was much, much smaller than he remembered, but the location and shape were the same. As he walked across the grass towards the pool, and his view of it grew clearer, Andy's head dropped. The pool was empty.

Andy walked slowly to the pool's edge, his heart thumping as he got closer. He was in luck. Two puddles lay at the bottom of a spotlessly clean basin. Coated in sky-blue paint, the pool was still being used, but must have been emptied recently. It was coming to the end of the day, so Andy guessed the pool was filled in the morning, and emptied in the early evening. From a metal tap in front of one of the huts snaked a slim, dark green hose, which disappeared into a low-lying bush.

Andy walked around to the other side of the pool, unsure of what to do. He could come back in the morning and, if his assumption was right, he would find the pool would be full. Or he could wait. Across the park the boys were leaving, their shadows stretching ahead of them. The sun was close to dipping below the roofs of the neighbourhood houses. He would wait.

Andy tried the door of both huts but they were locked. He sat down on a bench. The sky's orange darkened to red, the red to a dark purple the colour of eggplants, lit by the white bulb of a full moon and a scattering of sparkling stars.

Andy groped in the bush where the hose entered, and extracted the dripping end. He clasped it, walked over to the pool and lowered the hose into it. He returned to the hut, twisted the stiff head of the tap, and the water hissed and rumbled below his feet as the hose twitched. At the pool's edge Andy peered down. The puddles rippled as water gargled and burst out from the end of the hose. How long it would take to fill the pool, he didn't know, but he was in no hurry.

The Pool

Andy dragged the bench over to the poolside, lay down on it and watched the light of the moon reflected in the swirling water of the pool below.

Andy woke to a morning sun perched low in a hopeful sky. The pool was full. The waiting was over.

He kicked off his shoes, yanked off his socks and stripped, dropping his shirt and trousers onto the brick floor.

Not wanting to make a sound, he sat at the pool's edge, swivelled his body around and slithered into the water that had been warmed by the heat of the morning sun.

Andy pushed himself out to the centre of the pool and paddled, calming himself, readying himself. He steadied his breathing, softened, dropped his arms to his sides and slipped beneath the surface. He stretched out his legs and crossed his arms over his chest, letting the weight of his body pull him down to the bottom of the pool. For the second time, his back rested on the pool's bottom. Above, beyond the pool's surface, stretched the sky, as blue as it had been on that day. Andy gazed as cloud after cloud entered one side of the pool, drifted on the wind, and exited the other side. He was ready.

I'm back. I've come back for you.

In a corner of the pool, the water shifted and stirred. A flop of hair, red, atop a small boy who glided as smooth as a seal towards him, with a freckled face and a wide joyous smile Andy knew so well. Andy held out a hand and the boy reached for it. Their hands embraced, warmed and fused.

Forgive me, for all these years I've kept you waiting.

Their love flooded and consumed each other.

I'll never leave you again.

Anywhere but Nice

The end of another long day in the Square Mile. Anne steered her Mercedes around the underground car park, put her foot on the accelerator pedal and powered the car up the exit ramp to a striped barrier. The car sat, bathed in the haze of a red hazard light until, with a beep of recognition, the light turned green and the barrier rose.

Anne edged the car out towards the pavement, let a straight-backed businessman pass by, signalled left and entered the road. Chic's "Good Times" was playing on the radio, the roads were empty, and from experience Anne expected to be at her Hampstead apartment about thirty minutes later.

Although a long day, it had been a successful one. Another major client was on board, sales targets had been met and there was nothing to keep her awake that night. Still, she reminded herself, she had to loosen her grip. Although she was the managing director, she shouldn't be the last to leave the office every night.

Reaching Westminster—the halfway point—Anne turned the car north and thought about what to have for her evening meal. In her refrigerator sat leftover lasagna. She would warm that up in the microwave, throw a salad together and relax with a glass or two of wine, maybe from the bottle of Chianti resting on her wine rack. She wondered briefly where she had got the bottle, before seeing, too late, that the car in front had stopped. Anne thumped the brake pedal. The car's tyres shrieked. Almost at a standstill, the Mercedes' front bumper nudged the rear of the car in front, shunting it forwards a foot or so with a yelp of metallic pain.

"My car!" she screamed. "My new car!"

Anne groaned, backed her car up into the side of the road, prodded the dashboard's hazard light button and jumped out. The car in front was static. Anne recognized it as a Citroen 2CV. She marched to the driver's side window. Inside a young woman was turning the ignition key back and forth in a frantic attempt to bring the engine to life. Anne tapped the window. The woman glanced up, raised a palm as if to say "just a minute" then tried to start the car again.

Tired, hungry and out of patience, Anne rapped the window with her knuckles and made a "roll down" motion with her clenched fist.

The window lowered an inch.

"The engine's died," the woman yelled.

"I can see that," Anne yelled back, "but you're blocking the road."

"Damned car," the woman shouted at the 2CV's steering wheel, and got out. The woman was tall, slim, and dressed in a mismatch of styles and colours, a student Anne guessed, or a designer. The woman reached into the car, put her left hand on the steering wheel, put her right hand on the car's frame and pushed. Anne could tell she had done this before.

"Give me a hand?" the woman shouted over her shoulder. Anne sighed, stepped behind the 2CV and pushed. With the car parked at the side of the road, the woman pulled out a

222

smartphone from her jacket pocket and made a call. "Dad, it's Jane. The car's gone and died on me again. I know, I know. Can you help? I'm on the A5 heading north, just after Marble Arch."

Anne turned away to check her car. There didn't seem to be any damage at all. The 2CV was a different story, its rear bumper crumpled and hanging from the car's body, as if on a thread. A ruby-red rear light had also been shattered. Anne called the police then took close-up photos of the front of her car and rear of the 2CV, before crossing to the other side of the road to take wider shots of the scene.

Anne walked back over to the 2CV.

"I'm awfully sorry," the woman said. "My dad got me the car as a graduation present. I love it, but there's always something wrong with it."

Anne nodded. "Looks like the power supply this time. I've also mangled your bumper, sorry about that. It's just about hanging on. I think you're safer getting towed to a garage."

"My dad said he'd call the AA before coming. I wish I had a car like yours. Did your husband buy it for you?"

Anne smiled. "No, I bought it myself. I run a company, work hard and thought I'd treat myself."

"Oh, I'm sorry, I didn't mean to…"

"That's alright. I'm used to it. Did you ask your dad for a 2CV or did he just give it to you?"

"I asked him. They're so cute."

"They are indeed."

Later that evening, after Anne had finished her lasagna and was stretched out on her sofa in front of the television, she thought of Pascal.

In the late 1980s Anne lived in Nice for six months on a student exchange programme. She stayed with a French family, studied French at the University of Nice and worked in a cafe to make ends meet. That was where she met Pascal. He would drop by the cafe in the evenings with work colleagues, all dressed in suits, white shirts, loose ties and cute smiles.

Anne fell for Pascal the first time she saw him. She loved the way he spoke French in a deep, guttural voice that belied how slim he was. One day he entered the cafe by himself and they got talking. Anne said she wanted to see more of the Riviera. Pascal arranged to pick her up from the cafe at the weekend and take her for a drive in his car. That was the first time she had ever sat in a 2CV.

Pascal knew all there was to know about the car. Anne lost count of how many times he'd explained how the 2CV had been made for French farmers, why it was designed to be an "umbrella on wheels" and why he preferred it to that other "people's car", the Volkswagen Beetle. She watched with her heart in her mouth as Pascal spoke, intensely, both hands gesticulating, sometimes neither on the wheel.

To Anne, far from looking like an umbrella on wheels, the 2CV reminded her of an upturned wheelbarrow. She took an instant dislike to it, but after repeated trips to and from the beaches at Antibes, Villefranche-sur-Mer and Monaco, she relented and let it grow on her. She even made an effort to remember some of the information Pascal fired at her and tried hard to impress him by pointing out special edition models on the road such as the Charleston, Beachcomber and Cocorico.

Anne turned off the television, poured herself another glass of wine and entered her study. She powered on her laptop and typed "buy 2CV". A website opened with the words "32 Citroen 2CVs for sale right here, right now". There, on the fourth page, was one the same colour as Pascal's. "1988

CITROEN 2CV Dolly in Rhubarb and Custard livery" it read. "One careful owner. Excellent condition, handbrake suspect. £11,950".

Pascal had adored the colour of his car. He told Anne of his love of rhubarb pie, a famous dessert in the Alsace area of eastern France where he had grown up. Everyone grew rhubarb in their gardens, he said, and he promised to take her there one day and have his mother bake a pie for her.

Anne had to have the car. The location was listed as Dorset, a little far, but she would make the best of it, have some fun and see the sights. She clicked the "Message the sender" button and typed *Hello. I'd like to see the 2CV. Would it be possible to see it this weekend?*

In the morning she had a reply. *Thank you for your interest. The car will be sold on a first-come-first-serve basis, so may have been sold by the weekend, but if it hasn't, please drop by after 10 on Sunday morning. I'm in Bournemouth.*

Never having bought a second-hand car, Anne called her father for advice.

"Cars like that need a lot of attention," he cautioned her. "In your position you have better things to do with your time than fiddle with the engine or lie under the car looking for rust. However, if you must buy one, the first thing to do is lift up its floor mats and check for rust or holes. Don't buy it if you see holes. If you need a second pair of eyes, I'll go with you."

Anne turned down her father's offer. This was to be her project. She would travel alone and she wasn't fussed about a little rust here or there. The memories the car brought to life were important to her. The memories of being younger, carefree, taking risks and living for the day. These days she lived in the body of a cautious, middle-aged businesswoman who only made decisions after due consideration of all possible outcomes.

Come Sunday morning, Anne walked to West Hampstead station and caught the 7:23 train. She changed train at Clapham Junction and settled into her first class seat for the ride to Bournemouth. The train breached the M25, rocked through rolling countryside to Basingstoke, on to Winchester, followed by Southampton. As the train left the New Forest behind destined for Bournemouth, Anne gazed at the Channel, shimmering under the mid-morning sky.

Anne recalled how Pascal would pick her up from her flat early on Sunday mornings. They would drop by a local bakery to buy a baguette and then drive on to the glorious beaches of Antibes for a swim, picnic and nap. Anne's favourite location was Salis Beach, a curved heaven of white sand and shallow, glistening water.

The train came to a stop at Bournemouth station at just one minute after ten. Hungry, Anne popped into the station's cafe and had a quick latte and a warm croissant. She strode over to the taxi rank and got in the back seat of the first car and read out the address off her smartphone to the driver. A few minutes later, driver paid, Anne strode up to a detached house on a very respectable and well-kept estate. There was no sign of the 2CV but Anne guessed it was hidden behind the white door of the double garage at the top of the driveway.

The whine of a vacuum cleaner escaped from inside the house. Anne rang the doorbell and the whining stopped. A second or two later the door was opened by a woman of about the same age as Anne.

"You must be Anne about the car. I'm Claire. I'll just be a minute."

Anne watched Claire walk down the hallway and enter a front room, heard the vacuum cleaner's cord being unplugged and a rattle as the cord wound itself into the body. Claire appeared again, took a pair of shoes down off a shoe shelf and slipped them on. Claire removed a couple of keys from the key rack, one the classic 2CV ignition switch key that had been attached to a red enamel "2CV" key ring.

Claire pointed a remote control at the garage. The door clattered opened, revealing the 2CV parked next to an empty space.

"There used to be a Jaguar there, but my husband took that when he left me," Claire said, displaying no hint of sadness. "He left me with the 2CV. To be honest, I have to sell it. I need the cash."

Claire got in the car. The engine started with a whine that reminded Anne of her mother's old sewing machine, and the car rolled out into the sunlight.

Anne saw at a glance the car was clean and, on the surface at least, rust free.

Claire got out. "Why don't you take a look inside," she said.

Anne slid into the passenger side.

"That's the first time I've seen somebody do that," Claire said. "Don't you drive?"

Embarrassed, Anne laughed and shuffled over to the driver's seat. "I drive, but I've only ever been a passenger in one of these. Habit, I guess."

As she said that, Anne realized it wasn't true. Pascal had taught her how to drive the 2CV late one cool summer evening in the almost empty car park of a public beach at Antibes. She had stalled the car several times, to Pascal's annoyance, but had managed it in the end. Of course, Pascal hadn't let her drive the car back to Nice.

"Do you want to take it for a test drive?" said Claire.

"Sure, but just around the estate and back. I'll only be a minute."

Anne released the handbrake, clasped the black ball at the end of the gear lever and put it into first, then squeezed the accelerator pedal and set the car trundling down the driveway to the road.

Anne sensed how light and responsive the car was compared to her Mercedes. She found herself smiling, and had the car flying down the other side of the estate by the time it was in fourth gear. At this point, she remembered being told to do an emergency stop to test the car's brakes. With no car behind her she hit the brake pedal, bringing the car to a stop and stalling the engine in the process. Engine running again, she set off and was soon back at the house.

"That was quick," said Claire.

"Yes. It drives very well."

"It should. My ex was a member of a 2CV enthusiasts club and would always have the car ready for a get together with other members. Complete waste of time if you ask me. The last thing he mentioned was the handbrake being a little dodgy, something to do with a cable, but he was such a fusspot. It seems to be working fine to me."

"So it does."

"Do you want to look at the engine?"

"No, that's alright."

"Uh, how about underneath?"

"That's okay. It looks good. 11,950 pounds, wasn't it?"

"Er, yes. You want to buy it?"

"Sure."

"Wow. You're quick."

"Sometimes."

"Well, let's go inside and I'll show you the documentation."

After checking the service history of the car, Anne handed over the cash. She chatted with Claire, they exchanged phone numbers, and then Anne left with the car keys in hand.

Behind the wheel of the 2CV Anne turned out of the estate, looked for a signpost for the A35 and found it at the first roundabout she came to. She was heading for Poole.

As Anne drove, the memories flooded back of Pascal driving his 2CV along the Riviera with the sun's rays streaming down over the blue Mediterranean Sea. They had been special days, perhaps the best days of her life. They had talked a lot in the car, about everything. She hadn't felt the need to hold back with Pascal. She asked to meet his folks and he agreed, so she asked if he would like to visit England and meet her parents. She had been disappointed by his response.

"There's no sunshine in England, no? Even in summer, it is always, how do you say, raining dogs and cats."

"Cats and dogs."

"Whatever. You English have so many ways to describe your weather."

"It's not always raining, you know. The weather can be sublime at times," Anne had countered. "And anyway, it would only be for a few days."

Pascal persisted.

"Even your tennis tournament, Wimbledon. Every year, whole days are cancelled by rain. Everyone knows it will rain, and yet only the English are surprised when a day is washed up. It's so strange. And one year that singer, Crag Richard…"

"Cliff Richard. Cliff..."

"Whatever. Well, he sang in the rain to the audience who also sat there, smiling, in the rain. Only the English would do such a thing."

Eventually, after a lot of persuading, Pascal said he would go. But, as he didn't like flying, he would travel by train to Calais, then take the ferry to Dover.

Anne returned to England at the end of the exchange period. They called each other often. The distance at first was new, exciting and they couldn't get enough of each other's voices and laughed late into the night. Then, as the date of Pascal's arrival drew closer, Anne sensed Pascal's enthusiasm cool ahead of his long journey. She persuaded her mother to drive her to Dover to meet Pascal rather than have him make his way alone to their London home.

Anne and her mother stood in the passenger terminal building at Dover docks, waiting for the ferry from Calais. Anne passed the time talking of Pascal, how handsome he was, his exotic French accent, and how kind he had been to her in Nice. She spotted the ferry on the horizon, a white dot growing larger as the ferry closed in on Dover, looming close enough for Anne to read the ship's name, *Pride of Calais*. The ferry docked and the passengers began to disembark in ones and twos down the gangplank. Anne peered at them all, looking for Pascal's face and characteristic gait. Sometime after the last passenger had disembarked, Anne was interrupted by her mother's impatient voice.

"Pascal wasn't on the ferry, Anne. What should we do?"

Anne found the administration office in the terminal building and asked if Pascal had been a passenger.

"Nobody with that name was on the ferry," she was told.

"He must have missed it. He'll be on the next one," Anne reassured her mother.

But Pascal wasn't on the next ferry, or the first ferry of the afternoon. Anne's mother made an excuse and drove home, leaving Anne to wait for the last ferry of the day. The afternoon dragged, the ferry docked and its passengers dispersed. Anne rode on the train to London alone, in tears. Had she been stood up? Or had Pascal got the date wrong? When she got home she called Pascal's apartment but there was no answer. There was no answer for several days until, late one night, Pascal picked up the phone. He had set off on the train ride from Nice to Calais, he said, but on the way had spent a night in Paris with old friends. They'd had such a good time he stayed another day and had lost his desire to visit England. "I saw the weather predication. Rain in London. I wanted to be warm and dry in Nice," he said. He made his excuses in fast, fluid French, without the warmth Anne had been used to. "You'll find somebody else," were his last words. It was over.

Under a crisp, cloudless sky Anne steered the 2CV into Poole. As the car crossed Poole Lifting Bridge she saw a ferry docked in the distance. She brought the car to a stop at the back of the line of cars waiting to board the ferry, the cars all shiny glass, gleaming chrome and dripping exhaust pipes.

After being dumped by Pascal she lost the motivation to continue her study of French and of Art Restoration. She begged her parents to let her take a year out, and even though they and her tutors did their best to convince her to stay, she got her way. After weeks at home watching television and eating the refrigerator bare, her father ran out of patience and told Anne to find a job, holding out the carrot of a position at his own company. Anne took his offer, thinking she'd stay a few months to please him and then return to university. She hadn't expected to find sales so stimulating and a monthly pay packet to be so motivating. Years later, Anne had risen to board level and when her father came to retire, he was proud to have her take over. Her first task as managing director was to order the development of software for the company's clients to use. A few years later the company pushed out a cloud-based solution, the first one of its kind in the country and it was a roaring success. It was now her twenty-fifth year at the company. She often wondered if she had made the right choices in her career, and suspected that she had not.

Just before the gate for checking boarding documents, Anne turned the 2CV's steering wheel to the left and accelerated into an area used for loading and offloading ferry cargo. She kept the car running between the confines of two parallel yellow lines that skirted the area and brought the car to a stop about two metres from the quayside.

If only she could have that time again, knowing what she knew now.

Anne turned the engine off, got out and walked up to the edge and looked down at the treacly black seawater heaving there. Deep water. She turned back, her heart pounding, a white heat scorching her brain. She stood behind the car and, as nonchalantly as possible, leaned to her right, placing the palm of her outstretched right arm on the car's rear windscreen. The 2CV, free of its handbrake, inched forwards. She leaned a little harder and the car rolled a little further and began to gain momentum. Keeping her weight on the car, the two-metre gap narrowed to one and the 2CV's shadow crept closer to the edge.

Behind her, shouting. "What you doing? Hey, stop."

The words drowned in the clatter of heavy boots closing in. "Stop!"

The wheels of the 2CV kept turning.

"Out of the way," yelled a man, barging Anne aside and clasping a glove-covered hand onto the car's rear bumper. Another man rushed to his side and with their boots scouring the tarmac they brought the car to a stuttering standstill, an inch from the edge.

The two men lay back on the tarmac, breathing hard, faces red under their helmets, looking in turn at each other and then at Anne.

"What were you playing at?" the larger of the two men demanded. The other staggered to his feet, reached into the car and pulled on the handbrake.

Anne composed herself. "I've just bought it," she said. "The seller said its handbrake was a little dodgy but I didn't realize it was so bad. It just started rolling towards the edge. I tried to stop it…"

"You weren't trying very hard."

"Yeah," said the smaller man, "you looked like you were trying to push it."

"Look, it's a heavy car. I'm not strong enough to stop it by myself," Anne asserted.

"You don't seem that worried about nearly having ditched it," the larger man persisted.

"I am worried," Anne claimed. "I only just bought it this morning. Before I drive it back to London I thought I'd visit the quayside and see the ferry, well, for personal reasons. I completely forgot about the handbrake."

"You really shouldn't have parked so close to the edge, dodgy handbrake or not. You could have lost it in the harbour.

These cars are lovely, they don't make 'em like this anymore. I'd give my right arm for one."

Anne looked at the man and saw he meant it.

"If you like the car so much, why don't you take it?"

"What?"

"Take it. I'll give it to you."

"What you talking about? I can't just take your car."

"Look, the paperwork is on the seat, there's some petrol in the tank. You just need to fix the handbrake."

"You're crazy," the man said, shaking his head.

Anne laughed.

"Maybe I am. But I live in London and already have a car. I don't even have anywhere to park this one. You'd be doing me a favour. I admit I made a mistake buying the car. It really should go to a good home."

"Look, lady, I couldn't take…"

"Then don't. Buy it from me. How about, uh, ten pounds?"

"A tenner?"

"Yes, a tenner. That should cover a cup of tea and a sticky bun at the station cafe while I wait for the train back to London."

The man stared at Anne. Anne stared at the man.

"Okay, you're on. A tenner. I still think you're crazy though."

With a creased ten pound note in her wallet, Anne gave the man a gentleman's handshake and set off on her walk to Poole railway station, certain that if she looked back he would still be standing there, shaking his head.

On the train back to Hampstead, Anne assessed the day's events. If she had been stronger she would have had the car clean over the edge into the deep, black water of Poole Harbour. No matter where Pascal was these days, he would have seen a video of a rhubarb-coloured 2CV being extracted from the harbour by a huge crane, seawater bleeding from its orifices. Even after all these years, he would have got the message.

But maybe this outcome was for the better. At least now, whenever she saw a 2CV she wouldn't suppress her anger but would laugh. She had done enough to avenge the past. It was time to acknowledge the present and plan for the future. It was time to be honest with herself. She was lonely. She didn't enjoy her job and hadn't for a long time. But, she was still in her forties, single, with savings and, despite opinions to the contrary, she wasn't crazy. She was smart enough to turn this around. She would turn it around.

As the train pulled into West Hampstead station, Anne drew a line under the plan she had penned in her notebook. Tomorrow she would call an emergency meeting and inform the board, then start to mentor a colleague who would take over from her at the end of the year. She would search the internet for colleges in Paris where she would study Art Restoration. She would dream of weekend visits to art galleries and museums, of drinking coffee in cafes and sipping Calvados in Left Bank cocktail bars.

And, if not Paris, then northern France, perhaps Normandy. Yes, Paris or Normandy.

Anywhere but Nice.

Author's Note

I hope you enjoyed reading these stories. I'm sure you have your favourites, some that perhaps still linger in your mind, some that you've decided to read again or even discussed with family and friends.

"The Jogger" was the first short story I wrote in what must have been 1998, a few years after arriving in Japan. I did jog at the time, although only along the pavements of Kamiochiai in Shinjuku, where I lived. Perhaps the idea for the story came from my wish to run unrestrained in a park rather than having to dodge fellow pedestrians, continually stop at traffic lights, and pop into convenience stores to ask staff for directions after losing my way. I didn't have a car at the time either, and missed the freedom of movement driving would have given me, a yearning that found its way into the story.

The most recent story to appear in this collection is "The Choice". Clearly my experience of daily train commutes to work in Tokyo contributed to the story, as did my experience of leaving the making of life choices so late that I end up without a choice to make. It typically takes me one to two weeks to write the first draft of a story, but this time I forced myself to write the first draft of "The Choice" in one day (with the occasional visit to the toilet) in an attempt to maintain the tension of the story throughout. I won't be doing that again, but I am pleased with the result.

Thank you for reading.
Chris

Acknowledgments

Thank you to:

My parents, my wife Sachiyo and my daughter Amy for their support and patience while I wrote the stories in this collection.

My sister, Jenny, for being the first person to read each story and for her insightful and encouraging comments.

My copy-editor, Louise, for skillfully and sensitively working on the stories and helping to make them the best they can be.

Archna and the team at Neem Tree Press, for responding positively to my manuscript and for patiently guiding me through the process of getting this book published. I look forward to working with you all on the next short story collection!

About the Author

Christopher Green was born in Middlesbrough, UK, and grew up in various locations in the UK, Germany and South Africa. A long-time resident of Japan, he lives near Tokyo with his wife, Sachiyo, and daughter, Anna.

Christopher is a short story writer and the author of the children's book *On The Beach: The Winter Visitor*. His hobbies include writing haiku in Japanese and playing Park Golf, both with limited success. For exercise he walks along the banks of the Sakai river where, if he is lucky, an idea for his next story will pop into his head and remain there until he gets home.

For more information about Christopher and his books, please visit www.greeninjapan.com

About the Illustrator

Rebecca Purton is an accidental illustrator. She always loved making and drawing things, but had no idea she was an illustrator until someone kind told her she might be. Before that moment she did all sorts—taught English as a foreign language, folded clothes in a shop for middle-aged women, ticked lists in a film archive, met a Japanese man, married him, lived with him in Japan, lived with him in the UK, attended umpteen different dance classes (currently ballet and belly) and rekindled a vague love of watching birds. In between these stops on her haywire path through life, she wrote and she read. She still writes and she still reads: stories keep her marbles intact, and she's nothing without those marbles! Rebecca is based in Orpington or Tokyo, depending on the season and the prevailing wind.